CW00662005

Guido Almansi, Italian, is Professor of English and Comparative Literature at the University of East Anglia. He is interested in the dishonesty of literature, in the subterfuges used by language and its wily accomplice, the writer, in order not to say what they mean and not to mean what they say. His favourite author is Shakespeare.

Claude Béguin, Swiss, teaches French at the University of Siena, Italy. She likes squarers of circles, writers who, though conscious of the devious nature of language, attempt to be straight. Her favourite author is Diderot.

When the wind changes, the descriptions of their interests can be reversed. Literary dreams were an area of possible collaboration since at night there is not enough light to distinguish between honesty and dishonesty.

Guido Almansi and Claude Béguin are husband and wife.

Guido Almansi
And
Claude Béguin

THEATRE OF SLEEP

*an Anthology of
Literary Dreams*

published by Pan Books

First published 1986 by Pan Books Ltd
This Picador edition published 1987 by Pan Books Ltd,
Cavaye Place, London SW10 9PG
9 8 7 6 5 4 3 2 1
© Guido Almansi and Claude Béguin 1986
ISBN 0 330 28946 2
Photoset by Parker Typesetting Service, Leicester
Printed and bound in Great Britain by
Richard Clay Ltd, Bungay, Suffolk

This book is sold subject to the condition that it
shall not, by way of trade or otherwise, be lent, re-sold,
hired out, or otherwise circulated without the publisher's prior
consent in any form of binding or cover other than that in which
it is published and without a similar condition including this
condition being imposed on the subsequent purchaser

Contents

Many friends and colleagues have helped us in our search for extravagant literary dreams. We would like to thank them all, and in particular Marino Bosinelli, Bertrand Bouvier, Guido Fink, Richard Gordon, Hannah and Julian Hilton, André Hurst, Michel Jeanneret, Holgar Klein, Charmaine Lee, Godo Lieberg, Maria Grazia Profeti, Lorna Sage, Jean Starobinski, Pippo Vitiello, Arnold Wesker; Mark Roberts, librarian of the British Institute in Florence and all the librarians of the Université de Genève and of the University of East Anglia, Norwich.

Special thanks to the translators of passages not published in English before: Robert Clarke, Julie Dashwood, Mike Hollington, Charmaine Lee, John Lyons, Jonathan Romney and Clive Scott.

Finally we wish to thank all the friends who have *NOT* insisted on telling us their personal dreams.

Acknowledgements

Every effort has been made to contact copyright holders. In the event of an inadvertent omission or error, the editor should be notified at Picador, Pan Books Ltd, 18–21 Cavaye Place, London, SW10 9PG.

For permission to reprint the stories, poems, excerpts and translations in this anthology, acknowledgement is made as follows:

Apollinaire 'Oneirocritic' in *Oeuvres Poétiques*, Gallimard, copyright © 1965.

Ariosto, Ludovico 'Orlando and Angelica', from *Orlando Furioso*, translated by Barbara Reynolds, copyright by Penguin Books Ltd, 1975.

Aristotle 'Are Dreams Prophetic?', from 'De Divinatione per Somnum', translated by J. I. Beare. Reprinted from *The Oxford Translation of Aristotle* edited by W. D. Ross, vol. 3 (1931), by permission of Oxford University Press.

Artaud, Antonin 'The Bad Dreamer', in *Oeuvres Complètes*, copyright © Gallimard 1970, translated by Jonathan Romney. Reprinted by permission of John Calder Publishers Ltd.

Artemidorus 'Varieties of Incest', from *The Interpretation of Dreams*, translation and commentary by Robert J. White, Noyes Press, 1976.

Augustine 'The Angel', from *The Confessions*, translated by R. S. Pine-Coffin, Penguin, 1961.

Bachelard, Gaston 'Flying' and 'Air', from *L'air et les songes*, José Corti, copyright © by José Corti, 1944, translated by Jonathan Romney.

Baillet, A. 'Descartes' Dreams', from *La Vie de Monsieur Des Cartes*. Translated by Jonathan Romney.

Baudelaire 'The Monster', translated by Jonathan Romney.

Bishop, Elizabeth 'Sleeping Standing Up' from *The Complete Poems* by Elizabeth Bishop. Copyright © 1938, 1956 by Elizabeth Bishop. Copyright © 1983 by Alice Methfessel. Reprinted by permission of Farrar, Straus and Giroux, Inc.

Boccaccio 'The Wolf' from *Decameron*, translated by G. H. McWilliam, Penguin, 1972.

Bodel, Jean 'The Cock Market' ('Le Songe Desvez'), translated by Charmaine Lee.

Borges, J. L. 'Prologue' and 'The Enemy' in *El libro de sueños*, Torres Agüerro, 1976.

Borges, J. L. 'The Circular Ruins', in *The Aleph and Other Stories*, translated by Norman Thomas Di Giovanni, Picador.

Bossuet, Jacques 'The Parable of the Blind Man', from *Les Oraisons Funèbres*, translated by Jonathan Romney.

Brecht, Bertold 'Joan's Vision', from *Saint Joan of the Stockyards*, translated by Frank Jones, Eyre Methuen, 1976.

Brillat-Savarin 'Meditation Six' in *Physiologie du goût*, translated by G. Almansi.

Butor, Michel 'Dream Matter', from *Matière de Rêves*, copyright © by Gallimard, 1975. Translated by Jonathan Romney.

Calvino, Italo 'Zobeide', from *Invisible Cities*, translated by William Weaver, Secker & Warburg.

Chester Mystery Plays 'Joseph and the Angel', from 'The Nativity, in *The Chester Mystery Plays*, edited by Maurice Hussey, Heinemann Educational Books, 1967.

Cicero Various passages from *De Divinatione*, translated by W. A. Falconer, 'The Loeb Classical Library', 1964.

Cobo, Bernabé 'The Inca', from *Historia del Nuevo Mundo*. Translated by John Lyons.

Dahl, Roald 'The BFG', from *The BFG*, copyright © by Roald Dahl, 1982.

Damian, François Various passages from *L'autre rive*, copyright © Minuit, 1985. Translated by Jonathan Romney.

Dante 'The Siren', from *Dante Purgatory*, translated by Dorothy Sayers, Gollancz.

Desnos, Robert 'Dreams', published in *Littérature*, 1922. Copyright © The Estate of Robert Desnos. Translated by J. Romney.

Dostoevsky, Fiodor 'Cana of Galilee' from *The Brothers Karamazov*, translated by David Magarshack, Penguin, 1972, copyright © David Magarshack, 1958.

Dylan, Bob 'Bob Dylan's 115th Dream.'

Eça de Queiroz 'The Butcher', from *The Illustrious House of Ramirez*, translated by Ann Stevens, reprinted by permission of the Bodley Head, 1968.

Egypt 'The Translator's Dream' from R. P. Festugière, *La révélation d'Hermès Trismégiste*, copyright © by Gabalda, 1944. Translated by C. Béguin.

Egypt 'Thutmosis and the God', from the chapter by Serge Saungron 'Les songes et leur interprétation dans l'Egypte ancienne', in *Les songes et leur interprétation* (by several authors), translated by C. Béguin, copyright © Editions du Seuil, 1959.

Eluard, Paul 'I Dream I am not Sleeping', from 'Donner à voir', in *Oeuvres complètes*, Gallimard, 1979, copyright Gallimard © 1968. Translated by Jonathan Romney.

Encyclopédie 'Dreams', in *L'Encyclopédie*, translated by Clive Scott.

Eschenbach, Wolfram von 'Snake birth', from *Parzival*, translated by A. T. Hatto, Penguin, 1980.

Euripides Passages from *Rhesus, Hecuba, Iphigenia Taurica*, translated by A. S. Way, 'The Loeb Classical Library', 1942.

Flaubert, Gustave 'The Profanation of the Bread', from *Mémoires d'un fou*, quoted in R. L. Mégroz, *The Dream World*, Bodley Head, 1939.

Freud, Sigmund 'Seven White Wolves', from *The Occurrence in Dreams of Material from Fairy Tales*, from Volume 12 of *The Standard Edition of the Complete Psychological Works of Sigmund Freud*, translated and edited by James Strachey, by permission of Sigmund Freud Copyrights Ltd., The Institute of Psycho-Analysis and the Hogarth Press. Also from *Collected Papers*, Vol. 4, by Sigmund Freud, Authorized Translation under the supervision of Joan Riviere. Published by Basic Books, Inc. by arrangement with The Hogarth Press Ltd. and The Institute of Psycho-Analysis, London. Reprinted by permission.

Froissart, Jean 'The Mirror', from *L'Espinette Amoureuse*. Translated by Charmaine Lee.

Genet, Jean 'Harcamone', from *Miracle of the Rose*, Blond, 1965.

Gide, André 'The Madonna Appears to the Atheist' from *The Vatican Cellars*, translated by Dorothy Bussy, copyright © by Cassell/Macmillan, 1952.

Goethe 'The Pheasants' from *Travels in Italy*, translated by W. H. Auden and E. Mayer, Collins, 1962.

Gómez de la Serna, R. 'The Transference of Dreams', from *Caprichos*, Espasa-Calpe S.A., 1962. Translated by John Lyons.

Goytisolo, José Agustin 'The Good Little Woolf', in *Palabras para Julia*, copyright © Laia, 1982.

Graves, Robert 'The Shout' (passage) from *Occupation Writer*. By permission of Robert Graves.

Grillparzer, Franz 'Medea', from *Aus Grillparzers Tagebuch (1808–1859)*. Translated by M. Hollington.

Groussac, Paul 'Between Dreams', in *El Viaje Intelectual*. Translated by John Lyons.

Handke, Peter 'Who has ever...', from *A Moment of True Feeling*. Reprinted by permission of Farrar, Straus and Giroux, Inc. Excerpt from *A Moment of True Feeling* by Peter Handke. Translated by Ralph Mannheim. Translation copyright © 1977 by Farrar, Straus and Giroux, Inc.

Handke, Peter 'The Inverted World', from *The Innerworld of the Outerworld of the Innerworld* by Peter Handke. English translation copyright © 1984 by Michael Roloff. Reprinted by permission of The Continuum Publishing Company.

Hebbel, Friedrich 'The Elusive Poem', from *Tagebücher*. Translated by Mike Hollington.

Herodotus 'Xerxes and Artabanus', translated by A. D. Godley, 'The Loeb Classical Library', 1963.

Hervey Saint-Denis 'The Monsters' from *Les Rêves et les moyens de les contrôler*. Translated by Jonathan Romney.

Hervey Saint-Denis 'Suicide' from *Les Rêves et les moyens de les contrôler*. Translated by R. Clarke.

Hoffmann, E. T. A. 'The Mine', from 'The Mines of Falun', in *Selected Writings*, translated by L. J. Kent and E. C. Knight, University of Chicago Press, 1969.

Huch, Friedrich several excerpts from *Träume*, translated by Mike Hollington.

Ibsen, Henrik 'Human experience', quoted from R. Lothar *Henrik Ibsen* in R. L. Mégroz, *The Dream World – a Survey of the History and Mystery of Dreams*, Bodley Head, 1939. By permission of The Bodley Head.

Jouve, Pierre Jean 'Red', from *La Scène capitale*, copyright © by Mercure de France, 1961, translated by Jonathan Romney.

Kerouac, Jack 'The Pink Sweater', from *Book of Dreams*, copyright © 1961, 1981 by Jack Kerouac. Reprinted by permission of City Lights Books.

La Fontaine, Jean de 'The Two Friends' in *The Fables of la Fontaine*, translated by Marianne Moore. Copyright 1952, 1953, 1954, © 1964 by Marianne Moore. Copyright renewed © 1980, 1981, 1982 by Laurence E. Brinn and Louise Crane, Executors of the Estate of Marianne Moore. Reprinted by permission of Viking Penguin Inc.

Lautréamont 'The Hog', from *Maldoror*, translated by Alexis Lykiard, Allison and Busby, 1983.

Leiris, Michel 'The Address' and 'The Actor', from *Nuits sans nuit et quelques jours sans jour*, copyright © by Gallimard.

Lenau Nikolaus 'Dreampowers', translated by Mike Hollington.

Lobel, Arnold 'The Dream', in *Frog and Toad Together*, copyright © 1971, 1972 by Arnold Lobel. Reprinted by permission of World's Work Ltd.

Lucretius 'On Dreams' from *The Poem of Nature*, translated by C. H. Sisson, copyright © by C. H. Sisson, Carcanet, 1976.

Lynkeus 'The Rational Dreamer' from *Phantasien eines Realisten*. Translated by Mike Hollington.

Machado, Antonio 'Alvargonzález' from *Poesias completas*, copyright © The Estate of Antonio Machado 1940; copyright © Espasa-Calpe S.A. 1978. Translated by John Lyons.

Machado, Antonio Three poems from 'Proverbios y Cantares' in Antonio Machado, *Sunlight*, edited, translated and published by Ivor Waters, copyright © Ivor Waters, 1973.

Malerba, Luigi 'The Serpent', from *The Serpent*, translated by William Weaver, by permission of the author and of Agenzia Letteraria Internazionale.

Mandiargues, A. P. 'The Pink Bitch', from *Marbres*, Laffont, 1953, translated by Jonathan Romney.

Michaux, Henry 'The Mother', from *Poteaux d'angle*, copyright © by Gallimard, 1981. Translated by Jonathan Romney.

Montale 'The Prisoner's Dream', in *Selected Poems*, translated by G. Kay, copyright © by Eugenio Montale and George Kay, 1964.

Mossadegh 'The Oil Commission' quoted in J. L. Borges, *El libro de sueños*, copyright © by Torres Agüerro, 1976. Translated by Guido Almansi.

Nerval, Gérard de Two passages from *Aurélia*, translated by G. Wagner, Peter Owen, 1958.

Nodier, Charles 'The Bailiff of the Isle of Man', from *La Fée aux Miettes*. Translated by Clive Scott.

Novalis 'The Blue Flower', from *Henry von Ofterdingen*, translated by Palmer Hilty, Frederick Ungar Publishing Co., Inc., 1964.

Ovid 'A Cuckold', passage from *Amores*, in *The Erotic Poems*, translated by Peter Green, Penguin, 1982.

Padilla, Gastón 'The Woof', from *Memorias de un Prescindible*, 1974, quoted in J. L. Borges, *El libro de sueños*, copyright by Torres Agüerro, 1976.

Papini, Giovanni 'The Sick Gentleman's Last Visit', from *Il Tragico quotidiano*, 1906. Translation by Alberto Manguel.

Pascal Two passages from *Pensées*, translated by John Warrington, 'Everyman's Library', J. M. Dent & Sons Ltd, 1973.

Pérec, Georges several excerpts from *La boutique obscure*, copyright © Denoël, 1973, translated by Jonathan Romney.

Pirandello, Luigi 'The Reality of the Dream', in *Novelle per un anno*, copyright © The Estate of Luigi Pirandello. Translated by Julie Dashwood.

Plutarch 'Caesar's Death', from 'The Life of Caesar' in *Plutarch's Lives*, translated by Bernadotte Perrin, 'The Loeb Classical Library' 1971.

Proust, Marcel 'Swann's Dream', from *Swann's Way*, translated by Scott Moncrieff, by permission of Chatto and Windus (1928).

Pushkin, Alexander 'Tatiana's Dream', from *Eugene Onegin*, translated with a commentary by Vladimir Nabokov, copyright © by Vladimir Nabokov, reprinted by permission of Routledge and Kegan Paul plc.

Racine, Jean 'The Young Assassin', from 'Athaliah', in *Four Greek Plays*, translated by R. C. Knight, Cambridge University Press, 1982.

Resnik, Salomon 'The Wood', from *Il Teatro del Sogno*, Boringhieri, copyright © by Salomon Resnik, 1982, by authorisation of the author.

Rimbaud, Arthur 'Dawn' and 'Deserts of Love', in *Complete Works*, translated by Paul Schmidt, Harper and Row, 1966.

Saintine, X. B. 'The Victims' Ball', in *La Seconde vie*. Translated by Jonathan Romney.

Schubert, Franz 'My Dream', from the Diary, in Otto Eric Deutsch, *Schubert, a Biography*, translated by Eric Blom, Dent, 1956.

Seferis, George 'The Acropolis', from 'Glosses ston Artemidoro ton Daldiano', in *Dokimès*, Ikaros, 1975, by permission of Maro Seferis.

Sorel, Charles 'Francion', from *Histoire Comique de Francion*. Translated by Clive Scott.

Steiner, George 'Before Language' from 'The Historicity of Dreams', *Salmagundi*, Fall 1983, copyright © by Skidmore College, 1983.

Theocritus 'Fishermen' in *Theocritus*, edited and translated by A. E. S. Gow, Cambridge University Press, 1950.

Ts'ao Chan 'Bao Yu', from *The Dream of the Red Chamber*, translated by David Hawkes, Penguin, 1980, copyright © by David Hawkes, 1980.

Valéry, Paul 'Let me, Dream, Look You in the Eye', from *Questions du Rêve*, in *Cahiers Paul Valéry*, N° 3, edited by J. Levaillant, Gallimard, 1979, copyright © by Gallimard, 1979. Translated by Jonathan Romney.

Virgil 'Hector' from *The Aeneid*, translated by W. F. Jackson Knight (Penguin Classics 1956), copyright © G. R. Wilson Knight, 1956.

Vonnegut, Kurt 'Poo-tee-weet', from *God Bless You, Mr Rosewater*, copyright © 1965 by Kurt Vonnegut Jr. Reprinted by permission of Delacorte Press/Seymour Lawrence and Jonathan Cape.

Wagner, Cosima 'Sausages and Music', from *Diaries*, translated by Geoffrey Skelton, by permission of Collins, Publishers.

West, Nathanael 'The Trojan Horse', from *The Dream Life of Balso Snell*, in *The Day of The Locust*, Penguin, 1963, copyright © by Moss & Kamin, 1931.

Wilder, Thornton 'The Void', from *The Ides of March*, Longmans, Green, 1948.

Introduction

Les songes contiennent infiniment moins de mystère que le vul-
gaire ne l'imagine, mais un peu plus aussi que ne le croient les
esprits forts.   *Pierre Bayle*

In *The Faber Book of Aphorisms*, edited by W. H. Auden and Louis Kronen-
berger, we find the following observation about dreams: 'Dreaming permits
each and every one of us to be quietly and safely insane every night of our lives'
(Charles Fisher). Dreams, in other words, guarantee our freedom to evade
temporarily the shackles of reasonable life. This aphorism describes particularly well the situation of writers, who are often forced by the more obtuse
among their readers to be much more rational than they would like. If literature
is threatened with fossilization this is not so much the fault of the conformist
writer as of the conformist reader, this honest sincere genuine coward (not a
hypocrite but his opposite), whose rule threatens the freedom of literature. The
vitality of writing depends in the end on the open-mindedness of the *lector in fabula*.

For this reason we think that literary dreams have a crucial role to play: they
can lure the dull reader who just wants a nice story ('And I like a story to be a
story, mind, and my wife's the same' grumbles the writer's bogeyman in E. M.
Forster's *Aspects of the Novel*) outside his usual daily life. This tiresome reader
wants literature to copy his own experience of reality, or at times his own
experience of fantasy – which is rather scanty and thrives on palace hotels and
airports, jet-set and exotic adventures, brothels and noble mansions. But
although the fantasy of Forster's literal-minded reader is in bad repair, his
dreams might work better (God knows why: this is one of the many puzzling
riddles concerning dreams. Aristotle, in a passage reproduced in this book,
already wondered why the Gods should send some of their best prophetic
dreams to commonplace persons). Even the man who wants 'a nice story' might
be willing to follow the writer in the adventures of the dream because he cannot
deny that dreaming belongs to a reality shared by both of them. It could in fact
be the only reality they may have in common.

But dreams are an unpleasant subject. Again, in his quiet unassuming way,
Forster has summed up the issue. In *A Room with a View*, Lucy Honeychurch is
staying with the mother of her fiancé in her London flat; she goes to sleep in the
guest bedroom:

As she was dozing off, a cry – the cry of nightmare – rang from Lucy's room. Lucy could ring for her maid if she liked, but Mrs Vyse thought it kind to go herself. She found the girl sitting upright with her hand on her cheek.

'I am sorry, Mrs Vyse – it is these dreams.'

'Bad dreams?'

'Just dreams.'

'Just dreams.' These two simple words are a harsh comment on the dream world. An anthology of literary dreams must contain many of these 'Just dreams' which upset Lucy, and shall perhaps perturb the mental balance of the reader. But there is another side to the dream. Dreams, as we said above, are an unpleasant subject; but they can also, from a different point of view, be the most pleasant theme in the world. We are told that a group of Russian revolutionaries once asked the great leader: 'Comrade Lenin, are we allowed to dream?' The answer should have been 'no', since dreams are an escape from Communism, from the common world of waking people into the private fortress of the dreamer where the bourgeois hoards *his* desires and *his* fears, *his* memories and *his* fantasies. But not even the dictatorship of the proletariat could cancel this manifestation of individualism. Dreams are pleasant because, when we dream, we are free from all controls: no one can interfere with our experience. In Orwell's *1984* disobedience to Big Brother starts in a dream. Men are free because they can dream at will, and no tyrant can interfere with this activity.

We have already made various statements in the previous pages, and we feel guilty about them because one should never say anything about dreams. It is a subject on which nobody knows anything, and the only reaction should be a puzzled 'no comment'. But it is so difficult to keep quiet, and in spite of what we have learned we must go on babbling. Experience has taught us the virtue of silence where dreams are concerned; and we shall, as usual, ignore this lesson. During the last few years we have been gathering material for this anthology of literary dreams and in the course of our research we have read many books of dreams, on dreams, about dreams, and so on. Without any prevarication on our part, we have reached the positive certainty that there is no certainty in this field. We are convinced of the marvellous equivalence, from a logical or rational standpoint, of all explanations and interpretations concerning dreams. In this area everyone is entitled to say anything he likes without being checked; it is a free-for-all. As far as dreams are concerned, 'the most sovereign ontological positions have clay feet,' writes James Hillman, because the various dream philosophies cannot rid themselves of the archetypal fantasies which underlie their convictions. We owe our allegiance to the civilized world, so we tend to discard the most primitive forms of dream superstition, perhaps more out of imaginative incapacity and cultural conditioning than real distrust. Barring those, however, all the theories offered so far by social and/or occult sciences, by literature and fantasy, seem to us equally reasonable in the daylight of reason; and they are all impossible to prove.

The main differences are of an aesthetic or literary nature. Freud's *Interpretation of Dreams* is an infinitely richer work, from a poetic and imaginative point of view, than *Les rêves et les moyens de les contrôler* ('Dreams and How to Direct them') by Hervey Saint Denis. Artemidorus's *Oneirocritica* makes far more fascinating reading than Charles Rycroft's *The Innocence of Dreams*; Bachelard's books on dreams are more convincing, from a narrative angle, than *La mise-en-scène du rêve* ('The Theatre of Dreams') by Salomon Resnik. But there is no proof that could force us to choose – for motives other than aesthetic, literary or hedonistic – one interpretation rather than another; and no field of human knowledge would be of any use to us if we were forced to select one of them according to rational criteria.

Freud tells us that dreams represent our repressed desires and that they are a conceptualization and personification of the unconscious imagination largely contaminated by the conscious. For Jung, dreams are the expression of the collective subconscious of mankind, an encounter with the cultural archetypes, the primordial models of society. According to Jacques Lacan, dreams are 'like a charade where the participants must guess an utterance known to them, or its variant, with the sole help of a mimed scene.' In *The Innocence of Dreams* Charles Rycroft states that dreams are a kind of involuntary poetic activity; Roger Caillois in *L'incertitude qui vient des rêves* ('The Uncertainty Fostered by Dreams') ventures that dreams are a bedlam of empty simulacra, holding no secrets; James Hillman in *The Dream and the Underworld* claims that dreams 'belong to the Underworld and its Gods'; Francis Crick suggests that dreams during REM sleep are necessary to rid the brain of unwanted or parasitic modes of behaviour.

The experimental psychologist says that dreams are 'a multimodal perceptual simulation'; the sci-fi author pretends that dreams are messages sent from a planet outside our galaxy, Trafalmadore for instance, where people decide on the evolution of mankind for reasons unknown to us and transmit their instructions through these night visions. Liam Hudson believes that in dreams we try to resolve the complexity of waking life; one theologian tells us that dreams are divinely inspired while another claims that dreams are messages dictated by the devil, the Lord of the Night, who directs us through our oneiric faculty (we would thus be disc jockey playing at night the music from hell; this idea reappears under various guises in the works of several dream writers). We could carry on and on. All those versions are equally acceptable in the anarchy of dream interpretation. Let us add tentatively our own ironic definition: 'Dreams are what we know nothing about when we are awake: we do not know what they are; where they come from; where they are going to;

what is their function; what are their causes and purposes; what relation they have with waking or with the life of body and soul, feelings and instincts, reason and heart.' Who could prove us wrong?

Oneirology has made gigantic steps during these last years, thanks to the discovery of REMs (Rapid Eye Movements occurring during deep sleep while we dream) and to laboratory researches based on the dreams of human guinea pigs monitored by adequate instruments. Scientific oneirology has helped us understand *how much*, *when*, and *how* we dream (what mental circuits are aroused by the dreaming activity). But it has taught us nothing as to *why*, and almost nothing as to *what* we dream. The *why* question is outruled, like others on the line of 'What is the source of life?' or 'What is the purpose of the universe?' The problem of the cause, origin and purpose of the dream is so mysterious that *serious* researchers – I mean those who work according to verifiable parameters – do not even try to broach the issue (perhaps some breakthrough might occur in the field of ethology rather than in human psychology now that we know that many animals have nocturnal experiences similar to human dreams).

But the *what* problem is far more interesting. We all think we can answer that one because there is a scientific literature which transcribes the patients' dreams with rigorous criteria, and a literary literature which, from the Bible and Homer onwards, has documented lavishly the dreams – true or fictional – of mankind. But in fact no one knows anything on the subject, because of the fatal borderline between dreamt dream and narrated dream, of 'the obvious gap between what is experienced and what is recounted', in Lacan's words. We know everything about dreams as they are told or written down afterwards, since by then they belong to the common world of the awake. We know nothing about dreams as they are dreamt since they belong to the dreamer's private world, with the possible exception of our own oneiric experience. And perhaps we do not even know our own dreams, since when we recount them to ourselves, or reflect upon the events of the previous night using the autonomous circuits of our memory and thought-processes, we are forced to remodel, modify and adapt our dream experience according to the narrative conventions we are familiar with. These do not necessarily coincide with the narrative conventions of sleep. 'As we lie down to sleep the world turns half away/ Through ninety dark degrees' writes the American poet Elizabeth Bishop in a poem included in this anthology. But we could also speak of one hundred and eighty dark degrees, i.e. of a mirror-like reversal of the axial co-ordinates of our experience: inverting our conventional perspectives and the usual poles of attraction and repulsion; mixing up senses and feelings and perceptions and thoughts; playing on an evanescent extra-human reality which transcends the sensorial universe. If there is a sixth, oneiric sense, it challenges the experience of the five others.

Freud, who seems to deny the temporal and spatial dimensions of the oneiric experience, hints at the pluridimensional character of dreams; but nothing proves that our waking-life dimensions have any currency in our dream life. Perhaps we should borrow the mathematic system of notation and speak of dimension 1', dimension 2' etc., to indicate this other kind of 'dimension', also called 'dimension', which we find in dreams. The only person who could explain what these dream-dimensions are is the dreamer, who is by definition unable to recount his experience until he emerges from the dream and is reintegrated into the waking world, ruled by our usual dimensions.

'You might say it is not possible to observe a dream properly . . . It is like trying to study liquid iron from solid iron,' wrote Paul Valéry. The atoms may remain the same, but their organization and syntax have changed radically. The minute we wake up our dream becomes something else; the tale of a dream that follows the laws of story-telling and the conventions of our sight, hearing, taste, smell and touch. Bottom knew it when he extolled his 'Bottom's dream, because it hath no bottom': a bottomless dream because of its profundity and its existence outside the character called Bottom. The experience of this sixth, oneiric sense, i.e. of a faculty without organs which derives in turn from another faculty without organs, to wit the imagination, is translated into the language of the sensorium, our usual perceptive organs controlling the five senses, and the language of the brain, the busy organ of our daytime understanding. What does this translation entail? No one can answer this question, but we are at liberty to think that it is an impossible transfer, like Tchaikovsky's metamorphosis of a poem into music in *Francesca da Rimini*; or Aldous Huxley's rendition of a symphony in writing; or, in Rabelais, Panurge's presentation of a philosophical problem in a language of bodily signs, grimaces and winks. The passage from dreamt dream to narrated dream seems impenetrable. We would like to grasp the form and the content, the signifier and the signified, of the dreamt dream; but we have only the content, the signified, of the dreamt dream, transcribed into an inadequate language: the form, the signifier, of the narrated dream. As to the form of the dreamt dream, we know nothing about it because we cannot rely on an appropriate glossary in order to translate our experience from night life to day life; and we are wary of anyone who claims to possess this secret code.

When we remember a dream, we treat it as a story we would summarize from memory. This is a basic, yet inevitable mistake, since there is no alternative. 'To obtain the synthesis of a dream you would have to express it in its "atomic" constituents. For the story which one remembers is only a secondary fabrication, following an initial stage that is non-chronological, non-resumable, non-integrable' (Valéry again). Those who speak arrogantly of the meaning and interpretation of dreams are like art critics who try to analyse a non-extant fresco from an aesthetic point of view on the basis of its description by Pausanias; or to judge the colour scheme of one of the *Paintings from an Exhibition* from Mussorgsky's musical commentary. In this sense, dreams do not exist. Feuerbach said that death does not exist because the only competent person in the matter, the dead one, is constitutionally unable to report on it. The same paradox holds true for dreams because the only witness, the dreamer isolated in the privacy of his dream, does not speak. The dreamer's mouth is sealed by the dream.

Let us suppose that the fragments of a dream were connected, not by a linear development or circular pattern, as usually happens with narrations in waking life, but in a kind of Moebius ring (what Lacan calls a *huit intérieur*, an internal eight, though in a different context); or perhaps in a spiral progress from one point to the next. This is only a fancy hypothesis, of course, without any factual basis or logical proof, just like the interpretations by Freud or Jung, only rather less convincing and authoritative. But the idea is not without attraction since the Moebius ring or the spiral progression could explain the distorting effect we perceive in many dream situations, which could be due to the continuous curving of the narration in a dream. Once awake the dreamer, penetrated by the memory of his dream experience, does not possess a corresponding unfolding model in his mind. If he tries to reconstruct his dream afterwards, he must 'translate' it, changing the Moebius ring into a circle, the spiral movement into a linear one. Narrative laws are much stronger than the rules of sincerity. The dreamer may choose to be true or untrue to his memory of the event, but he cannot disobey narrative conventions, be they his own or society's, since he has literally no choice. He is married to one type of narration, and he must be faithful because there is no alternative.

In one of the most authoritative texts of contemporary oneirology, *A Grammar of Dreams*, David Foulkes claims, we do not quite know on what basis, that dreams are ' "ordinary" rather than "exotic"; linear rather than unlinear; propositional and dichotomous rather than ineffably, primitively unifying, and well capable of being expressed in words' (*sic*). And again: 'The typical REM dream has a linear narrative structure, much like the structure of a verbal narrative: first this, then this, then this; with the various "this's" having some sensible thematic connection with one another'. This is a very bold statement. If the narrative structure of the dream is similar to the narrative structure of waking life and language, surely this depends on the translative process. Shakespeare sounds very French in Voltaire's translation; dreams seem very linear, ordinary, literarily structured because they have already been translated into non-oneiric language.

The interpretation of a dream is already a dream, writes Salomon Resnik following an old aphoristic tradition ('The inquiry into a dream is another dream,' George Saville, Marquis of Halifax). But we could turn this idea upside down: 'a dream is already a kind of interpretation'; or, as Jung put it, 'the dream is its own interpretation.' When it comes out of the protective cocoon of sleep, the dream is open to any kind of interpretation: historical, stylistic, rhetorical or aesthetic. This is true both of the neutral and scientific descriptions, where the author tries to give the most unbiased account of the night experience, and of the dreams which are inserted in a novel or in any other form of fiction. The biographical, or literary-biographical records of writers' dreams present striking affinities with their own fictive stories. Be it Kerouac's *Book of Dreams*, Pérec's *La Boutique obscure. 149 rêves*, Luigi Malerba's *Diario di un sognatore* or Butor's several volumes of *Matière de rêve*, which all claim to be transcriptions of dreams written down in the morning, they all read like their author's short stories. We are not saying that Kerouac, Malerba, Pérec or Butor are lying: we are only suggesting that the author of the narrated dreams is perhaps lying to the author of the dreamt dream.

This is one of the paradoxes about literary dreams. On the one hand, a literary dream is an artificial document since it is manipulated by the writer according to the rules of rhetoric and narrative strategy. On the other hand, it is a natural document since these rules are the same ones that we apply every morning when we wake up and try to evoke the dreams of the past hours 'naturally': for ourselves; for a spouse or a friend; or for a psychologist after a REM experiment in a laboratory. Where dreams are concerned the absurd distinction between natural and cultural discourse disappears because everything is culture, in the memory as well as in the verbal reproduction of the dream experience. In Northern Italy, when someone talks in an artificial and highly mannered way, the standard demotic rebuke is 'Parlett come te magnett'; 'Talk the way you eat'; but one cannot say 'Talk the way you dream' because the homology is impossible. The dream of the 'natural' sleeping dreamer is entrusted to the awakened dreamer, who is *per force* a cultural being, submitted to the conventions of language and narrativity. Luckily for us, everything is cultural; and we can thus defend ourselves from being invaded by the dreams, from this expansion of the nocturnal madness of the dream: 'the overflow of the dream into real life' which, for instance, caused Nerval's madness and suicide. Dreams must be kept at bay.

Almost every writer since the beginning of recorded history has invented or transcribed dreams. We were therefore confronted with an *embarras de richesses* as our eclectic criteria allowed us to pick any dream in any period of any literature, classical or modern (though in the end, for obvious cultural reasons, we limited ourselves to texts from Western Europe and North America with a few excursions towards Russia and more exotic areas). We have tried to give an adequate sampling of dreams in Western literature, from the Bible to Kerouac, choosing the texts for their representativeness, their psychological interest, their aesthetic value, their stylistic exuberance – but mainly for their capacity to please us, titillate our curiosity and stimulate our reflections in this area. Setting aside the issue of exhaustiveness – which in this field would be a preposterous ambition – we would like to forestall criticism with a preliminary declaration. All the readers who think that we have neglected the most important, the most beautiful, the most significant, the most extraordinary dream in Western literature are right, and we apologize in advance for any inconvenience caused to the public by our omissions.

Robert Benchley, the *New Yorker* humorist, maintained that: 'There may be said to be two classes of people in the world: those who constantly divide the people of the world into two classes, and those who do not.' This is particularly true of culture, where there are classifiers and confusionists, variants of Lévy-Strauss' distinction between *ingénieurs* and *bricoleurs*. We are incurable members of the second category, and every time we thought we had found a way of organizing our material, we immediately discovered possible exceptions that would destroy our scheme. What were we to do with that heap of dreams we were meant to administer? According to Robert Herrick, 'Here we are all by day; by night w'are hurled / By dreams each one onto a sev'rall world'. This implies that there are as many worlds and categories of dreams as there are dreamers; or perhaps more, because each dreamer has a vast repertory of private dreams with their recurrences and variations, not to mention the infinite number of possible combinations between our waking experience and our night fantasy which create every single dream. And beyond those infinite possible dreams, we must add all the impossible dreams invented by writers (but is there such a thing as an *impossible* dream? We do not have an answer to this spell-binding question). It is already difficult to classify our daytime narrative lore, engendered by the commonwealth of waking people; but it is well-nigh impossible to find satisfactory categories in this galaxy of individual narrative worlds spawned by the dreams; or in this hybrid mixture of dream experience and narrative know-how, the library of literary dreams from which we have amply borrowed.

Hence the division we are offering here because of anthological conventions, editorial simplicity and facility of reading is not only arbitrary: it is an avowed fake we have adopted with all the honest dishonesty of cultural operators who are aware of the compromises entailed by any sort of intellectual activity. We first thought of starting from a central pigeon-hole which we would have called 'real', from which we intended to derive three new ones: 'subreal', 'surreal' and 'unreal'. These three categories, together with the main one, were to form the four classes of narrated dreams: 'subreal' dreams, which apparently emerge from deep instinctive sources; 'real' dreams, which are in close relation with the day world; 'surreal' dreams, where reality is transformed according to metaphorical models which might perhaps be interpreted; and 'unreal' dreams, with a prevailing influence of the fantastic element. Out of modesty and for mnemonic reasons we have abandoned this terminology in favour of the four following adjectives: 'instinctive', 'realistic', 'symbolic' and 'fantastic'. We are well aware that every dream participates to some extent in all those four fictitious categories (and probably in a few more) in a crazy cocktail of instinctive forces, residues of experience, symbolic representations and fantastic flights. And even if there were 'genuine' examples of these four categories, we know that they would be the product of complex compromises. The *fantastic* dream story is based on data taken from reality, modified by the symbolic urge and influenced by instinctive motivations; the *symbolic* one feigns to stage a surreal model in which symbol and symbolized thing correspond in an ideal metaphorical embrace, but in practice it must make do with imbalances created by the claims of sensorial and imaginative compulsions; the *instinctive* one has to go through our rational censorship, and yet tries to avoid it by assuming symbolic or fantastic guises; the *realistic* one duplicates reality as in a mirror, but this mirror is deformed by the three other forces; and so on. It is like Alice's *Caucus-race*, with everybody running in circles, so that you can't tell the pursuer from the pursued. Or like a snake eating its tail, as the one seen in dream by Kekule when he was trying to define the model of an organic molecule. To him, the mocking Uroborus brought the solution of his problem (the carbon atoms are arranged in a circular and not a linear structure); we, on the other hand, are left where we were. But among the models of false classification we have considered, this one, though it might not be the least false, is probably the most practical, both for our and the reader's sake.

Instinctive dreams

The dreams we have chosen to call instinctive are apparently the consequence of a speleological descent in the deep strata of our being, or alternatively of an emersion out of those depths. As George Steiner suggests in the passage here reproduced, there are dreams which seem to be born 'before language', or without a linguistic mediation: dreams which do not need words, or concepts, or symbols, or verbal images in order to exist. Dreams, as 'multi-modal perceptual simulations' (according to the terminology of today's oneirological psychology), might not need exterior help to imitate the experience of the 'simulated' sense. 'The eye of man hath not heard, the ear of man hath not seen, man's hand is not able to taste, his tongue to conceive, nor his heart to report, what my dream was', says Bottom in *A Midsummer Night's Dream*. Touch, sight, hearing, smell and taste, which should find expression through the appropriate organs (skin, eyes, ears, nose, tongue), by-pass them through an alternative system of communication: dreaming. This short-circuit results in an instinctive dream which seems to have a direct grasp on the reality of the body (dare we say 'of the ego'?) – defying the primacy of language which has been the main tenet of modern thought (for instance in linguistic philosophy and in semiotics). The dream, when dreamt, is a short-cut, though the same dream, once it is being told, must follow again the large curves of the linguistic main road.

The instinctive dream, which takes place in 'the civil wilderness of sleep' (Robert Herrick), can for example disturb the normal balance between having a body and being conscious of having a body. The subversive power of the dream may turn this body inside out like a sock, in what we would like to call ironically 'a process of interiorization', by deliberately misapplying the term designating the intimacy of the soul to the intimacy of our organs. We say that something is beautiful, attractive, titillating when we look at it from outside. We see the Venus de Milo, or the body of a woman, or a beautiful mountain, and we express our admiration.

But dreaming can alter the coordinates of our vision. What would become of the three examples chosen above if they were seen from the inside? This is the disturbing, traumatic experience evoked by Jean Genet in the passage selected from *The Miracle of the Rose* where judges, guardians and priests explore the inner shafts and galleries of the body of Harcamone, the man condemned to death. His true essence, his real being of flesh, muscles and flowing blood, appears thus in visions where veins and arteries, gullets and windpipes, are transmuted in a utopian landscape. The assessment of Har- camone's beauty, or sex-appeal, or seductiveness, is thus subordinated to the experience – which can only be oneirical – of seeing him from the pipes and capillaries which run through his body. This idea makes the mind reel, a rather frequent experience when you deal with dreams. Try to think of the mouth of a beloved woman: these lips you want to press, bite, suck, know in the intimacy of a kiss or of a touch. Now invert the angle of vision, and imagine the same lips as seen from within the barrier of the teeth, the mouth as the monstrous opening of a cave sheltering the terrifying clamp of the jaws. The lips open to admit air for breathing, water for drinking – or worse still, food, to be crushed mashed and mushed between teeth, tongue and palate, and eventually reduced to a disgusting chewed pulp, before descending to the dark digestive recesses. This is the kind of turn dreams can perform, by spinning the angle of vision and exchanging the usual poles of attraction and repulsion, playing on an elusive reality that by-passes the sensorial universe. As if there were a sixth, oneiric sense controverting the evidence of the five others.

We said that a dream could be a descent: into the depths of our bodily reality, as in Genet; or of a metaphor of the body, as in the mine of E.T.A. Hoffmann's tale, which we quote here at length (this story is rather symp- tomatic of the spirit of a time when the actual development of the mining industry suggested that sort of symbolization – another example would be the mine seen as a digestive system in Zola's *Germinal*). Or in the vertical shaft of the individual's past, be it in the family country house of Rimbaud's child- hood, or in the rich attires of adolescent disguises in Schnitzler; or in the other dark shaft of our genetic past, among those removed amoebic ancestors evoked by Huch, whom the dreamer clumsily tries to destroy with a knife, hacking them into fragments, reducing these embryos of form to 'formless little black lumps' in an attempt to escape from his paleontological heredity. Or in the nether world where Lenau's 'wicked guests' and Apuleius' chthonian gods weave their plots, broadcasting them in our dreams; or in a reversal to primeval chaos, the anarchy of 'bizarre combinations' mentioned in the item of the *Encyclopédie*.

Reaching the bottom, the dream rediscovers the habitual elements of instinctive life: blood, violence and lust. The world of dreams abounds with blood. In Dante's Hell, an oneiric territory almost by definition, the sinners who have committed violence are immersed in the Phlegeton, a stream of boiling blood. Yet this river has a tendency to overflow and invade the heath of our dreams. From yawning wounds blood flows freely to quench our instincts. The haemodynamics of dreams outmatches in liquid volume, strength and passion, the already conspicuous haemodynamics of reality. In the passage from Lautréamont, quoted here, we find the thick blood of the pig which exalts the glorious *suinitas* of the dreamer, so much superior to the *humanitas* that covered him when he was awake. Incongruously, a portentous nose-bleeding in the text by Pierre Jean Jouve drenches the underpants used as a handkerchief by the dreamer to compensate for the absence of red lipstick; and blood seeps out of the piously broken bread in Flaubert's cannibalistic dream. The whole tale of Apuleius reproduced here is a slow preparation for the awesome fount of blood that spouts from Socrates' neck. Violence is expressed by bites, scratches, wounds, tearings, beheadings, penetrations (sexual or not). In the omnipotence of dreams, man kills easily: relatives, parents, children, acquaintances – perhaps more readily his friends than his enemies, the innocents than the culprits, the loved ones than the hated ones, subverting thus the coordinates of our feelings. And almost all dreams are pervaded by sex, unadulterated by the fiction of love, distilled to its purest essence of madness and lust.

The unsatisfied woman in Bodel's *fabliau* may love her husband, or think that she loves him, or be aware of her conjugal happiness: but the evidence of the dream frees the Eros from the slag of feelings and affections. The woman is condemned to a temporary dissatisfaction by the excessive drinking of her husband, and to perpetual dissatisfaction by the difference between the dreamed cocks and the reality of her husband's sexual appendage. In Schnitzler's novel, the lustful night roamings of Fridolin fade before the shattering arrogance of Albertine's dreamed infidelities. Everything is over-thrown by the might of the sexual instinct in the freedom of the dream: destroyed are the religious feeling and the quiet routine of the ecclesiastical profession (Gautier); the nobility of Orlando's lofty love (Ariosto); the respectability of the intellectual (Leiris); the awareness of one's humble social rank (Voltaire). In Charles Sorel the object of desire is even reduced to pieces: legs, breasts, belly, arms, tongue etc., which must be put back together as a wooden doll before the final ceremony of consummation.

Maybe some women, when awake, crave for love with a lorry-driver who would treat them with the same delicacy he would use in changing a wheel of his juggernaut; maybe some men crave for a quick roll in the hay, a swift, hasty act of love, 'he took her, short and sharp and finished, like an animal' (D. H. Lawrence, in *Lady Chatterley's Lover*). But dreams can lower the level even further, accelerate the pace, stress brutality and bestiality, cancel all foreplay and postcoital languor: 'Wham Bam' without even the 'Thank you, Ma'am' or 'Sorry, Sam' which is *de rigueur* in the traditional joke. This is not without consequences to the economy of the psyche in general and of the dream in particular. One is tempted to say that any manifestation of aggressive or lustful instincts in dreams produces a kind of recoil, a rebound, so as to compensate the temporary imbalance between instinct and conscience. The toll is paid in fear, remorse, guilty feelings, self-hatred, or a sensation of forced immobility, of paralysis. 'Dreams are preponderantly unpleasant,' says Alfred Ziegler, an experimental psychologist. The low pleasures of dreams entail the high pains of dreams.

We do not always dwell in our dreams: at times we only visit them with the timorous attitude of a tourist in a foreign land. 'Who's there?' 'Nay, answer me and unfold yourself': in the first scene of Hamlet these words are uttered by Barnardo and Francisco who are also frightened by possible oneiric visitations. We may as well say: 'Who's there?' 'Nay, answer me and unfold yourself' when we meet another human being; perhaps another 'I', down there in Dreamland. 'Every bit of the dream, including the dream "I", is a metaphorical image' (James Hillman). The so-called *primitives* consider their own images in their dreams as a sort of *double*: while they sleep, their *double* lives a thousand compromising adventures in another universe. In Proust Swann sees from outside, or experiences from inside, the sensations of a second Swann who is able to control his jealousy because of Odette's affair with Napoleon III. But this second Swann meets a 'strange young man', who was still Swann; and the latter 'bursts into tears' when he hears this news, so much so that the second Swann must dry the eyes of the third Swann. In the Chinese dream of Bao-Yu, here included, we would thus have an 'I' who dreams another 'I' who meets a third 'I': a disturbing *mise-en-abyme* for us Westerners, slaves of our pompous individualism which we aspire to impose upon both sides of the threshold of sleep. But the dream experience shatters the pathetic limitations of our individualistic conception of what constitutes a human being, and forces upon us a dialogue, not always a pleasant one, with alternative realities of our 'I'.

The dream is the 'mirror mirror on the wall' that always answers our wishes with unpleasant truths. In all the horror literature of the nineteenth century, the most frightening scene is probably the moment in which Jàkov Petròvitch Goliàdkin meets another Jàkov Petròvitch Goliàdkin on the embankment of the Fontanka: 'an unknown person whom he thought was partially known', in Dostoevsky's *The Double*. It is not Dr Jekyll meeting Mr Hyde, but something far worse: Dr Jekyll meeting Dr Jekyll. In a way, dreams are a kind of daily repetition of this fatal encounter, where the dreamer meets the protagonist of his dreams, a duplicate of himself, who commits improper and reprehensible actions. This is perfectly illustrated in the opening of Peter Handke's novel, included in this anthology, in which the main character, after committing a murder in a dream, can no longer confront himself or his family when he wakes up, and finds himself totally alienated from what he thought, or fancied, he was. This theme of the double reappears in several texts of this section: Sheridan Le Fanu, Leiris, Baudelaire, Gautier, Huch. In Le Fanu's story Judge Harbottle, who pays for the immorality of his life with the death penalty in his nightmare (and with suicide in his life, in a section of the short story which is not included in this anthology), meets a duplication of himself who bears the significant name of Judge Twofold.

Yet not all encounters with the *double* are sinister. When Jekyll finds himself transformed after drinking his fatal potion, he feels 'younger, lighter, happier in body'. This might also be true of the duplicated dreamer, who has ambivalent feelings towards his reflected image. The ambivalence is confirmed by the recurring theme, both in the common experience and in our choice of texts, of nakedness, of finding your clothes wet (in Butor's 'Dream Matter'), of losing your pants or skirts, or walking about with your prick hanging out of your fly: an experience which seems to satisfy both our exhibitionistic drives and self-punishing desires. Of course these dreams, for all their 'instinctiveness', are also symbolic, and the attraction/repulsion towards one's own sexual organs signify also the attraction/repulsion towards other pudenda, towards these things we are also ashamed of: the pudenda of our instincts, the naked avowal of our desires, the intimacy deprived of all covering or masking. Hence a dream of nakedness, according to our hypothesis of a quadripartite division, must be exquisitely instinctive and arrogantly symbolic at the same time.

But there is another kind of dream, still within the region of the instinctive, which seems immune to this ransoming process: this is the dream that rises from the depths instead of plunging downwards, when the instincts are used as a launching pad towards the upper regions. This happens in particular in the dreams of flight, perhaps the most satisfying of oneiric experiences. Dreams often enable us to move in the fourth dimension, to overcome the severe limitations of time past and time future and dive into yesterday's or leap into tomorrow's world. But in our opinion no one has sufficiently stressed that the main privilege granted us by dreams is the freedom of movement in the third, and not in the fourth, dimension. In real life, we can almost always freely choose whether we want to go forward or backwards, left or right; but we cannot decide to go up or down, unless we are in a lift (see the dream of Brillat-Savarin in this section). In dreams we enjoy this freedom of kicking our heels and soaring like Superman in a wingless flight (Bachelard's description on this point is very convincing). This is perhaps the happiest, the most exhilarating of dream experiences, which frees us from 'the sin of gravity', to use Nietzsche's expression, and gives us the liberty and innocence of weightlessness. The study of dreams, both the literary sort and those occurring in real life, should expand from the nightmare to its opposite, the boundless joy of oneiric flight.

Of course dreams of flying can also be symbolic, when the flight stands for something else: a social climb, for example; or, according to Artemidorus, it can be diagnostic or prophetic, indicating the prospect of a future journey or a project of emigration. Malerba's character, the greatest flyer in this anthology, declares that he can 'steer his dreams, not the way you steer a car or a bicycle, but the way you steer a boat that always veers a little and can't take narrow curves'. This is probably the neatest formulation in all oneirological literature of the labile connection between our will and our dreams (Hervey Saint-Denis, in his *Les rêves et les moyens de les diriger*, 'Dreams and how to steer them', had come to the same conclusion in his heavy pseudo-scientific style). But in spite of Malerba's ironic claim to program his imaginative night-life, the dream in the passage from his novel, *The Serpent*, reproduced here, seems to be gloriously instinctive, free from the conventions of steering and the responsibility of control. We would like to insist on the primary meaning of the dream of flight, which is in fact flying itself, with all due deference to Freud and his acolytes.

Psychoanalysis links the dream of flight to the child's delight in movement, interpreted in a sexual key: I would fly in the overt dream to remove the fact that, in the latent meaning of the dream, I am having intercourse. And if the contrary were true, as affirmed by Ludwig Duerf, Freud's antagonist (whose very name is the diametric opposite of his Viennese colleague's)? Duerf, who is recalled in two small pages of *The New Statesman* by the poet and wit Robert Conquest, is supposed to have invented a counter theory to Freud's, which he published in the *Acta linguistica Cracoviensa*. The dreams and symbols of flight do not stand for the details of our repressed sexual fantasy but vice-versa: among the aviatorily repressed, sexual dreams and symbols stand for the unconscious desire to fly, or maybe to become a pilot. D. H. Lawrence's *Lady Chatterley's Lover* should be read as a repressed literary sublimation, in its wealth of sex and phalli and vulvae and pubic hair and open-air copulations, of the aviatory libido of the author. The novel actually demonstrates that the writer, D. H. Lawrence, craved to imitate his famous cousin by marriage Baron von Richtofen, the ace of the German Air Force (a complex Lawrence shares with Snoopy). Symbols, as Bachelard taught us, always work both ways – else, what kind of symbols would they be? Neither Freud nor Duerf can find proof of their interpretations since they are not submitted to the laws of verifiability. Between the two of them, our preference goes of course to Duerf. If I dream I am riding a horse, this might *mean* I want to ride a woman; and if I dream I am riding a woman, this might *mean* I want to ride a horse. The discourse of instinct helps to muddle the waters.

PLATO

Imitation of dreams

The theme of *Phaedo* is the immortality of the soul. From a narrative point of view the setting of the dialogue – in the cell of Socrates before he drinks hemlock – places it between *The Apology* and *Crito*. These two dialogues were, however, written shortly after Socrates' death in 399 BC, whereas *Phaedo*, like *The Symposium*, *The Republic* and *Phaedrus*, are works of Plato's maturity, written probably around 380 BC.

Socrates, sitting up on the couch, began to bend and rub his leg, saying, as he rubbed: How singular is the thing called pleasure, and how curiously related to pain, which might be thought to be the opposite of it; for they never will come to a man together, and yet he who pursues either of them is generally compelled to take the other. Their bodies are two, and yet they are joined to a single head; and I cannot help thinking that if Aesop had noticed them, he would have made a fable about God trying to reconcile their strife, and how, when he could not, he fastened their heads together; and this is the reason why when one comes the other follows, as I find in my own case pleasure comes following after the pain in my leg which was caused by the chain.

Upon this Cebes said: I am very glad indeed, Socrates, that you mentioned the name of Aesop. For that reminds me of a question which has been asked by others, and was asked of me only the day before yesterday by Evenus the poet; and as he will be sure to ask again, if you would like me to have an answer ready for him, you may as well tell me what I should say to him. He wanted to know why you, who never before wrote a line of poetry, now that you are in prison are putting Aesop into verse, and also composing that hymn in honour of Apollo.

Tell him, Cebes, he replied, that I had no idea of rivalling him or his poems; (which is the truth, for that, as I knew, would be no easy task). But I wanted to see whether I could purge away a scruple which I felt about the meaning of certain dreams. In the course of my life I have often had intimations in dreams 'that I should compose music.' The same dream came to me sometimes in one form, and sometimes in another, but always saying the same or nearly the same words: Compose and practise music, said the dream. And hitherto I had imagined that this was only intended to exhort and encourage me in the study of philosophy, which has always been the pursuit of my life, and is the noblest and best of music. The dream was bidding me do what I was already doing, in the same way that the competitor in a race is bidden by the spectators to run when he is already running. But I was not certain of this, as the dream might have meant music in the popular sense of the word, and being under sentence of death, and the festival giving me a respite, I thought that I should be safer if I satisfied the scruple, and, in obedience to the dream, composed a few verses before I departed. And first I made a hymn in honour of the god of the festival, and then considering that a poet, if he is really to be a poet, should not only put together words, but should invent stories, and that I have no invention, I took some fables of Aesop, which I had ready at hand and knew, and turned them into verse. Tell Evenus this, and bid him be of good cheer; say that I would have him come after me if he be a wise man, and not tarry; and that today I am likely to be going, for the Athenians say that I must.

Translated by B. Jowett

APULEIUS

The Witch

We have very little information about Apuleius, the author of *The Golden Ass*, who lived in the second century AD. The passage chosen here is at the very beginning of the story. Lucius, on his way to Hypata, meets two friends who are discussing the truth of magic. In spite of the jokes of his sceptical companion, one of the two, Aristomenes, tells the story of another friend, Socrates, and the witch Merope. In a half-comic half-gruesome manner this story gives the tone of the future magic misadventures of Lucius, who shall be transformed into an ass by the blunderings of a would-be witch.

Certes sir I thanke you for your gentle offer, and at your request I wil proceed in my tale; but first I will sweare unto you by the light of this Sunne that shineth here, that those things that I shall tell be true, least when you come to the next city called Thessaly, you should doubt any thing of that which is rife in the mouthes of every person, and done before the face of all men. And that I may first make relation unto you, what and who I am, and whither I go, and for what purpose, know ye that I am of Egin, travelling these countries about from Thessaly to Etolia, and from Etolia to Boetia, to provide for honey, cheese, and other victuals to sell againe: and understanding that at Hippata (which is the principall city of all Thessaly) is accustomed to be sould new cheeses of exceeding good taste and relish, I fortuned on a day to goe thither, to make my market there: but as it often happeneth, I came in an evill houre; for one Lupus a Purveyor had bought and ingrossed up all the day before, and so I was deceived.

Wherefore towards night being very weary, I went to the Baines to refresh my selfe, and behold, I fortuned to espy my companion Socrates sitting upon the ground, covered with a torne and course mantle; who was so meigre and of so sallow and miserable a countenance, that I scantly knew him: for fortune had brought him into such estate and calamity, that he verily seemed as a common begger that standeth in the streets to crave the benevolence of the passers by. Towards whom (howbeit he was my singular friend and familiar acquaintance, yet halfe in despaire) I drew nigh and said, Alas my Socrates, what meaneth this? how fareth it with thee? What crime has thou committed? verily there is great lamentation and weeping made for thee at home: Thy children are in ward by the decree of the Provinciall Judge: Thy wife (having ended her mourning time in lamentable wise, with face and visage blubbered with teares, in such sort that she hath well nigh wept out both her eyes) is constrained by her parents to put out of remembrance the unfortunate losse and lacke of thee at home, and against her will to take a new husband. And dost thou live here as a ghost or hogge, to our great shame and ignominy?

Then answered he to me and said, O my friend Aristomenus, now perceive I well that you are ignorant of the whirling changes, the unstable forces, and slippery inconstancy of Fortune: and therewithall he covered his face (even then blushing for very shame) with his rugged mantle, insomuch that from his navel downwards he appeared all naked.

But I not willing to see him any longer in such great miserie and calamitie, took him by the hand and lifted him up from the ground: who having his face covered in such sort, Let Fortune (quoth he) triumph yet more, let her have her sway, and finish that which shee hath begun. And therewithall I put off one of my garments and covered him, and immediately I brought him to the Baine, and caused him to be anointed, wiped, and the filthy scurfe of his body to be rubbed away; which done, although I were very weary my selfe, yet I led the poore miser to my Inne, where he reposed his body upon a bed, and then I brought him meat and drinke, and so wee talked together: for there we might be merry and laugh at our pleasure, and so we were, untill such time as he (fetching a pittifull sigh from the bottome of his heart, and beating his face in miserable sort) began to say.

Alas poore miser that I am, that for the onely desire to see a game of triall of weapons, am fallen into these miseries and wretched snares of misfortune. For in my returne from Macedonie, whereas I sould all my wares, and played the Merchant by the space of ten months, a little before that I came to Larissa, I turned out of the way, to view the scituation of the countrey there, and behold in the bottome of a deep valley I was suddenly environed with a company of theeves, who robbed and spoiled me of such things as I had, and yet would hardly suffer me to escape. But I beeing in such extremity, in the end was happily delivered from their hands, and so I fortuned to come to the house of an old woman that sold wine, called Meroe, who had her tongue sufficiently instructed to flattery: unto whom I opened the causes of my long peregrination and carefull travell, and of myne unlucky adventure: and after that I had declared unto her such things as then presently came to my remembrance, shee gently entertained mee and made mee good cheere; and by and by beeing pricked by carnall desire, shee brought mee to her own bed chamber; whereas I poore miser the very first night of our lying together did purchase to my selfe this miserable face, and for her lodging I gave her such apparel as the theeves left to cover me withall.

Then I understanding the cause of his miserable estate, sayd unto him, in faith thou art worthy to sustaine the most extreame misery and calamity, which has defiled and maculated thyne owne body, forsaken thy wife traiterously, and dishonoured thy children, parents, and friends, for the love of a vile harlot and old strumpet. When Socrates heard mee raile against Meroe in such sort, he held up his finger to mee, and as halfe abashed sayd, Peace peace I pray you, and looking about lest any body should heare, I pray you (quoth he) take heed what you say against so venerable a woman as shee is, lest by your intemperate tongue you catch some harm. Then with resemblance of admiration, What (quoth I) is she so excellent a person as you name her to be? I pray you tell mee. Then answered hee, Verily shee is a Magitian, which hath power to rule the heavens, to bring downe the sky, to beare up the earth, to turn the waters into hills, and the hills into running waters, to lift up the terrestrial spirits into the aire, and to pull the gods out of the heavens, to extinguish the planets, and to lighten the deepe darkenesse of hell. Then sayd I unto Socrates, I pray thee leave off this high and mysticall kinde of talke, and tell the matter in a more plaine and simple fashion. Then answered he, Will you heare one or two, or more of her facts which she hath done, for whereas she inforceth not onely the inhabitants of the countrey here, but also the Indians and the Ethiopians the one and the other, and also the Antictons, to love her in most raging sort, such are but trifles and chips of her occupation, but I pray you give eare, and I will declare of more greater matters, which shee hath done openly and before the face of all men.

In faith Aristomenus to tell you the truth, this woman had a certaine Lover, whom by the utterance of one only word she turned into a Bever, because he loved another woman beside her: and the reason why she transformed him into such a beast is, for that it is his nature, when hee perceiveth the hunters and hounds to draw after him, to bite off his members, and lay them in the way, that the hounds may be at a stop when they finde them, and to the intent it might so happen unto him (because he fancied another woman) she turned him into that kinde of shape.

Semblably she changed one of her neighbours, being an old man and one that sold wine, into a Frog, in that he was one of her occupation, and therefore she bare him a grudge, and now the poore miser swimming in one of his pipes of wine, and well nigh drowned in the dregs, doth cry and call with an hoarse voice, for his old guests and acquaintance that pass by. Likewise she turned one of the Advocates of the Court (because he pleaded and spake against her in a rightfull cause) into a horned Ram, and now the poore Ram is become an Advocate. Moreover she caused, that the wife of a certain lover that she had should never be delivered of her childe, but according to the computation of all men, it is eight yeares past since the poore woman began first to swell, and now shee is encreased so big, that shee seemeth as though she would bring forth some great Elephant: which when it was knowne abroad, and published throughout all the towne, they tooke indignation against her, and ordayned that the next day shee should most cruelly be stoned to death. Which purpose of theirs she prevented by the vertue of her inchantments, and as Medea (who obtained of King Creon but one days respit before her departure) did burne all his house, him, and his daughter: so she, by her conjurations and invocations of spirits (which she useth in a certaine hole in her house, as shee her selfe declared unto me the next day following) closed all the persons in the towne so sure in their houses, and with such violence of power, that for the space of two dayes they could not get forth, nor open their gates nor doore, nor break downe their walls, whereby they were inforced by mutuall consent to cry unto her, and to binde themselves strictly by oaths, that they would never afterwards molest or hurt her: and moreover, if any did offer her any injury they would be ready to defend her. Whereupon shee, mooved by their promises, and stirred by pitty, released all the towne. But shee conveyed the principal Author of this ordinance about midnight, with all his house, the walls, the ground, and the foundation, into another towne, distant from thence an hundred miles, scituate and beeing on the top of an high hill, and by reason thereof destitute of water, and because the edifices and houses were so nigh built together, that it was not possible for the house to stand there, she threw it downe before the gate of the towne. Then I spake and said, O my friend Socrates you have declared unto me many marvellous things and strange chances, and moreover stricken me with no small trouble of minde, yea rather with great feare, lest the same old woman using the like practice, should fortune to heare all our communication. Wherefore let us now sleepe, and after that we have taken our rest, let us rise betimes in the morning, and ride away hence before day, as far as we can possible.

In speaking these words, and devising with my selfe of our departing the next morrow, lest Meroe the Witch should play by us as she had done by divers other persons, it fortuned that Socrates did fall asleepe, and slept very soundly, by reason of his travell, and plenty of meat and wine wherewithall hee had filled him selfe. Wherefore I closed and barred fast the doores of the chamber, and put my bed behinde the doore, and so layed mee downe to rest.

But I could in no wise sleepe, for the great feare which was in my heart, untill it was about midnight, and then I began to slumber. But alas, behold suddenly the chamber doores brake open, and lockes, bolts, and posts fell downe, that you would verily have thought that some Theeves had beene presently come to have spoyled and robbed us. And my bed whereon I lay being a truckle bed, fashioned in forme of a Cradle, and one of the feet broken and rotten, by violence was turned upside downe, and I likewise was overwhelmed and covered lying in the same. Then perceived I in my selfe, that certaine affects of the minde by nature doth chance contrary. For as tears oftentimes trickle down the cheekes of him that seeth or heareth some joyfull newes, so I being in this fearefull perplexity, could not forbeare laughing, to see how of Aristomenus I was made like unto a snail in his shell. And while I lay on the ground covered in this sort, I peeped under the bed to see what would happen. And behold there entred in two old women, the one bearing a burning torch, and the other a sponge and a naked sword; and so in this habit they stood about Socrates being fast asleep. Then shee which bare the sword sayd unto the other, Behold sister Panthia, this is my deare and sweet heart, which both day and night hath abused my wanton youthfulnesse. This is he, who little regarding my love, doth not onely defame me with reproachfull words, but also intendeth to run away. And I shall be forsaken by like craft as Vlysses did us, and shall continually bewaile my solitarinesse as Calipso. Which said, shee pointed towards mee that lay under the bed, and shewed me to Panthia. This is hee, quoth she, which is his Counsellor, and perswadeth him to forsake me, and now being at the point of death he lieth prostrate on the ground covered with his bed, and hath seene all our doings, and hopeth to escape scot-free from my hands, but I will cause that hee shall repent himselfe too late, nay rather forthwith, of his former untemperate language, and his present curiosity. Which words when I heard I fell into a cold sweat, and my heart trembled with feare, insomuch that the bed over me did likewise rattle and shake. Then spake Panthia unto Meroe and said, Sister let us by and by teare him in pieces, or tye him by the members, and so cut them off. Then Meroe (being so named because she was a Taverner, and loved well good wines) answered, Nay rather let him live, and bury the corps of this poore wretch in some hole of the earth; and therewithall shee turned the head of Socrates on the other side, and thrust her sword up to the hilts into the left part of his necke, and received the bloud that gushed out, into a pot, that no drop thereof fell beside: which things I saw with myne owne eyes, and as I thinke to the intent she might alter nothing that pertained to sacrifice, which she accustomed to make, she thrust her hand downe into the intrals of his body, and searching about, at length brought forth the heart of my miserable companion Socrates, who having his throat cut in such sort, yeelded out a dolefull cry and gave up the ghost. Then Panthia stopped the wide wound of his throat with the Sponge, and said, O Sponge sprung and made of the sea, beware that thou passe not by running

River. This being sayd, the one of them moved and turned up my bed, and then they strid over mee, and clapped their buttocks upon my face, and all bepissed mee till I was wringing wet. When this was ended they went their wayes, and the doores closed fast, the posts stood in their old places, and the lockes and bolts were shut againe. But I that lay upon the ground like one without soule, naked and cold, and wringing wet with pisse, like to one that were more than halfe dead, yet reviving my selfe, and appointed as I thought for the Gallowes, began to say, Alasse what shall become of me to morrow, when my companion shall be found murthered here in the chamber? To whom shall I seeme to tell any similitude of truth, when as I shal tell the trueth in deed? They will say, if thou wert unable to resist the violence of the women, yet shouldest thou have cried for helpe; Wouldst thou suffer the man to be slaine before thy face and say nothing? Or why did they not slay thee likewise? Why did they spare thee that stood by and saw them commit that horrible fact? Wherefore although thou hast escaped their hands, yet thou shalt not escape ours. While I pondered these things with my selfe the night passed on, and so I resolved to take my horse before day, and goe forward on my journey.

Howbeit the wayes were unknowne unto me, and thereupon I tooke up my packet, unlocked and unbarred the doors, but those good and faithfull doores which in the night did open of their owne accord, could then scantly be opened with their keys. And when I was out I cried, O sirrah Hostler where art thou? open the stable doore, for I will ride away by and by. The Hostler lying behinde the stable doore upon a pallet, and halfe asleepe, What (quoth hee) doe you not know that the wayes be very dangerous? What meane you to rise at this time of night? If you perhaps guilty of some heynous crime, be weary of your life, yet thinke you not that wee are such Sots that we will die for you. Then said I, It is well nigh day, and moreover, what can Theeves take from him that hath nothing? Doest thou not know (Foole as thou art) if thou be naked, if ten Gyants should assaile thee, they could not spoyle or rob thee? Whereunto the drowsie Hostler halfe asleepe, and turning on the other side, answered, What know I whether you have murthered your Companion whom you brought in yesternight, or no, and now seeke the meanes to escape away? O Lord, at that time I remember the earth seemed to open, and me thought I saw at hell gate the Dog Cerberus ready to devour mee; and then I verily beleeved, that Meroe did not spare my throat, mooved with pitty, but rather cruelly pardoned mee to bring mee to the Gallowes. Wherefore I returned to my chamber, and there devised with my selfe in what sort I should finish my life. But when I saw that fortune would minister unto mee no other instrument, than that which my bed profered mee, I sayd, O bed, O bed, most dear unto me at this present, which hast abode and suffered with me so many miseries, judge and arbiter of such things as were done here this night, whome onely I may call to witnesse for my innocency, render (I say) unto me some wholsome weapon to end my life, that am most willing to dye. And therewithal

I pulled out a piece of the rope wherewith the bed was corded and tyed one end thereof about a rafter by the window, and with the other end I made a sliding knot, and stood upon my bed, and so put my neck into it, and when I leaped from the bed, thinking verily to strangle my selfe and so dye, behold the rope beeing old and rotten burst in the middle, and I fell downe tumbling upon Socrates that lay under: And even at that same very time the Hostler came in crying with a loud voyce, and sayd, Where are you that made such hast at midnight, and now lies wallowing abed? Whereupon (I know not whether it was by my fall, or by the great cry of the Hostler) Socrates as waking out of a sleepe, did rise up first and sayd, It is not without cause that strangers do speake evill of all such Hostlers, for this Caitife in his comming in, and with his crying out, I thinke under a colour to steale away somthing, hath waked me out of a sound sleepe. Then I rose up joyfull with a merry countenance, saying, Behold good Hostler, my friend, my companion and my brother, whom thou didst falsly affirme to be slaine by mee this night. And therewithall I embraced my friend Socrates and kissed him: but hee smelling the stinke of the pisse wherewith those Hagges had embrued me, thrust me away and sayd, Clense thy selfe from this filthy odour, and then he began gently to enquire, how that noysome sent hapned unto mee. But I finely feigning and colouring the matter for the time, did breake off his talk, and tooke him by the hand and sayd, Why tarry we? Why lose wee the pleasure of this faire morning? Let us goe, and so I tooke up my packet and payed the charges of the house and departed: and we had not gone a mile out of the Towne but it was broad day, and then I diligently looked upon Socrates throat, to see if I could espy the place where Meroe thrust in her sword: but when I could not perceive any such thing, I thought with my selfe, What a mad man am I, that being overcome with wine yester night, have dreamed such terrible things? Behold, I see Socrates is sound, safe, and in health. Where is his wound? where is the Sponge? Where is his great and new cut? And then I spake to him and sayd, Verily it is not without occasion, that Physitians of experience do affirme, That such as fill their gorges abundantly with meat and drinke, shall dreame of dire and horrible sights: for I my selfe, not tempering my appetite yester night from the pots of wine, did seeme to see this night strange and cruel visions, that even yet I think my self sprinkled and wet with human blood: whereunto Socrates laughing made answer and said, Nay, thou art not wet with the blood of men, but thou art imbrued with stinking pisse; and verily I my selfe dreamed this night that my throat was cut, and that I felt the paine of the wound, and that my heart was pulled out of my belly, and the remembrance thereof makes me now to feare, for my knees do so tremble that I can scarce goe any further, and therefore I would faine eat somewhat to strengthen and revive my spirits. Then said I, Behold here thy breakefast, and therwithall I opened my script that hanged upon my shoulder, and gave him bread and cheese, and we sate downe under a great Plane tree, and I eat part with him; and while I beheld him eating greedily, I perceived that he waxed meigre and pale, and that his lively colour faded away, insomuch that beeing in great fear, and remembring those terrible furies of whom I lately dreamed, the first morsell of bread that I put in my mouth (which was but very small) did so sticke in my jawes, that I could neither swallow it downe, nor yet yeeld it up, and moreover the small time of our being together increased my feare, and what is hee that seeing his companion die in the high-way before his face, would not greatly lament and bee sorry? But when that Socrates had eaten sufficiently he waxed very thirsty, for indeed he had well nigh devoured all a whole Cheese: and behold evill fortune! there was behinde the Plane tree a pleasant running water as cleere as Crystal, and I sayd unto him, Come hither Socrates to this water and drinke thy fill. And then he rose and came to the River and kneeled downe upon the side of the banke to drinke, but he had scarce touched the water with his lips when as behold the wound of his throat opened wide, and the Sponge suddenly fell into the water, and after issued out a little remnant of bloud, and his body being then without life, had fallen into the river, had not I caught him by the leg and so pulled him up. And after that I had lamented a good space the death of my wretched companion, I buried him in the Sands there by the river.

Which done, in great feare I rode through many Outwayes and desart places, and as culpable of the death of Socrates, I forsooke my countrey, my wife, and my children, and came to Etolia where I married another Wife.

This tale told Aristomenus, and his fellow which before obstinatly would give no credit unto him, began to say, Verily there was never so foolish a tale, nor a more absurd lie told than this. And then he spake unto me saying, Ho sir, what you are I know not, but your habit and countenance declareth that you should be some honest Gentleman, (speaking to Apuleius) doe you beleeve this tale? Yea verily (quoth I) why not? For whatsoever the fates have appointed to men, that I beleeve shall happen. For many things chance unto me and unto you, and to divers others, which beeing declared unto the ignorant bee accounted as lies. But verily I give credit unto his tale, and render entire thankes unto him, in that by the pleasant relation thereof we have quickly passed and shortned our journey, and I thinke that my horse also was delighted with the same, and hath brought me to the gate of this city without any paine at all. Thus ended both our talke and journey, for they two turned on the left hand to the next villages, and I rode into the City.

Translated by W. Aldington

BODEL

The Cock Market

Jean Bodel of Arras, the first known author of *fabliaux*, lived between the twelfth and thirteenth centuries. We know that he was interned as a leper in 1210. The title of this *fabliau*, which is here reproduced in its entirety, is usually given as *Li sohaiz desvez*, ('The Foolish Dream'); but recently the word 'desvez' has been transcribed as 'des vez', i.e. 'des viz', 'of the cocks'; and not 'desvez', i.e. 'foolish, mad'.

I will tell you briefly of an adventure that I heard at Douai; it's about what happened to a man and his wife, whose names, however, I do not know. She was a good woman and he a good man, but I can assure you that each loved the other very much.

One day this good man had some business to do out of town; he was away for at least three months looking for new wares. His business went so well that he returned happy and content to Douai one Thursday evening. Do not think that his wife was sorry to see him, she showed such joy towards her lord, which was also what her duty as a wife required of her, that he never felt so happy before. When she had hugged and kissed him she prepared a low comfortable chair so that he could be at his ease; supper had been ready for some time and they ate as much as they wished, sitting on a cushion by the fire that burned brightly and smokelessly. The room was well-lit and cheerful; they ate two courses: meat and fish, they had wine from Auxerre and Soissons, a white tablecloth and good food. The lady was eager to serve him: she gave her husband the best portions and poured him wine at every morsel to increase his enjoyment. The lady was very keen to offer him her services for she expected that he in his turn should welcome her too. But she was not very careful about one thing: she gave him so much wine that he was completely overcome by it, so that when it was bedtime he quite forgot that other pleasure. His wife, however, who came to lie beside him, remembered it well; she was not waiting for his invitation, she was quite ready for everything. He took no notice of his wife who would have liked to have some fun and stay awake a little longer. Do not think that the lady was pleased when she discovered her husband was asleep. 'Ah!' she said, 'This is proof of the filthy, smelly peasant that he is; he ought to be awake but he's asleep! I'm very annoyed about this; I haven't slept with him for two months nor he with me, and now the devil has sent him to sleep, and may he take him too!' The lady does not say what she thinks, but meditates and pushes aside the thoughts that arouse her; she does not wake or touch him for he would consider her insatiable. For this reason the lady forgot the thoughts and desires she felt towards him and fell asleep, angry and upset.

Now in all truth I tell you that while she was asleep the lady had a dream and dreamt that she was at an annual fair of which you have never heard the likes. There were no stalls or yard-sticks, no tarpaulins or shops, no money changers nor tables nor any place where people sold grey or squirrel fur, nor linen or woollen cloth, nor alum, dye or cochineal, nor anything else, it seemed, but balls and cocks; of these there was no lack. The houses, rooms and attics were full of them and every day porters would arrive weighed down by cocks; and they came by the cartload too. And even if many came, it was not in vain, for everybody sold his share. For thirty sous you could have a good one, and for twenty a nicely shaped one, and there were poor people's cocks too; you could have fun with a little one for ten, nine or eight sous. They were sold retail and wholesale, the biggest were the best, the most expensive, the most sought after. The lady looked everywhere, and struggled and strove until she came to a stall where she had seen a big long one. She stayed near there: it was big at the back, big all over and had a large bold snout. To tell you the truth, you could throw a cherry, send it flying into the eye and it would go all the way to the sack containing the balls that were as big as a shovel; never was there anything like it. The lady began to bargain for the cock, she asked the man the price: 'Even if you were my sister you would not pay less than two marks. This cock is neither poor nor feeble; indeed, it is the best in Lorraine and its balls are from Lorraine too: they've worked well this year! Take it, you won't regret it,' he said, 'seeing as though you're being begged to do so.' 'My friend, what's the point in dillydallying? I'll give you fifty sous if you think that's enough; you'll never get anything more anywhere and I'll give you a penny tip, may God give me joy.' 'I've practically given it away,' he said, 'because I don't want to press you further, and may I receive all that you will wish upon me when you try it out; I think you'll say many a prayer and a psalm for me yet.' Then the lady raised her hand and aimed with such strength for she thought she was striking his palm, but instead she hit her husband, she struck him so hard with the palm of her hand on his cheek as to leave the mark of her five fingers. The slap made him tremble and burn from ear to chin, he was astonished and woke up and on awaking he started, and the lady, who would have preferred to go on sleeping longer, also woke up with a jolt for her joy was turned to sorrow. On awaking she lost the pleasure that she had had in her dream: this was why she would have slept still. 'My love,' he said, 'do tell me what you were dreaming about when you gave me that slap. Were you asleep or awake?' 'My lord, I did not hit you,' she said. 'Don't mention it again, for our love and peace of mind.' 'For the trust you have in me, please tell me what you saw then, do not conceal anything for any reason.'

Know then that the lady began to tell her tale, willingly or perhaps not, of how she had dreamt about the cocks, how there were bad ones and good ones, how she had bought one for herself that was the biggest and the fattest for fifty sous and a penny. 'My lord,' she said, 'this is what happened: the deal had to be concluded; when I thought I was striking his hand, I slapped you hard on the cheek; I did it while I was asleep. For the love of God, do not be angry if I behaved foolishly, I admit my guilt to you and beg your pardon with all my heart.' 'But of course, my dear,' said he, 'I forgive you and may God do so too!' Then he put his arms round her and hugged her tightly and kissed her sweet mouth; and his member began to stretch for she aroused and excited him. Then he put his cock in her hand and when he felt somewhat satisfied he said: 'My dear, by the faith that you owe me, and may God give you great honour, what price would the one you are holding in your hand have fetched at the fair?' 'My lord, if I live to see tomorrow, even if someone had a coffer full of these, he would not find anyone willing to make an offer or to pay a penny for it; even the poor men's cocks were such that one of them would have been worth more than twice as much as this one; I can tell you that there yours would not have been looked at or asked for from afar or near.' 'My dear,' he said, 'I don't really care, but take this one until you can get something better.' And I think this is what she did.

They spent a happy night together, but I believe she was quite brazen in that the next day she went round telling everybody to the point that the news reached the ears of Jean Bodel, a writer of *fabliaux*, who thought it a good story and added it to his own compositions. To cut a long story short, this is where the lady's tale ends.

Translated by Ch. Lee

ARIOSTO

Orlando and Angelica

This passage comes from *Orlando furioso*, a romantic epic written by Ludovico Ariosto in the early sixteenth century, which describes the madness of Orlando, paladin of Charlemagne and chief defender of the Christian faith against the Moors. Before the poem starts, Orlando and his cousin Rinaldo fight for the possession of Angelica, the beautiful daughter of the Great Khan of Cathay; Charlemagne promises Angelica to 'which of them, in the impending fight/More Infidels impaled upon his sword'. But the Christian army is defeated that day, and Angelica flies away. Now Orlando dreams of perils threatening his beloved.

Orlando that same night lies wide awake,
His thoughts, distracted, rambling here, now there.
He tries to concentrate but cannot make
His troubled conscience settle anywhere,
As on the crystal surface of a lake
The trembling shafts of sunlight mirrored are,
Leaping to roof-top, and, at random glancing,
Sparkle and gleam, in all directions dancing.

And to his anguished mind his love returns.
Though never absent, now while he's at rest
She kindles him anew and brighter burns
The flame which seemed by day to have quiesced.
Over and over in his thoughts he churns
How he had travelled with her to the West
As far as from Cathay, how at Bordeaux
He lost her and now seeks her high and low.

His conduct he repented grievously
And often he reproached himself in vain.
'My love,' he said, 'how reprehensively
I have behaved towards you! To think (what pain!)
I might have had you night and day with me
(If my devotion you did not disdain),
But into Namo's hands instead I gave you,
Not knowing from such outrage how to save you.

'Had I not reason to oppose this course?
And Charles perhaps would not have said me nay.
And who against me would have dared use force,
Or who by violence take you away?
And ought not I to arms have had recourse,
My breast presenting to the bitter fray?
In the event, not Charles with all his might
Could have despoiled me of you in fair fight.

'Would he had placed her in another's care,
In Paris, or some citadel well guarded!
To Namo he entrusted her, aware
That she'd escape and would not be awarded
To me as guerdon. No one anywhere
Deserved her more, yet I'm thus ill-rewarded.
I'd have protected her; ah, how I rue
That what I could have done I did not do!

'O my sweet life, where are you now, alone,
Far from my help, so lovely and so young,
Like a lost lamb which, when the day is flown,
Meanders in a wood, in hopes ere long
The shepherd will locate her bleating tone;
But from afar the wolf has heard among
The plains her voice uplifted in the night,
And all in vain the shepherd mourns her plight.

'My hope, where are you now, where can you be?
Alone you wander yet on ways untracked?
Or did the wolves destroy you cruelly
When your Orlando's faithful arm you lacked?
And that sweet flower, the height of bliss, ah me!
Which scrupulously I preserved intact,
Lest I offend a maidenhood so chaste,
By force has now been taken and laid waste?

'Alas! what do I long for but to die,
If men have robbed me of that sweetest bliss?
Send down on me, I pray, O God on high,
All other sufferings, but spare me this!
If it be true, I'll end my life with my
Own hands and send my soul to the Abyss.'
Such were the words Orlando uttered, sighing
And weeping, restless on his pallet lying.

All creatures on the earth to rest their bones,
Or to refresh their souls, now took their ease,
Some on soft beds and others on hard stones,
Some on the grass, still others in the trees;
But you, Orlando, amid tears and groans,
Your eyelids scarce have closed to gain release,
Those irksome, goading thoughts give no respite,
Not in your sleep, so fitful and so light.

In broken slumber thus Orlando dreams:
Upon a bank where flowers his soul refresh,
He gazes upon ivory which seems
By Nature tinted to resemble flesh,
And on two radiant stars, of which the beams
Serve to revive the soul which they enmesh:
I mean her eyes and face (as you have guessed),
By which his heart is riven from his breast.

He felt the greatest happiness and joy
That ever a requited lover knew;
When there arose a tempest to destroy
The plants, the trees, the flowers and all that grew.
No winds, the globe around, such force employ
When in their jousts and tourneys they fall to.
He seemed to seek now here, now there, for shelter,
Lost in a desert, running helter-skelter.

The unhappy man meanwhile (he knows not how)
Has lost his lady in the darkling air.
He calls her name, now in the forests, now
In open country, echoes everywhere
Awakening. 'What powers', he cries, 'allow
That from a sweetness such as this, so rare,
Poison so bitter comes?' Entreating aid,
Her voice is heard in valley, hill and glade.

To left and right, up hill, down dale, in vain
Pursuing her, breathless he seemed to race
Wherever he could hear her voice. The pain
Of fearing that her lovely eyes and face
He'd never in his life behold again
Tortured his anguished heart. From a new place,
A new voice called: 'Confirmed are all your fears!'
Then he awoke, his pillow drenched with tears.

Forgetting that in dreams the things we see,
Inspired by fear or longing, are inclined
To be untrue, firmly convinced was he
His lady was in danger, or repined
In degradation and humility,
And from the restless couch where he reclined
He sprang and, taking shield and coat of mail,
He mounted Brigliadoro and made trail.

He took no squire, nor, lest dishonour might
Attach to his good name (one of the chief
Concerns of chivalry), his coat of white
And crimson quarterings, in the belief
That dubious paths would beckon (as was right);
But chose instead, in keeping with his grief,
A coat of inky black, which he put on,
A trophy he had from an emir won;

And silently, at midnight, stole away.
No courtesy to Charlemagne he showed,
Nor yet to Brandimarte did he say
Farewell, the friend to whom great love he owed;
But when, her golden locks in disarray,
The Dawn had risen from the rich abode
Of her Tithonus, darkness scattering,
His absence was then noticed by the king.

Translated by B. Reynolds

DONNE

Elegie X – The Dreame

This is one of the *Elegies* by John Donne. Another celebrated poem about dreams by Donne, with the same title, *The Dreame*, is in the *Songs and Sonets* ('Deare love, for nothing lesse then thee').

Image of her whom I love, more then she,
　　Whose faire impression in my faithfull heart,
Makes mee her *Medall*, and makes her love mee,
　　As Kings do coynes, to which their stamps impart
The value: goe, and take my heart from hence,
　　Which now is growne too great and good for me:
Honours oppresse weake spirits, and our sense
　　Strong objects dull; the more, the lesse wee see.
When you are gone, and *Reason* gone with you,
　　Then *Fantasie* is Queene and Soule, and all;
She can present joyes meaner then you do;
　　Convenient, and more proportionall.
So, if I dreame I have you, I have you,
　　For, all our joyes are but fantasticall.
And so I scape the paine, for paine is true;
　　And sleepe which locks up sense, doth lock out all.
After a such fruition I shall wake,
　　And, but the waking, nothing shall repent;
And shall to love more thankfull Sonnets make,
　　Then if more *honour, teares*, and *paines* were spent.
But dearest heart, and dearer image stay;

Alas, true joyes at best are *dreame* enough;
Though you stay here you passe too fast away:
For even at first lifes *Taper* is a snuffe.
Fill'd with her love, may I be rather grown
Mad with much *heart*, then *ideott* with none.

SOREL

Francion

Charles Sorel's *Histoire comique de Francion*, a masterpiece of seventeenth-century fiction little known outside France, appeared in 1623. This irreverent picaresque tale was then diluted and expurgated in two successive editions (1626 and 1633). The novel begins *in medias res*: Francion has a rendezvous with his beloved Laurette, after sending her old husband away on an unlikely magic cure for impotence, but their meeting is disrupted by the arrival of thieves. Francion falls from a ladder he was using to reach the window of his mistress, and is taken to an inn where he meets a gentleman, Raymond. He tells him of his love for Laurette and they both go to bed. An old woman, a retired procuress who had Laurette as her pupil and employee before her marriage, has heard the story, and decides to have a look at Francion. Half awakened by the light of her candle, Francion mistakes her for Laurette and kisses her passionately. The old bawd then tells him about Laurette's past and goes away. The next day, Francion recounts to Raymond the dreams he has had during the night.

Sir, since your subtle mind craves the diversion of dreams, let me recount to you the most fantastic the human ear has ever been privy to. And let this principle of my own devising govern my discourse: that if I am found guilty, in the telling, of boring you with nonsense, I will stop as soon as you mention it. 'You would never get to the end of your story,' the Burgundian gentleman interrupted, 'were you to wait for me to enjoin silence upon you: for you are incapable of saying anything which does not bear absorbingly on your subject and which does not bring the listener exquisite pleasure. Even if the things you have dreamed are utterly without rhyme or reason, I will not allow my attention to waver an instant, so that, afterwards, I may thoroughly scrutinize them and find an explanation for them.' I will give you full satisfaction then, the pilgrim said, even though I am sure that Artemidorus himself would have been at a loss in so difficult an undertaking.

Having bid you goodnight after the recital of my history, I gave myself up to an infinite variety of thoughts, and constructed incomparable castles in the air relative to my love-life and fortune, the two concerns which tyrannize my life. So preoccupied was I by these, that sleep took me unawares, and from the very beginning, because my mind was filled with what had befallen me the day before, it seemed to me that I was still in a tub, but unbound and quite naked. I was floating on a huge lake and was very much surprised to see several other men, as naked as I was, and borne along in tubs like mine. They all came from some unidentifiable place by way of a small canal, and after a time there were so many of them that I was afraid lest their tubs so encumbered mine that it would no longer have room to move. But this was not the source of my greatest anxiety, for other things demanded my attention. There was a hole in my vessel which I had to keep permanently plugged with my hands for fear of drowning. My only and meagre consolation was that all the others were in similar straits. No matter, this predicament would have been tolerable to us, had we not at the same time been rained upon by an assortment of cucumbers, melons, mortadellos and other sausages which we hardly dared pick up for fear of letting the water in while we did so.

Those gnawed at by hunger took what they could with one hand, keeping the other firmly over the hole. Others more gluttonous and inventive (for the desire to satisfy the stomach is a master of all arts and sciences) used their members as plugs and set about seizing hold of the sweet manna, which fell from heaven, with both hands. I, who to begin with had done nothing more than open my mouth as a gutter for the rain, was so bold as to follow their example, which produced excellent results. Alas for the misfortunes of some of my companions who sought to emulate me. Their pathetic members were so small, that instead of serving as plugs, they could only act as taps. Consequently they were drowned in pitiful circumstances, all because they had not managed to plug up the hole in their vessels.

For my own part, I had no fear of falling victim to this misfortune, largely because I was as well endowed as anyone with what was necessary; so I had no care in the world other than to fill my belly with sausages, which struck me as the most regal of feasts. Once I had eaten my fill, I diverted myself with the contemplation of a beautiful island in the middle of our lake, where I saw dishes far more exquisite than those on which I had just surfeited myself.

Who can it be who condemns us to such misery? said I. Why does he not cast us up on this delightful island I see before me? Or if it is the hatred he bears us which prevents him doing so, why has he allowed us to carry on living this long?

After uttering these words and realizing that I could not steer my vessel as I wished, because I had no oars, I threw myself headlong into the lake, with the intention of swimming to the island; but I paid the price for my imprudence, for the island which I thought was very close by was in fact a great distance off, and even seemed to recede at the same rate as I progressed towards it, as though it was swimming just as I was.

My despair of ever reaching it reduced my strength to nothing; and my body being no longer borne up by the movement of my arms and feet, I was engulfed by the waves which just then swelled up, with all the unbridled force of sea-waves.

However I fell into a place without sustaining the slightest injury, for the ground was covered with young breasts, stuck together in pairs, like balloons, balloons which I took much time and pleasure rolling about on. Finally I stretched myself out on my back, with all my muscles relaxed, when a beautiful lady came and knelt beside me. She put a funnel in my mouth and, holding a vase in her hands, told me that she wanted me to taste a delicious liquor. I needed no further invitation, but opened my mouth wider than the Bard did when he swallowed a mouse while taking a drink. Then, lifting herself up a little, she pissed more than a pint of urine, and a very generous pint at that, which I had no option but to swallow.

I quickly leapt up to punish her, and had no sooner given her a sharp cuff than her whole body fell to pieces. Her head was on one side, her arms on another, her legs a little further away; in short everything was put asunder. And what made me marvel the more was the fact that, shortly afterwards, all these members and organs resumed their normal functions and operations. The legs began walking about the cave, the arms came over to give me a beating, the head pulled ugly faces and the tongue hurled abuse at me. My fear lest I be accused of having murdered this woman impelled me to search out some way of bringing her back to life. I though that if all the parts of her body could be reassembled, she would recover her former state, since there was no part of her which was not ready to resume all its normal activities. So I collected all the pieces together except her arms and head, and seeing her belly so invitingly attractive, I took the bold step of fondling it, to make my peace with her; but her tongue cried out that I had not chosen the breasts that belonged to her, and that the ones I had re-attached to her body were some others I had picked up in the cave. Immediately I set about discovering hers, and when I had fixed them in their appointed place, the head and arms lost no time in taking up their appropriate postitions, desirous as they were of partaking of the pleasure, along with the other members. The mouth kissed me and the arms tightly embraced me, until a blissful langour made me abandon my caresses.

Translated by C. Scott

RACINE

The Young Assassin

Like Racine's other tragedy inspired by a Biblical story, *Esther*, *Athaliah* was written for the girls' school of Saint-Cyr, where it was represented in 1691. The story is based on 2 Kings, 8–11. Two main factions are confronted: the Kingdom of Judah, true to the Jewish faith; and the Kingdom of Israel, which has become pagan. But Joram, King of Judah, marries Athaliah, daughter of Ahab, King of Israel and Queen Jezebel. Athaliah converts her husband to paganism. Joram dies, and is succeeded by his son Ochosias. Meanwhile, Israel has gone back to the true faith under the reign of Jehu, oncle of Ochosias, who kills his nephew together with all the descendants of Achab, and throws Jezebel to the dogs. Athaliah, who wants to remain Queen of Judah, massacres in the meantime all the children of Ochosias. But one of them, Joas, is saved by the great priest, who hides him in the temple till he can claim his kingship. At the beginning of the tragedy Athaliah is haunted by this premonitory dream.

> *Athaliah*　But these last days, a care has come to ruffle
> The even course of my prosperity:
> A dream – that ever I should come to fear
> A dream! – oppresses and devours my heart.
> I flee it everywhere, it never leaves me.
> It was a night of horror and thick dark,
> And Jezebel my mother stood before me,
> Clad richly, as the day she met her death;
> Nothing had dimmed her spirit, on her cheeks
> Still glowed the borrowed beauty of the colour
> That she had painted on them, to repair
> The irreparable cruelty of time.
> 'Tremble,' she said, 'true daughter of your mother,
> The terrible God of the Jews will conquer you
> As he did me; and it is hard to fall
> Into those hands, my child.' With this, the ghost
> Seemed to bend forward to my bed; and I
> Stretched out my arms to it, only to find
> A mass of mangled flesh and bone, and slime,
> And tatters rolled in blood, and ghastly limbs
> Fought over by the dogs that fed on them.

Abner Great God!
Athaliah After these horrors, I perceived
A little child in linen, dazzling white,
Such as the priests about the Temple wear.
The sight revived me, and my anguish ceased;
But as I looked and marvelled at his air
Of gentleness and noble modesty,
Suddenly he whipped out a treacherous blade
And drove it in my breast. – Perhaps these visions
so disparate, so incongruous, seem to you
A trick of chance; and I was first ashamed
Of having feared a figment of sick fancy.
But it remains with me; and twice again
I have dreamed the self-same dream, and twice again
In slumber I have seen the self-same child
About to stab my body as at first.

Translated by R. C. Knight

ENCYCLOPEDIE

Dreams

The text is taken from the *Encyclopédie* edited by Diderot and D'Alembert, published between 1751 and 1772 in twenty-eight volumes.

The imagination of the waking consciousness is a civilized republic, kept in order by the voice of the magistrate; the imagination of the dreaming consciousness is the same republic, delivered up to anarchy; it should be said, however, that passions are themselves frequent offences against the authority of the law-giver, even when his powers are being fully exercised. There is a law of the imagination for which experience provides incontrovertible proof, namely that the imagination connects objects in the same pattern in which our senses present them to us, and that in the process of remembering, it acts in conformity with that pattern. This is such common knowledge that it would be otiose to dwell upon it. Let us suppose we see a stranger today, for the first time, at some entertainment, in such and such a place, in the company of other individuals: if in the evening our imagination recalls the image of this stranger, either involuntarily or because we will it, it will automatically take it upon itself to represent to us, simultaneously, the place of the entertainment, the seat occupied by the stranger, and the people we noticed in his immediate vicinity; and if we happen to see this same stranger somewhere else, after a year or ten years or more, depending on the power of our memory, even as we see him this whole escort of images, if I may so express it, will gravitate around him.

Such being the manner, therefore, in which images are arranged in our brains, it is hardly suprising that so many bizarre combinations result; but this must be insisted upon, because it explains the outlandishness and apparent absurdity of dreams; and it is not just two objects which are connected in this way, but ten, a thousand, indeed the enormous conglomeration of all our images, of which not one has been registered without some other, and that other without a third, and so on. By recalling any single image, you can, one after the other, summon up all the others, by routes mapped out not by chance, as it might seem, but by the order and circumstances which governed their first entry into our minds; our minds are, if you like, a wood intersected by a thousand pathways; you find yourself on such and such a path, in other words your mind is busied by such and such a sense-impression; if you yield to its enticements, as one does either voluntarily when one is awake, or willy-nilly in the dreams which draw one along this path, you will take a second path, then a third, according to whether they have been made or not; and your itinerary, however irregular it seems, will depend on your point of departure and the lay-out of the wood, so that at another place or in a wood differently intersected, you would have taken another route, been plunged in another dream.

Given these principles, let us now use them to solve the problem of dreams. Dreams occupy us during sleep, and when a dream comes to us, we emerge from the kind of total lethargy into which deep sleep had plunged us, and perceive a sequence of images which are more or less well-defined, depending on the intensity of the dream; this is the popular conception of dreaming. We can only be said to be dreaming when we become conscious of these images, when these images imprint themselves on our memories and we are able to say that we have had such and such a dream, or at least that we have been dreaming. But, in the strictest sense, we are dreaming all the time, that is to say that as soon as sleep has taken possession of our mental operations, the mind is subject to an uninterrupted series of representations and perceptions; but sometimes they are so confused or so dimly registered, that they do not leave the slightest trace, and this is in fact what we call 'deep sleep'; but we would be wrong to regard it as a total absence of any sort of perception, as complete mental inertia.

Translated by C. Scott

VOLTAIRE

The One-Eyed Street Porter

An expurgated version of the tale *The One-Eyed Street Porter* first appeared anonymously in *Le Journal des Dames* of March 1774. The translation given here corresponds to the slightly bawdier version first published in Kehl's posthumous edition of Voltaire's *Oeuvres* (1784).

Our two eyes do not render our condition any the better; one of them enables us to see the good, and the other the evil of life; very many people have the bad habit of closing the first, and very few close the second, – this is why there are so many who would rather be blind than to see all that they do see. Happy are the one-eyed who are deprived only of that bad eye which spoils everything that is looked at! Of these, Mesrour is an example.

It would have been necessary to have been blind not to have seen that Mesrour was one-eyed. He had been so from birth; but he was a one-eyed so contented with his condition that it had never occurred to him to desire another eye; it was not in the least the gifts of Fortune which consoled him for the wrongs of Nature, for he was simply a street-porter, and had no other treasure than his shoulders; but he was happy, and he showed clearly that one eye the more and the inconvenience of having one less had very little to do with happiness – money and appetite came to him always in proportion to the exercise he took; he worked in the early part of the day, ate and drank in the evening, slept at night, and considered all days as so many separate lives; in such fashion that care for the future never troubled him in the enjoyment of the present. He was, as you see, at once one-eyed, street-porter, and philosopher.

He happened to see, passing in a brilliant chariot, a great princess who had one eye more than he, which did not prevent him from thinking her very beautiful; and, as the one-eyed differ from other men only in having an eye the less, he fell violently in love with her. It might be said perhaps that when one is street-porter and one-eyed, it is not at all necessary to fall in love, above all with a great princess, and, what is still more, with a princess who has two eyes. I will admit that there is much cause to fear that one may not please; however, as there is no love without hope, and as our porter loved, he hoped. As he had more legs than eyes, and as they were good ones, he followed for the distance of four leagues the chariot of his goddess, which her six great white horses drew with much rapidity. The fashion at that time, for the ladies, was to ride without lackeys and without a coachman, and to drive themselves; the husbands wished that they should be always alone, in order to be more sure of their virtue, which is directly opposed to the sentiment of the moralists who declare that there is no virtue in solitude. Mesrour ran steadily along by the wheels of the chariot, turning his good eye on the lady, who was astonished to see a one-eyed man of this agility.

Whilst he was thus proving that one is indefatigable for her who is beloved, a wild beast, pursued by the hunters, crossed the high road and frightened the horses, who, having taken their bits in their teeth, dragged the beautiful lady toward a precipice; her new lover, more frightened even than she, – although she was very much so, – cut the traces with a marvellous agility, the six white horses leaped over the precipice alone, and the lady, who was not less white than they, got off with the fright. 'Whoever you may be,' she said to him, 'I shall never forget that I owe my life to you; ask of me whatever you like; everything that I have is yours.' 'Ah! I can with much more reason,' replied Mesrour, 'offer the same to you; but in offering it to you, I should offer you always less; for I have only one eye, and you have two, – but one eye that looks at you is worth more than two eyes that do not see your own.' The lady smiled, for the gallantries of a one-eyed man are still gallantries, and gallantries always provoke smiles. 'I should like very well to be able to offer you another eye,' she said to him, 'but it is your mother alone who could have made you that present: but follow me still.' With these words she descended from her chariot and continued her route on foot; her little dog descended also and walked on foot beside her, barking at the strange figure of her attendant squire. I am wrong in giving him the title of squire; for, no matter how much he might offer her his arm, the lady was never willing to accept it, under the pretext that it was too dirty; and you are going to see how she was obliged to pay dearly for her cleanliness, – she had very little feet, and shoes still smaller than her feet, so that she was neither built nor shod in such a manner as to be able to sustain a long march.

Pretty feet may console for having poor legs, when one's life is passed in a reclining-chair surrounded by a crowd of fops; but of what use are slippers embroidered in spangles in a rocky road, where they can be seen only by a street-porter, and above all by a porter who has only one eye? Mélinade (that was the lady's name, which I have had my reasons for not giving until now, because it was not yet invented) advanced as best she could, cursing her shoemaker, tearing her shoes, skinning her feet, and spraining her ankles at every step. It was about an hour and a half that she had been walking at the pace great ladies usually take, that is to say that she had already made nearly a quarter of a league, when she fell with fatigue on the spot. The Mesrour, whose aid she had refused whilst she was still on her feet, now hesitated to offer it to her, in the fear of soiling her by touching her; for he knew very well that he was not clean, the lady had made it sufficiently clear to him, and the comparison which he had made himself on the road, between himself and his mistress, had made him see it still more clearly. She wore a dress of a light silver stuff, sown with garlands of flowers, which allowed all the beauty of her figure to appear brilliantly; and he wore a brown, laborer's frock, spotted in a thousand places, full of holes and patches; in such sort that the patches were beside the holes, and not above them, where they would have been, however, better placed; he had compared his hands, sinewy and converted into callosities, with two little hands more white and more delicate than the lilies; finally, he had observed the beautiful blond hair of Mélinade, which could be seen through a light veil of gauze, partly gathered up and partly twisted into curls, and he had to place beside that only black horse-hair, bristly and frizzled, and having for sole ornament a torn turban.

Meanwhile, Mélinade endeavoured to rise, but she presently fell again, and so unfortunately that she allowed Mesrour to perceive that which deprived him of the little reason which the sight of the princess's countenance had left him. He forgot that he was a street-porter, that he was one-eyed, and he no longer thought of the distance which Fortune had placed between Mélinade and him; scarcely did he remember that he was a lover, for he was wanting in the delicacy which is said to be inseparable from true love, and which constitutes sometimes its charm and much oftener its weariness; he made use of the rights which his quality of porter gave him to brutality, he was brutal and happy. The princess was then doubtless in a swoon, or she would certainly have sighed over her fate; but, as she was just, she surely blessed destiny that every misfortune brings with it its consolation.

Night had extended her veil over the horizon, and she concealed in her shadows the veritable happiness of Mesrour, and the pretended unhappiness of Mélinade; Mesrour tasted the pleasures of perfect lovers, and he tasted them like a street-porter, that is to say (to the shame of humanity), in the most perfect manner; the weakness of Mélinade constantly overcame her, and her lover constantly regained his forces. 'Powerful Mahomet,' he once exclaimed like a man transported, but like a bad Catholic, 'there is lacking to my felicity only that it should be felt by her who causes it; whilst I am in thy paradise, divine prophet, grant me still one more favour, – that is, to be in Mélinade's eyes that which she would be in my eye if it were day;' he finished praying and continued enjoying. Aurora, always too diligent for lovers, surprised Mesrour and Mélinade in the attitude in which she might have been surprised herself a moment previously with Tithonous. But, what was the astonishment of Mélinade when, opening her eyes at the first rays of the sun, she saw herself in an enchanted spot with a young man of noble figure, whose visage resembled the luminary whose return the earth was then awaiting; he had rosy cheeks, coral lips; his large eyes, tender and lively at once, expressed and inspired voluptuousness; his quiver of gold, ornamented with precious stones, was suspended from his shoulders, and pleasure alone made his arrows rattle; his long, floating hair, retained by a diamond band, floated freely down to his loins, and a transparent stuff, embroidered with pearls, served him for a garment whilst concealing none of the beauties of his body.

'Where am I, and who are you?' cried Mélinade in the excess of her surprise. 'You are,' he replied, 'with the wretch who had the happiness to save your life, and who has so well paid himself for his trouble.' Mélinade, as contented as astonished, regretted that the metamorphosis of Mesrour had not commenced sooner. She approached a brilliant palace which attracted her eyes, and read this inscription over the door: 'Keep far away, profane ones, these doors open only to the master of the ring.' Mesrour approached in his turn to read the same inscription; but he saw other characters, and read these words: 'Knock without fear.' He knocked, and immediately the doors opened of themselves with a great noise. The two lovers entered to the sound of a thousand voices and a thousand instruments in a vestibule of Parian marble; from there they passed into a superb hall, where a delicious feast had been awaiting them for twelve hundred and fifty years, without any one of the dishes growing cold, – they seated themselves at the table and were served each one by a thousand slaves of the greatest beauty; the repast was accompanied by concerts and dances; and when it was ended, all the genii came in the most perfect order, divided into different troops, with costumes as magnificent as they were singular, to take the oath of fidelity to the master of the ring, and to kiss the sacred finger on which he wore it.

Meanwhile there was at Bagdad a very devout Mussulman, who, not being able to go and perform his ablutions at the mosque, caused the water from the mosque to be brought to his house, in consideration of a slight recompense which he paid the priest. He had just completed the fifth ablution, in order to dispose himself for the fifth prayer; and his maid-servant, a heedless young thing, very little given to devotion, got rid of the sacred water by throwing it out of the window. It fell upon an unfortunate who was sleeping profoundly in the corner by a post which served him for a pillow. He was inundated and awoke. It was the poor Mesrour, who, returning from his enchanted sojourn, had lost on his way the ring of Solomon. He had shed his superb garments and had resumed his coarse frock; his fine quiver of gold had changed into a porter's wooden pack, and he had, to complete his misfortunes, left one of his eyes on the road. He then remembered that he had drunk the evening before a great quantity of brandy which had made his senses drowsy and heated his imagination. He had up to this time loved this liquor for its taste, he began now to love it through gratitude, and he returned gaily to his work, quite resolved to employ his wages in purchasing the means of finding again his dear Mélinade. Another might have been in despair at being a villainous one-eyed man after having had two beautiful eyes; to have to put up with the refusal of the sweepers of the palace, after having enjoyed the favours of a princess more beautiful than the mistresses of the Caliph; and to be in the service of all the tradespeople of Bagdad, after having reigned over all the genii; but Mesrour did not have that eye which sees the evil side of things.

Translated by W. Walton

TS'AO CHAN

Bao Yu

This text is taken from Ts'ao Chan's *The Dream of the Red Chamber*, an eighteenth-century Chinese novel which tells the story of the Jia Family (the author is also known as Cao Xueqin, and the novel has various other titles, among which is *The Story of the Stone*). Just before the beginning of our passage, some relatives have come to visit Lady Jia, Bao Yu's grandmother.

Grandmother Jia pursued her questioning:

'Your young master lives with his grandmother, then?'

'Yes, madam.'

'How old is he? Has he started school yet?'

'Thirteen this year,' said the woman. 'He *has* started school, but he is always playing truant. He has always been naughty, since he was little. He's a good-looking boy, though, and his grandmother's favourite, so there's not much his father and mother can do about it.'

Grandmother Jia was greatly diverted.

'Just like us! And what is his name?'

'Well, because she says he is her "treasure" and because he has such a milky-white complexion, his grandmother calls him "Bao-yu". That means "Precious Jade", you see.'

Grandmother Jia turned to Li Wan, laughing:

'Fancy that! He's even *called* Bao-yu, too.'

Li Wan inclined politely:

'Coincidences over names have always been common, whether among contemporaries or among people of different periods.'

'We did wonder, after he was given this name, whether there wasn't some family of our acquaintance in the capital in which the name had already been used,' said the woman; 'but as it was ten or more years since we'd been there, we couldn't remember for sure whether there was or not.'

'It's my grandson's name,' said Grandmother Jia. 'Come here, someone.'

'Hei!' shouted the womenservants in attendance, and a few of them stepped forward.

'Go over to the Garden and tell our Bao-yu to come here so that our visitors can have a look at him and tell us how he compares with *their* Bao-yu.'

The women hurried off in obedience to her order and returned after ten minutes or so with Bao-yu in their midst. When the four women from the Zhen household saw him enter, they hurriedly rose to their feet.

'You gave us quite a turn,' they said. 'If we hadn't been here and had met you in some other place, we'd have thought that our own Bao-yu must have followed after to join us!'

They took him by the hand and made much of him, plying him with all sorts of questions. Bao-yu smiled back at them and greeted them politely.

'Well, how does he compare with yours?' Grandmother Jia asked them.

'It would appear that the two Bao-yus are very like each other from what they have already said,' Li Wan remarked.

'I don't doubt such a coincidence is possible,' said Grandmother Jia. 'Children of the upper classes, especially if they are reared delicately and provided they are not pock-marked or ill-favoured, are all much of a muchness as far as good looks are concerned. There would be nothing remarkable in a slight resemblance between them.'

'In appearance he is exactly like our Bao-yu,' said the women; 'but though Your Ladyship was saying just now that he is mischievous, I think your Bao-yu must be better-tempered than ours.'

'Oh?' said Grandmother Jia, immediately interested. 'Why do you think that?'

'Because he let us hold his hand just now when we talked to him. If it had been *our* young gentleman, he would have called us "old fools". We are not allowed to lay a finger on any of his things even, let alone take him by the hand. The only servants he will have about him are young girls—'

Before they could go on, Li Wan, Tan-chun and Bao-chai had burst out laughing. Grandmother Jia was laughing too:

'I'm sure that if I were to send some of my women to see your Bao-yu now and *they* took *him* by the hand, he would somehow or other contrive to put up with it. Children brought up in families like ours, no matter how odd or eccentric they may be, will always conduct themselves in a courteous, well-bred manner in the presence of strangers. Otherwise their eccentricity would not be tolerated. In fact, the reason why grown-ups are so fond of them, though partly because of their good looks, is mainly because their beautiful manners – much better than many a grown-up's – make it such a pleasure to be with them. No one meeting them can help liking them, and that makes us more tolerant of what they do on their own, when they are out of sight. But if they were to carry on in exactly the same way all the time, never allowing the grown-ups to get a word in edgeways, they would be fit for nothing but a whipping.'

'That's true, madam,' said the women, smiling. 'Although our Bao-yu is so odd and mischievous, he can at times, when he is with visitors, behave himself better than a grown-up, so that it's a pleasure to watch him. No one who meets him can help liking him. Often they ask us what his father should want to beat him for, not realizing what a holy terror he can be inside the family. Sir Zhen and Lady Zhen are driven half distracted by him. If it were just his wilfulness, which is fairly normal in a child, it could be cured in time; so could his extravagance, which is normal in the sons of well-to-do people; and so could his hatred of study, which again is fairly normal in a young person. But this weird perverseness of his seems to be inbred: there seems to be no cure for it.'

Just then Lady Wang's return was announced. She went straight up to Grandmother Jia on entering and saluted her, after which she received the salutations of the four visitors and exchanged a few words with them.

'You are tired,' said Grandmother Jia. 'Go and rest.'

Lady Wang served her mother-in-law with some tea before withdrawing to her own apartment. Shortly after she had gone, the four women took their leave of Grandmother Jia and went to join her. Lady Wang chatted with them for a while about family affairs before sending them on their way – suitably primed, of course, with messages and gratuities: but those are details which need not concern us.

Greatly tickled by what the women had told her, Grandmother Jia, for some time after their visit, would announce to anyone who came to see her:

'There is another Bao-yu, you know, exactly like our Bao-yu in every particular.'

The other members of the family, bearing in mind that the world was a large place and instances of the same name among its innumerable upper-class families probably of not very rare occurrence, and that a grandmother who doted on her grandson was a fairly unremarkable phenomenon, were unimpressed by the coincidence and gave little thought to it. But Bao-yu, convinced, like many another young gentleman, of his own uniqueness, dismissed what the four women had said as a fabrication designed to give pleasure to his grandmother. He was taunted about it by Xiang-yun when he visited her in her sick-room in the Garden to see how she was getting on.

'You'll be able to get up to all sorts of mischief now,' she said. 'Previously it was a case of

> The single strand made not a thread
> Nor the single tree a wood.

We thought there was only one of you. But now you know you are a pair, there will be no stopping you. If your father beats you really badly, you can always run off to Nanking and get this other Bao-yu to stand in for you!'

'You don't believe that rubbish, do you?' said Bao-yu. 'How *could* there be another Bao-yu?'

'There was a Lin Xiang-ru in the Warring States period and a Si-ma Xiang-ru under the Former Han,' said Xiang-yun.

'Yes, but this one's supposed to *look* the same as well,' said Bao-yu. 'That's not something you can find precedents for, surely?'

'What about when the men of Kuang mistook Confucius for Yang Huo?' said Xiang-yun.

'Confucius and Yang Huo may have looked the same,' said Bao-yu, 'but they didn't have the same name. Lin Xiang-ru and Si-ma Xiang-ru had the same name but they didn't look alike. We are supposed both to have the same name and to look the same. It isn't possible.'

Xiang-yun, unable to think of a reply, took the easy way out.

'Pleathe yourthelf. Whether it is or whether it isn't, it's of no concern to me.'

And she lay back on the bed and closed her eyes.

But Bao-yu's confidence was shaken. *Had* he a double? When he told himself that he couldn't possibly, he now began to feel that perhaps after all he had. On the other hand how could he be sure that he had when he had never seen him? Brooding on this uncertainty, he went back to his room and lay down on his bed to ponder it in silence. Soon he had drifted into sleep.

He was in a garden, which, he remarked with surprise, bore some resemblance to Prospect Garden. While he was still puzzling over the similarity, he became aware that some girls were coming towards him, all of them maids. Again he was surprised:

'Strange that there should be another lot of maids here like Faithful and Aroma and Patience!'

He observed that they were laughing at him:

'Bao-yu, what are you doing here?'

Bao-yu, naturally supposing that they meant him, smiled back at them:

'I've strayed in here by accident. I think this garden must belong to some friend or other of my family. Won't you take me with you and show me round it?'

'It isn't our Bao-yu after all,' said the girls. 'He's not bad-looking, though, and he *sounds* reasonably intelligent.'

'Tell me,' said Bao-yu eagerly, 'is there another Bao-yu here then?'

'*Bao-yu?*' rejoined one of the girls sharply. '*We* have Her Old Ladyship's and Her Ladyship's orders to use that name as much as possible as a means of bringing him luck and Bao-yu likes to hear us use it; but what business has a boy like you from some remote place outside to be making free with it? Don't let them catch you doing that here, *boy*, or they'll flay your backside for you!'

'Come, let's be going,' said another. 'We don't want Bao-yu to see him.'

'Don't let's stand here talking to the nasty creature,' said a third. 'We shall be contaminated!'

And they hurried off.

Bao-yu was nonplussed:

'No one has ever been as horrid as that to me before. I wonder why they are? And I wonder if there really *is* another person exactly like me here.'

As he mused on the unaccountable hostility of the maids, his feet were carrying him along in no particular direction and presently he found himself inside a courtyard. He looked around him in some surprise:

'Strange! There's even a place like Green Delights here.'

He mounted the steps of the verandah and walked inside the building. Someone was lying there on a bed. On the other side of the room were some maids, some of them sewing, some of them giggling over a game they were playing. Presently the person on the bed – it was a youth – could be heard to sigh and one of the maids laughingly inquired what he was sighing for.

'Aren't you asleep, Bao-yu? I suppose you are worried about your cousin's illness again and imagining all sorts of foolish things about her.'

Bao-yu heard this with some astonishment. He listened while the youth on the bed replied:

'I heard Grandmother say that there is another Bao-yu in the capital who is exactly like me, but I didn't believe her. I've just been having a dream in which I went into a large garden and met some girls there who called me a "nasty creature" and wouldn't have anything to do with me. I managed to find this Bao-yu's room, but he was alseep. What I saw was only an empty shell lying there on the bed. I was wondering where the real person could have got to.'

'*I* came *here* looking for Bao-yu. Are *you* Bao-yu then?' Bao-yu could not help blurting out.

The youth leaped down from the bed and seized Bao-yu by the hands:

'So *you* are Bao-yu, and this isn't a dream after all?'

'Of course it isn't a dream,' said Bao-yu. 'It couldn't be more real!'

Just then someone arrived with a summons:

'The Master wants to see Bao-yu.'

For a moment the two Bao-yus were stunned; and then one Bao-yu hurried off and the other Bao-yu was left calling after him:

'Come back, Bao-yu! Come back, Bao-yu!'

Aroma heard him calling his own name in his sleep and shook him awake.

'Where's Bao-yu?' she asked him jokingly.

Though awake, Bao-yu had not yet regained consciousness of his surroundings. He pointed to the doorway:

'He's only just left. He can't have got very far.'

'You're still dreaming,' Aroma said, amused. 'Rub your eyes and have another look. That's the mirror. You're looking at your own reflection in the mirror.'

Bao-yu leaned forward and looked. The doorway he had pointed to was his dressing-mirror. He joined Aroma in laughing at himself.

Seeing him awake, maids were already at hand with a spittoon and a cup of strong tea for him to rinse his mouth with. Musk recalled Grandmother Jia's strictures against young people having too many mirrors around them.

'She says that when you're young your soul isn't fully formed yet, and if you're reflected in mirrors too often, it can give your soul a shock which causes you to have bad dreams. Fancy putting your bed right in front of that great mirror! It's all right as long as it's kept covered, but sometimes when you've been out to the front, especially in hot weather when you're feeling tired, they forget to cover it. That's what must have happened just now. And you must have been looking at yourself in it before you dropped off to sleep. That would be a sure way of bringing on a bad dream. And it would explain why you were calling your own name out in your sleep. Let's move this bed inside, away from the mirror, for goodness sake!'

Translated by D. Hawkes

HOFFMANN

The Mine

This text is from one of the tales included in the collection *The Brothers of Saint Serapion* by E.T.A. Hoffmann, the German Romantic short-story writer. The tale, *The Mines of Falun*, was written in 1818, and seems to be based on a real fact: in 1719 the miraculously preserved body of a young miner, who had died in 1670, was found in the mines of Falun, in Sweden. At the beginning of the story Elis Fröbom, a young sailor, has just discovered on coming home that his mother, the last surviving relative, has died. He is sitting sadly in front of the inn where his companions are feasting their return, when an old miner appears to him, tempting him away from the sea to the mines of Falun.

The old man sat down on the bench beside Elis and began to describe in great detail what went on in a mine and tried to give the ignorant boy a clear and vivid picture of everything. He talked about the mines of Falun, in which, he said, he had worked since childhood. He described the huge opening with the blackish brown walls, and he spoke of the immeasurable wealth of the mine with its beautiful stones. His account became more and more vivid, his eyes glowed brighter and brighter. He roamed through the shafts as if through the paths of a magic garden. The minerals came to life, the fossils stirred, the marvelous iron pyrites and almandine flashed in the gleam of the miner's lights; the rock crystals sparkled and shimmered.

Elis listened intently. The old man's strange way of talking about the marvels under the earth as if he were in their midst engaged his whole being. He felt oppressed. It seemed to him as if he had already descended to the depths with the old man and that a powerful magic was holding him fast so that he would never again see the friendly light of day. And then it seemed to him again as if the old man had opened up to him an unknown world in which he belonged and that all the enchantment of this world had long ago been revealed to him in his earliest boyhood as strange, mysterious presentiments.

'I have,' the old man finally said, 'I have revealed to you, Elis Fröbom, all the splendours of a calling for which nature has actually destined you. Take counsel with yourself, and then do what your mind prompts you to do.'

With that the old man jumped quickly up from the bench and strode away without saying goodbye or looking around again. He soon vanished from sight.

Meanwhile it had become quiet in the inn. The power of the strong ale and brandy had triumphed. Many of the sailors had slipped away with their girls; others lay in corners and snored. Elis could not go to his accustomed home, and at his request, he was given a little room for the night.

Tired and weary as he was, he had scarcely stretched out on his bed when a dream touched him with her wings. It seemed to him that he was drifting in a beautiful ship in full sail on a crystal clear sea, a heaven of dark clouds arching above him. But when he looked down into the waves, he realized that what he had thought was the sea was a solid, transparent, sparkling mass in the shimmer of which the whole ship dissolved in a marvellous manner so that he was standing on a crystal floor; and above him he saw a dome of darkly gleaming minerals, which he had at first thought were clouds in the sky. Driven by an unknown power, he strode on; but at that moment everything around him began to stir and, like curling waves, there shot up all around him marvellous flowers and plants of glittering metal, the blossoms and leaves of which curled upward from the depths and became intertwined in a most pleasing manner. The ground was so transparent that Elis could clearly see the roots of the plants; but when he looked down deeper and ever deeper, he saw in the depths innumerable, charming female forms who held each other locked in embrace with white, gleaming arms, and from their hearts there sprouted forth those roots and flowers and plants; when the maidens smiled, sweet harmony echoed through the domes, and the wondrous metal flowers thrust ever higher and became ever more gay. An indescribable feeling of pain and rapture seized the youth. A world of love, of desire, and of passionate longing expanded within him. 'Down – down to you!' he cried, and he threw himself down with outspread arms on to the crystal ground. But it dissolved beneath him and he hovered in the shimmering air.

'Well, Elis Fröbom, how do you like it here among these splendours?' a hearty voice called. Elis saw the old miner beside him; but as he stared at him, the miner changed into a gigantic shape, as if cast in glowing metal. Before Elis had time to be afraid, there was a sudden flash of lightning from the depths, and the solemn visage of a majestic woman became visible. Elis felt the rapture in his breast turn increasingly into crushing fear. The old man seized him and cried, 'Take care, Elis Fröbom. That is the Queen. You may look up now.'

Unconsciously he turned his head and saw that the stars in the night sky were shining through a crack in the dome. A gentle voice called his name in hopeless sorrow. It was his mother's voice. He thought he saw her figure through the cleft. But it was a charming young woman who stretched out her hand towards the dome and called his name.

'Carry me up there,' he cried to the old man. 'I belong to the upper world and its friendly sky.'

'Take care,' said the old man sombrely, 'take care, Fröbom! Be faithful to the Queen to whom you have given yourself.'

But as soon as the youth looked down again into the majestic woman's rigid face, he felt his being dissolve into the shining minerals. He screamed in nameless fear and awoke from the strange dream, the rapture and horror of which resounded deep within his heart.

'That was inevitable,' said Elis when he had pulled himself together with an effort. 'That was inevitable. I had to dream such strange stuff. After all, the old miner told me so much about the splendour of the subterranean world that my whole head was full of it. But never in my whole life have I felt as I do now. Perhaps I am still dreaming – no, no – I am probably ill. I'll go outdoors. A breath of fresh sea air will cure me.'

He pulled himself together and ran to Klippa Harbour where the revels of the *Hönsning* were beginning again. But he noticed that he did not feel happy, that he could not hang on firmly to any thoughts, and that presentiments and wishes which he could not name crisscrossed his mind. He thought sorrowfully of his deceased mother; then it seemed to him as if he were longing to meet that girl again who had spoken to him yesterday in such a friendly way. And then he feared that if the girl should appear in this or that little street, it would really only be the old miner whom he feared, although he could not say why. And yet he would have liked to have had the old man tell him more about the marvels of mining.

Tossed about by all these impelling thoughts, he looked down into the water. Then it seemed to him as if the silver waves were being transformed into a sparkling solid in which lovely, large ships were dissolving and as if the dark clouds that were rising into the pleasant sky were massing and solidifying into a dome of stone. He was dreaming again; he saw the majestic woman's solemn viasage, and that destructive yearning desire seized him anew.

His comrades shook him out of his reverie; he had to go along with them. But now it seemed to him as if an unknown voice were whispering constantly in his ear: 'What do you still want here! Away! Away! Your home is in the mines of Falun. There all the splendours that you dreamed of will be revealed to you. Away! Away to Falun!'

For three days Elis Fröbom roamed around the streets of Göteborg, constantly pursued by the strange figments of his dreams, constantly admonished by the unknown voice.

On the fourth day Elis was standing by the gate through which the road to Gefle led. A large man was just passing through ahead of him. Elis thought he recognized the old miner, and irrestistibly driven, he hurried after him but was unable to catch up with him.

On and on Elis went without stopping.

He knew very well that he was on the road to Falun, and it was this knowledge that calmed him in a special way, for he was certain that the voice of destiny had spoken to him through the old miner who was now leading him towards his true vocation.

Translated by L. J. Kent and E. C. Knight

BRILLAT-SAVARIN

Meditation xix

This is an extract from Jean Anthelme Brillat-Savarin's *Physiologie du Goût ou Méditations de gastronomie transcendente; ouvrage théorique, historique et à l'ordre du jour dédié aux gastronomes parisiens,* published in Paris in 1825.

One night I dreamt that I had found a secret way to free myself from the laws of gravity, so that my body could indifferently rise or sink since I could do either at will with equal facility. This condition seemed to me delightful. Perhaps many people have dreamt something similar; what is extraordinary is that I remember I could explain to myself with great clarity (at least so it seemed to me) the means by which I had reached this result. They seemed to me so simple that I wondered why they hadn't been found before. When I woke up, this explanatory part was completely obliterated from my mind, but the conclusion was still there. Since then, I cannot help being convinced that sooner or later a more enlightened genius will make this discovery, and just in case I put my name down.

Translated by G. Almansi

PUSHKIN

Tatiana's Dream

The complete version of Alexander Pushkin's masterpiece, *Eugene Onegin*, came out in 1833. Onegin, a young fashionable man, leaves St Petersburg for the country after inheriting from an uncle. With his friend Lenski, a poet, he starts visiting Mrs Larin and her two daughters, Tatiana, a romantic and melancholic girl, and the merrier Olga to whom Lenski becomes engaged. Tatiana falls in love with Onegin and declares herself in a letter, but the young *blasé* answers with a sermon on the dangers for young girls of giving in to their passions. Out of boredom he starts courting Olga during a ball. His friend Lenski challenges Onegin to a duel and is killed by him. Several years later Onegin meets Tatiana again, who is now married to a general. This time he falls in love with her, but their passion is by now impossible. Tatiana's dream is in the early section of the poem. We are giving here Nabokov's translation of the poem.

> On the nurse's advice, Tatiana,
> planning that night to conjure,
> has ordered in the bathhouse secretly
> a table to be laid for two.
> But suddenly Tatiana is afraid. . . .
> And I – at the thought of Svetlana –
> I am afraid; so let it be . . .
> we're not to conjure with Tatiana.
> Tatiana has removed
> her silken sash, undressed,
> and gone to bed. Lel hovers over her,
> while under her pillow of down
> there lies a maiden's looking glass.
> Now all is hushed. Tatiana sleeps.
>
> And dreams a wondrous dream Tatiana.
> She dreams that she
> over a snowy lawn is walking,
> surrounded by sad gloom.
> In front of her, between the snowdrifts,
> dins, swirls its wave
> a churning, dark, and hoary torrent,

by the winter not chained; two thin poles, glued
together by a piece of ice
(a shaky, perilous small bridge),
are laid across the torrent; and before
the dinning deep,
full of perplexity,
she stopped.

As at a vexing separation,
Tatiana murmurs at the brook;
sees nobody who from the other side
might offer her a hand.
But suddenly a snowdrift stirred,
and who appeared from under it?
A large bear with a ruffled coat;
Tatiana uttered 'Ach!' and he went roaring
and a paw with sharp claws
stretched out to her. Nerving herself,
she leaned on it with trembling hand
and worked her way with apprehensive steps
across the brook; walked on –
and what then? The bear followed her.

She, to look back not daring,
accelerates her hasty step;
but from the shaggy footman
can in no way escape;
grunting, the odious bear keeps lumbering on.
Before them is a wood; the pines
are stirless in their frowning beauty;
all their boughs are weighed down
by snow flocks; through the summits
of aspens, birches, lindens bare
the beam of the night luminaries shines;
there is no path; shrubs, precipices, all
are drifted over by the blizzard,
plunged deep in snow.

Into the forest goes Tatiana; the bear follows;
up to her knee comes yielding snow;
now by the neck a long branch suddenly
catches her, or by force it tears
out of her ears their golden pendants;
now in the crumbly snow sticks fast

a small wet shoe come off her charming foot;
now she lets fall her handkerchief –
she has not time to pick it up,
is frightened, hears the bear behind her,
and even is too shy to raise
with tremulous hand the hem of her dress;
she runs; he keeps behind her;
and then she has no force to run.

Into the snow she's fallen; the bear deftly
snatches her up and carries her;
she is insensibly submissive;
stirs not, breathes not;
he rushes her along a forest road;
sudden, 'mongst trees, there is a humble hut;
dense wildwood all around; from every side
'tis drifted over with desolate snow,
and brightly glows a window;
and in the hut are cries and noise;
the bear quoth: 'Here's my gossip,
do warm yourself a little in his home!'
and straight he goes into the hallway
and on the threshold lays her down.

Tatiana comes to, looks:
no bear; she's in the hallway;
behind the door there's shouting and the jingle
of glasses as at some big funeral.
Perceiving not a drop of sense in this,
she furtively looks through the chink
– and what then? She sees . . . at a table
monsters are seated in a circle:
one horned and dog-faced;
another with a rooster's head;
here is a witch with a goat's beard;
here, prim and proud, a skeleton;
yonder, a dwarf with a small tail; and there,
something half crane, half cat.

More frightful still, and still more wondrous:
there is a crab astride a spider;
there on a goose's neck
twirls a red-calpacked skull;
there a windmill the squat-jig dances

and rasps and waves its vanes.
Barks, laughter, singing, whistling, claps,
the parle of man, the stamp of steed!
But what were the thoughts of Tatiana
when 'mongst the guests she recognized
him who was dear to her and awesome –
the hero of our novel!
Onegin at the table sits
and through the door stealthily gazes.

He gives the signal – and all bustle;
he drinks – all drink and all cry out;
he laughs – all burst out laughing;
knits his brows – all are silent;
he is the master there, 'tis plain;
and Tanya is already not so awestruck,
and being curious now she opens
the door a little. . . .
Sudden the wind blows, putting out
the light of the nocturnal flambeaux;
the gang of goblins flinches;
Onegin, his eyes flashing,
making a clatter rises from the table;
all rise; he marches to the door.

And fear assails her; hastily
Tatiana strains to flee:
not possible; impatiently
tossing about, she wants to scream –
cannot; Eugene has pushed the door,
and to the gaze of the infernal spectres
the girl appears; ferocious laughter
wildly resounds; the eyes of all,
hooves, curved proboscides,
tufted tails, tusks,
moustaches, bloody tongues,
horns, and fingers of bone –
all point as one at her,
and everybody cries: 'Mine! Mine!'

'Mine!' Eugene fiercely said,
and in a trice the whole gang vanished;
the youthful maid remained with him
twain in the frosty dark;

Onegin gently draws Tatiana
into a corner and deposits her
upon a shaky bench
and lets his head sink on her shoulder;
all of a sudden Olga enters,
followed by Lenski; light gleams forth;
Onegin brings back his raised arm
and wildly his eyes roam,
and he berates the unbidden guests;
Tatiana lies barely alive.

The argument grows louder, louder: Eugene
suddenly snatches a long knife, and Lenski
forthwith is felled; the shadows awesomely
have thickened; an excruciating cry
resounds . . . the cabin lurches . . .
and Tanya wakes in terror . . .
She looks – 'tis light already in the room;
dawn's crimson ray
plays in the window through the frozen pane;
the door opens. Olga flits in to her
rosier than Northern Aurora
and lighter than a swallow. 'Well,'
she says, 'do tell me,
whom did you see in dream?'

Translated by V. Nabokov

GAUTIER

Clarimonde

Théophile Gautier, 'the perfect magician of French letters' in
Baudelaire's dedication to *Les Fleurs du mal*, was one of the leading
poets and fiction writers of the Romantic movement. His most
famous novel is *Capitaine Fracasse*. *La mort amoureuse*, translated
into English as *The Beautiful Vampyre*, from which we have selected
a long extract, is one of the first appearances in European literature of the female vampyre, together with Sheridan Le Fanu's
Carmilla. It first appeared in *La Chronique de Paris* in 1836.

I had now entirely recovered and had resumed my accustomed duties. The memory of Clarimonde and the old Abbé's words were always in my mind; however, no extraordinary event had occurred to confirm Sérapion's gloomy forebodings, and I began to think that his fears and my own terrors had been exaggerated; but one night I had a dream. I had hardly fallen asleep when I heard the rings of my bed-curtains slide along the rods with a loud clatter; I raised myself sharply upon my elbow and saw the shadowy form of a woman standing before me.

At once I recognized Clarimonde.

She held in her hand a small lamp like those which are placed in tombs, and its rays gave her slender fingers a rosy transparence which spread upward, fading by insensible degrees into the dull, milky white of her bare arm. She had no other garment than the linen shroud that covered her on her death-bed, the folds of which she held to her breast as if ashamed of being so scantily clothed, but her little hand was too small for the task; she was so pale that the colour of the drapery, under the faint rays of the lamp, was confused with that of her flesh. Wrapped in this fine tissue which revealed all the outlines of her body, she looked like a marble statue of an antique bather rather than a woman endowed with life. Dead or living, statue or woman, shade or body, her beauty was always the same; only the green sparkle of her eyes was a little dulled, and her mouth, before so vermilion, was now only tinged with a soft faint rose almost as pale as that of her cheeks. The little blue flowers I had noticed in her hair were quite withered and had lost nearly all their petals; but none the less she was charming, so charming that, despite the strangeness of the adventure and the mysterious manner in which she had entered my room, I was not for one moment afraid.

She placed the lamp on the table and seated herself on the foot of my bed; then, leaning towards me, she spoke in that voice, at once silvery and soft as velvet, which I have never heard from any lips but hers:

'I have kept you waiting a long time, dear Romuald, and you must have thought that I had forgotten you. But I have come a very long way, from a place from which no one has ever yet returned; there is neither sun nor moon in the country I come from; nothing but space and shadow; neither road nor pathway; no earth for the foot, no air for the wings; and yet I am here, for love is stronger than death and will conquer it in the end. Ah! what gloomy faces, what terrible things I have seen on my journey! How difficult it has been for my soul, come back to this world by the power of my will, to find its body and take up its abode there! What efforts I had to make before I could lift the stone with which they had covered me! See! the inside of my poor hands is all bruised. Kiss them and heal them, dear love!'

She pressed the cold palms of her hands, in turn, to my lips; I did indeed kiss them again and again, and she watched me do so with a smile of inexpressible content.

I confess to my shame that I had wholly forgotten the Abbé Sérapion's advice and the sacred character I had assumed. I had fallen without resistance and at the first assault. I had not even made an effort to repel the tempter; the coolness of Clarimonde's hand penetrated mine, and I felt voluptuous shivers run over my body. Poor child! In spite of all that I have seen of her, I can still hardly believe that she was a demon; at least she had not the appearance of one, and never has Satan better hidden his claws and hoofs. She had tucked her heels under her and sat on the edge of my couch in an attitude full of unstudied coquetry. Now and again she passed her little hand through my hair and rolled it into curls, as if to try how new ways of arranging it would suit me. I submitted to this with a most guilty satisfaction, and she kept up an accompaniment of the most charming prattle.

It is remarkable that I felt no astonishment at such an extraordinary adventure, and with that faculty which one has in dreams of accepting the most bizarre events as quite ordinary, I saw in it nothing that was not perfectly natural.

'I loved you long before I saw you, dear Romuald, and sought you everywhere. You were my ideal, and when I saw you in the church at the fatal moment, I said at once 'It is he!' I gave you a look into which I put all the love that I had, and that I was to have for you; a look to damn a cardinal, to bring a king to his knees at my feet before all his court. You remained obdurate and preferred your God to me.

'Ah! how jealous I am of God, Whom you loved and still love better than me!

'How unhappy I am! I shall never have your heart for my very own; I, whom you recalled to life with a kiss; I, the dead Clarimonde, who, for your sake, has broken the doors of the tomb, and has come to devote to you the life which she has only resumed to make you happy!'

These words were broken by intoxicating caresses which benumbed my senses and my reason to such a point that I did not fear, in order to console her, to utter a frightful blasphemy and tell her that I loved her as much as God.

New life came into her eyes; they shone like chrysoprases.

'Truly? truly? as much as God!' she said, clasping me in her beautiful arms. 'If it is so, you will come with me, you will follow me where I wish. You will leave your ugly black robes. You will be the proudest, the most envied of cavaliers; you will be my lover. To be the acknowledged lover of Clarimonde, who has refused a Pope, think of it! Ah! the happy life, the golden existence that we shall lead! When shall we start, my gallant?'

'Tomorrow! Tomorrow!' I cried, in my delirium.

'Tomorrow, then!' she replied. 'I shall have time to change my clothes, for these are a little scanty and not suited for travelling. I must also tell my servants, who believe me to be dead in good earnest and are broken-hearted.

Money, clothes, carriages, everything will be ready. I will come and fetch you at this time tomorrow. Farewell, dear heart.'

She touched my forehead with her lips. The lamp went out, the curtains closed again, and I saw no more; a leaden dreamless sleep weighed me down and held me torpid until next morning. I woke later than usual, and the recollection of that strange vision disturbed my mind throughout the day; I persuaded myself at last that it was a mere product of a heated imagination. Yet the sensations had been so vivid that it was difficult to believe that they were not real, and it was not without fear of what was going to happen that I went to bed, after praying God to banish evil thoughts from my mind and to watch over my sleep.

I was soon fast asleep, and my dream continued. The curtains were drawn apart, and I saw Clarimonde, not, as the first time, pale in her white shroud and with the hues of death upon her cheeks, but gay, lively and elegant, in a magnificent travelling-dress of green velvet edged with gold and looped up on one side to show a satin skirt. Her fair hair escaped in large curls under a large black felt hat trimmed with white feathers fancifully twisted; she held in her hand a little riding-whip, the handle of which ended in a golden whistle. She touched me lightly with it and said:

'Well, fair sleeper, is this how you make your preparations? I counted on finding you waiting. Get up quickly; we have no time to lose.'

I jumped out of bed.

'Come, dress and let us be off,' she said, pointing to a small parcel she had brought; 'the horses are impatient and are champing their bits at the door. We ought to be ten leagues from here already.'

I dressed myself in haste, and she herself handed me the articles of clothing, going into fits of laughter at my awkwardness and showing me how to put them on when I made mistakes. She dressed my hair with a light touch and, when this was done, put into my hand a little pocket mirror of Venetian crystal framed in silver filigree, saying:

'What do you think of yourself? Would you take me into your service as valet?'

I was no longer the same person. I did not recognize myself. I was no more like my old self than a finished statue is like a block of stone. The face I knew seemed but a coarse sketch of the face the mirror reflected. I was handsome; and my vanity was roused by the transformation. The fine clothes, the rich embroidered waistcoat, made quite another man of me; and I marvelled at the power of a few ells of cloth cut in a certain fashion. The spirit of my costume found its way under my skin, and in ten minutes I was a passable coxcomb.

I walked round the room several times to give myself an easy bearing. Clarimonde watched me with an air of motherly pride, and seemed well pleased with her work.

'Come, we have been childish long enough; we must be off, dear Romuald!

We have far to go and we shall not get there in time.'

She took me by the hand and led me away. All the doors opened to her immediately she touched them, and we passed the dog without waking him.

At the door we found Margheritone, the groom who had already been my guide; he held by their bridles three horses, black like the first, one for me, one for himself, and one for Clarimonde. Those horses must have been Spanish jennets out of mares by Zephyr; for they went as fast as the wind, and the moon, which had risen at our departure to light us on our way, rolled through the sky like a wheel broken loose from its chariot; we saw it on our right leaping from tree to tree as if it lost breath in pursuit of us. Soon we came to a plain where, by a clump of trees, a carriage drawn by four powerful beasts was waiting for us; we got into it, and the postillions set off at a furious gallop. I had one arm round Clarimonde and I held one of her hands clasped in mine; she laid her head on my shoulder, and I felt her half-uncovered bosom against my arm. I had never known such perfect happiness. In that moment I forgot everything, and I no more remembered having been a priest than I remembered what I had done in my mother's womb, so great was the fascination the malignant spirit exercised over me.

From that night onward my nature was in some way doubled; there were within me two men, neither of whom knew the other. Sometimes I thought I was a priest who dreamed every night that he was a nobleman, sometimes that I was a nobleman who dreamed that he was a priest. I could no longer distinguish dreams from real life; I did not know where reality began and illusion ended. The dissolute, supercilious young lord jeered at the priest, and the priest abhorred the dissipations of the young lord. Two spirals, entwined and confused, yet never actually touching, would give a good idea of this two-headed existence of mine. Despite the strangeness of the situation, I do not believe that I was ever insane. I always retained quite clearly the perception of my two existences. Only, there was one absurd fact that I could never explain to myself; this was that the feeling of the same identity should exist in two such different men. It was an anomaly I could not account for, whether I believed myself to be the curé of the little parish of C——— or Signor Romualdo, the acknowledged lover of Clarimonde [. . .]

Translated by P. Hookham

FLAUBERT

The Profanation of the Bread

This dream is taken from Gustave Flaubert's *Mémoires d'un Fou* ('Memories of a Madman') written in 1838 when the author was seventeen. This book, known as the first version of *L'éducation sentimentale* ('A Sentimental Education'), is an autobiographical attempt to reconstruct the hallucinations which haunted his early youth.

'At night time I heard steps, someone came up the stairs, a draught of air, like a bad-smelling scent came upon me. The door opened by itself and a number of men entered, perhaps seven or eight, I had scarcely time to count them. They were both big and small, with thick black beards and all had daggers between their teeth. When they approached my bed their teeth made a crunching noise. That was awful . . . They drew back the white curtains round my bed and each finger left a bloodstain. They gazed at me from great lidless eyes; I looked at them in return but was unable to stir a limb, I wanted to shout, it seemed as if the house rose up from its foundation, as if a lever had been inserted underneath it. For a long time they stared at me, then drew away and I saw that one side of their faces was without skin and that this side was bleeding. They lifted all my clothes up and left bloodmarks on each garment. Next they sat down to eat and from the bread they broke, blood spurted and trickled, drop by drop. Then they laughed and their laughter was like the death-rattle of dying men. When they had disappeared, everything was stained with blood, the wainscoting, the stairs, the floor. I felt a choking sensation and it seemed as though I had eaten flesh. I heard a long cry . . .'

Translated by R. L. Mégroz

LENAU

Dreampowers

According to Sophie Löwenthal, Lenau's beloved, this poem was
caused by a dream Lenau had on 16 February 1838. It was written and
published very fast: it appeared in the *Wiener Zeitschrift* on the 22
February 1838. Cesare Lombroso, the well known nineteenth-
century psychologist and criminologist, thinking erroneously that this
poem was written in 1844 after Lenau's suicide attempt which
precipitated him into madness, wrote: 'It is a tremendously chaotic
poem, the last ray of light in the night, the fruit of a genius who
managed for the last time to stamp down the demon of delirium. It is a
frighteningly true evocation of the hallucination that preceded or
accompanied Lenau's suicide attempt. The careful reader can notice
the lack of coordination, the fragmentation of thought and sentences
which is characteristic of people caught in feverish delirium.'

> The dream was so wild, the dream was so mad,
> So overwhelming and hopelessly sad.
> I gladly wish that I could say,
> I've been at rest at my sleep,
> I've had no dreams at my sleep.
> But here they still are, those tears that I weep,
> I hear my heart beating away.
>
> I've woken up in exhausted fright,
> A soaked handkerchief lay near my head,
> As if I'd returned from a funeral rite.
> Did I clutch it, as I dreamt in my bed
> To dry the tears away?
> I cannot say.
> But the wicked guests were there, the beasts
> Were gathering for their nightly feasts.
>
> As I slept, my house given up to their reign
> They led their disgusting lives again.
> Now they've gone, those savage creatures,
> In these tears I can trace their features,
> All they've left here littered about
> And over the table they've spilled the wine out.

Translated by M. Hollington

BAUDELAIRE

The Monster

Charles Asselineau, the addressee of this letter, was Baudelaire's biographer and edited, together with Théodore de Banville, the first complete edition of Baudelaire's works. At the time of this letter he was probably working on a volume of short stories, *La Double Vie*, which was published late in 1858 and thus reviewed by Baudelaire: 'One of Mr Asselineau's great talents is his precise understanding and rendering of the legitimacy of the absurd and the uncanny. He catches and reproduces, sometimes with strict fidelity, the strange reasonings of dreams. In such passages, his manner without mannerisms, a crude and clear protocol, reaches a great poetical effect'. This partly explains why this letter was written to him. As to Baudelaire himself, the first volume of his translation of Edgar Allan Poe's stories had come out the day before the date of this letter. His most important collection of poems, *Les Fleurs du mal* ('The Flowers of Evil'), appeared the year after, in 1857.

(To Charles Asselineau)   *(Paris) Thursday March 13 1856*

My dear friend, since you like hearing about dreams, here is one which I am sure will not fail to please you. It is 5 o'clock in the morning, so it is still quite fresh. Of course, it is only one specimen out of a thousand that beset me, and I do not need to tell you that their utter strangeness, and the fact that they are generally quite alien to my personal pursuits and adventures, always lead me to believe that they form an almost hieroglyphic language to which I have no key.

It was 2 or 3 o'clock in the morning (in my dream), and I was walking alone in the streets. I ran into *Castille*, who I think had several errands to attend to, and I told him I would accompany him and take advantage of the carriage to run an errand of my own. So we took a carriage. I felt it a *duty* of sorts to present the madam of a large whorehouse with a book of mine which had just come out. When I looked at the book in my hand, *it turned out* to be an obscene one, which explained *the necessity* of presenting the work to that woman. Moreover, in the back of my mind, this necessity was really a pretext, a chance to screw one of the house tarts in passing – which suggests that if I hadn't had to present the book, I wouldn't have dared go into such a house. I said nothing of this to *Castille*, but stopped the carriage at the door of the house, and left *Castille* in it, fully intending not to leave him waiting too long. No sooner had I rung and entered than I noticed my cock was hanging out of my unbuttoned fly, and I couldn't help feeling it was improper to appear in such a state, even in a place like that. What is more, noticing that my feet felt very wet, I looked down and found *they were bare*, and that I had stepped into a pool of liquid at the bottom of the stairs. Too bad, I thought, I'll wash them before I screw and before I leave the house. I went upstairs. After that, there was nothing more about the book.

I found myself in vast adjoining galleries, ill-lit and dingy, with the faded look of old cafés, old reading-rooms or seedy gaming-houses. The tarts were scattered around these great galleries, chatting with men, among whom I noticed some schoolboys. I felt very sad and very uneasy; I was afraid someone might see my feet. Looking down, I noticed that one of them had a shoe on it. Shortly after, I noticed there were shoes on both.

What struck me was that the walls of these vast galleries were decorated with all kinds of drawings in frames. Not all were obscene. There were even architectural drawings and Egyptian figures. As I was feeling more and more nervous and didn't dare approach any of the girls, I amused myself by making a thorough examination of all the drawings.

In a remote corner of one of the galleries, I found a very peculiar series. There was a whole array of little frames containing drawings, miniatures and photographic prints. Some depicted coloured birds with very brilliant plumage and with eyes that were *alive*. Sometimes, *there was only half a bird*. Others depicted bizarre, monstrous, almost *amorphous* beings, not unlike *meteorites*. In the corner of each picture was a note: '*Such and such a tart, age . . . . , gave birth to this foetus in the year such and such*', and other notes of that kind.

It occurred to me that this sort of drawing was not really very conducive to thoughts of lovemaking.

Another thought I had was this: Only one newspaper in the world, namely *Le Siècle*, would possibly be stupid enough to open a brothel and set up a sort of medical museum in it at the same time. Indeed, I suddenly realized, it was *Le Siècle* that had put up the funds for this brothel enterprise, and the medical museum was explained by its mania for *progress, science, and the spreading of enlightenment*. So, I reflected, the folly and stupidity of the modern age are useful in their mysterious way, and what has been done for evil can often turn to the good, through the workings of some perverse providence.

I admired the accuracy of my philosophical reasoning.

But among all these creatures was one that lived. It was a monster born in the house, and which sat all day on a pedestal. Although it was alive, it was actually part of the museum. It was not ugly. Its face was even pretty, very swarthy, of an oriental colour, and it had a lot of pink and green in it. It sat crouched, but in a strange contorted position. There was also something blackish twisted several times round it and round its limbs, like a big snake. I asked the creature what it was, and he told me it was a monstrous appendage that grew out of his head, an elastic thing rather like rubber, and so very long that if he were to coil it round his head like a braid of hair, it would be much too heavy to support; and so he had no choice but to wear it wrapped round his limbs – but this in any case looked much nicer. I had a long chat with the monster, and he confided to me all his troubles and woes. For several years now, they had made him sit in this room, up on this pedestal, to satisfy the public's curiosity. But his main worry came at supper time. Since he was a living being, he was expected to eat with the ladies of the house – to stagger with his rubber appendage to the dining-room, where he had to keep it wrapped around him, or leave it on a chair, like a bundle of rope; for if he let it trail on the ground, it would pull his head over backwards. To make matters worse, he was obliged, squat little thing that he was, to sit at table next to a big shapely girl. All this, though, he explained to me without any bitterness. I didn't dare touch him, but I was interested in him.

At this point (this is no longer part of the dream), my wife made a noise in her room with a piece of furniture, and woke me up. I woke up tired, absolutely worn out and aching in my back, legs and hips. I must have been sleeping in the same contorted position as the monster. I don't know if you will find all this as funny as I do.

Yours,
Ch. Baudelaire

Translated by J. Romney

SAINTINE

The Victims' Ball

X. B. Saintine published 'The Victims' Ball' in *La seconde vie*: the title is a homage to Gérard de Nerval, who used this expression to define dreams (see the passage from *Aurélia*, page 334). All the short stories in Saintine's collection purport to be dreams.

Among my dreams are some which are light, gay or even grotesque; these are easily kept in check by the will which still remains me, and procure me what is known as a sleep of smiles; but I have others which are restive, violent and terrible, which carry me off through catacombs, into charnel-houses, among the dead, among horrors and deathly visions.

This time I was at a court ball. On this occasion, by special favour, representatives of the middle classes and of the working people too, were present along with the highest nobility of the kingdom. The rooms were vast and numerous, splendidly lit; from every side, light glittered and shimmered on the gold, the cut glass, the mirrors, on the duchesses' diamonds, just as it did on the silky robes of the middle-class ladies and even on the imitation jewels of the women of the people.

However, I was aware of a strange greyish vapour which hung on this festive atmosphere; now and then, the glitter of the chandeliers seemed to dull, and faces, beaming a moment earlier, now frowned in anxious thought.

Suddenly, outside, the drums beat the salute, guns ring out in a simultaneous burst; inside the salons, excitement is at its peak and everyone can feel a sort of electric thrill; they all rush to the great entrance door; the orchestra strikes up a song of triumph and welcome; a great commotion is heard: the KING has just been announced.

King Louis XVI entered hand-in-hand with his wife, whose distinguished air, grace and beauty were the object of much admiration; she smiled, and her smile was mirrored in the faces of all those she looked at. Behind them, head slightly bowed, came Princess Elizabeth, graceful in a different way, slightly less charming, perhaps, but with incomparable serenity; then followed several great lords of their intimate circle, among whom, however, were none of the princes of the blood, for they were at present absent from France. At the thought of this absence, some faces in the crowd glowered, as if there were something menacing about it.

Among those who lined up in the royal company's path were leading magistrates, farmers-general, even some scientists, Bailly, Lavoisier, Lamoignon-Malesherbes, and a host of others. Cazotte, the man of letters, after joining in for a moment, had retired to a window-seat in the corner, and there, sad and sombre, a tear in his eye, he was lost in his bitter prophetic visions.

The king opened the ball with the Princesse de Lamballe; the queen chose Monsieur de Malesherbes as her partner. The orchestra played its latest dance tunes, which, admittedly, went right back to the old Trenitz quadrille, for it was several years since anyone had danced in France; also, despite the musicians' zeal, their lack of practice showed in the weakness of their execution, and their lack of unity; sharp and strident notes issued from the flutes and violins; a dull and doleful bass accompanied their liveliest harmonies. What was even more bizarre was that the greyish mist condensed in the salons was growing thicker and thicker; the chandeliers and the candles were proportionately diminishing in brightness; a strange pallor spread over the faces of all the dancers, who were now exchanging only a few faintly muttered words.

They continued to dance, however. What happened then was that, in the second step of a quadrille, one of the dancers suddenly began to shake, and his head, falling from his shoulders, rolled on to the floor. At this, a movement of alarm ran through the assembled company. But it quickly passed. The dance resumed, and at every step, in one or other of the two rooms, you would hear an 'oh!' . . . an exclamation, sometimes a jibe, or even a witticism; it was a head falling off.

Before long, no one paid any more attention to it.

A moment came when the phenomenon even took place in Their Majesties' set; the king himself . . . Then faces turned from pale to livid; in the orchestra, the flutes seemed to sob; the violins groaned a *De Profundis*; the candles flickered to life for an instant, but with the sickly glow of Bengal lights; just the lighting for some scene in a melodrama; and then everything fell back into almost total darkness.

Then, so many heads fell at once that the dancers could not help kicking the heads as they got underfoot, and sent them rolling left, right and centre; and from time to time a woeful voice, *vox ingens*, would ring out at the door, announcing that the carriage of Monsieur le comte . . . , or of Monsieur le marquis . . . , or of so and so, was waiting by the lobby, and a sound of wheels would shake the building with a low rumble; and those whose names had been called would go looking for their heads, picking them up from under the seats, and with their necks neatly severed between their shoulders, would go down to their carriages.

Their carriage was the guillotine wagon.

Soon, the ball, losing all sense of rhythm, was more like a free-for-all, a devil's dance; all ranks mixed together, but now in combat, uttering curses and cries of rage.

Heads continued to roll on the floor; people began to use them as projectiles of war; then others, less bellicose, had the idea of using them for a game of bowls. Since there was no more dancing, they needed to amuse themselves somehow.

An hour later, no one even bothered to wait for the heads to fall; they were calling out for the heads of nobles and bourgeois alike, and the people's too, pointing them out with a knife; each faction, each part of each faction got hold of the knife in turn; it was a battle of wild beasts, an orgy, a feast of blood; they were up to their hands and feet in blood, smearing it over themselves, drinking it, drunk on it, spitting it in each other's faces . . .

Till then huddled up in his window-seat, the good Cazotte, Cazotte the visionary, stood up. He tried to speak; since he had predicted the revolution and pointed out in advance its principal victims, perhaps he might now announce how long it would last; but despite all his efforts, he was quite unable to utter a word. The reason for this dumbness was that his head had already met the same fate as so many others, without his noticing. He was so absent-minded.

A thick, opaque red cloud had spread over this scene of desolation; the musicians had broken their instruments defending themselves against men armed with pikes; a smoking torch had replaced all the illuminations of the ball; the voice which an hour earlier had called out in such sinister tones now rang out again, and among the names of the victims, I thought I heard my own! . . . I awoke, clutching my neck.

It was broad daylight, which helped disperse the last chill impressions of that hideous dream. Now I wondered where it could have come from, to what sinister, fatal cause I could possibly attribute it!

In a glass of water on my bedside table stood a magnificent tea-rose . . . I know what they say about the suffocating emanations from flowers, and the danger of being shut up with them, especially at night; but could I really believe that this magnificent rose, so graceful in appearance, given to me the night before by my pretty neighbour, could have engendered such monstrosities in my brain? No! no! . . . I searched for some other explanation.

Close to the glass of water containing the rose, I noticed a pile of books, placed there that very morning, without my knowledge, by my servant; they were the volumes of Lamartine's *Les Girondins*, which a friend, enraptured with the work, had sent me without prior warning. The book shared something of the sombre historical tone of my dream . . . The era and the characters were the same . . . This coincidence struck me greatly. But a book only speaks when read; it produces neither sounds, nor any emanations which might reveal the subject it deals with and the mysteries it contains . . .

And yet, why should I not return to the supposition that, while our senses are numbed by sleep, our soul, taking wing, can freely cast itself abroad, or limiting its flight to the near vicinity, ferret about all around us? What if this fair traveller of mine, skimming through the book, perhaps even without opening it, had come to know Lamartine's *Girondins* before me, and bearing back her reading impressions, had communicated them to me on her return? . . . So many things are revealed to us in this way, things we ascribe to our own perspicacity! Yes, I must decide in favour of this explanation of the phenomenon; it is enough for me. I far prefer it to one which would denounce my lovely tea-rose as the cause of that horrible nightmare.

Translated by J. Romney

LAUTREAMONT

The Hog

Les chants de Maldoror, known in English as *Maldoror*, were published in 1868–9 by a young man, Isidore Lucien Ducasse, whose life has remained a partial mystery. He used the pen-name of Comte de Lautréamont. He became posthumously one of the founding fathers of the Surrealist movement in France. André Breton and his followers considered him as their most important precursor.

I was asleep on top of the cliff. He who has chased an ostrich through the desert for a day without being able to catch it has not had time to take sustenance or close his eyes. If that man read me now, he is, at a pinch, likely to guess what drowsiness was weighing me down. But when the storm, with the palm of its hand, has thrust a vessel vertically to the bottom of the sea; if, on that raft, only one man out of the entire crew remains, broken by weariness and every kind of privation; if the billow belabours him like flotsam for hours longer than the life of man; and if a frigate later ploughing through these desolate latitudes of staved keels sights the unfortunate whose wasted carcass bobs upon the ocean, and brings him help that is almost too belated, I believe this shipwrecked fellow would understand still better the degree to which the drowsiness of my senses was carried. Mesmerism and chloroform, when they take the pains to do so, sometimes know how to bring on similar lethargic catalepsies. They bear no resemblance to death: it would be an outright lie to say so. But let us get to the dream without delay, so that the impatient – hungry for this sort of reading – do not start bellowing like a school of macrocephalous sperm-whales fighting among themselves over a pregnant female.

I dreamed that I had entered the body of a hog, that it was not easy to extricate myself, and that I was wallowing – my bristles in the muddiest marshes. Was this a reward, the aim of my desires, that I no longer belonged to humanity?! Thus *I* interpreted it, and thence experienced a more than profound joy. However, I was busily hunting for whatever deed of virtue I had performed to deserve this signal favour on Providence's part. Now that my memory has gone over the various phases of this frightful flattening against the granite's belly, during which the tide twice passed without my noticing it over an irreducible mixture of dead matter and living flesh, it is perhaps not futile to proclaim that this degradation was probably only a punishment inflicted upon me by divine justice. But who knows his intimate needs or the cause of his plaguy joys? To my eyes the metamorphosis never appeared as anything but the exalted and magnanimous echo of a perfect happiness I had long awaited. It had come at last, the day I became a hog! I tried out my teeth on tree-bark; my snout I contemplated with delight. Not the least whit of divinity remained: I knew how to raise my spirit level with the excessive height of that ineffable sensual bliss.

Hear me then, and do not blush, endless caricatures of the beautiful, who take the laughable braying of your supremely contemptible souls seriously, and who do not understand why the Almighty in a rare moment of splendid buffoonery which certainly does not exceed the great general laws of the grotesque, one day had the mirific pleasure of populating a planet with singular microscopic beings called *humans* whose substance resembles that of rosy coral. You are indeed right to blush, bones and fat, but hear me out. I do not invoke your intelligence: you would make it spout blood out of the horror it evinces for you. Forget it, and be consistent with yourselves ... There, no more constraint! When I wanted to kill, I killed; that very thing happened often and no one restrained me. Human laws still pursued me with their vengeance although I did not attack the race I had so calmly abandoned. But my conscience reproached me not at all.

During the day I would fight with my new fellow creatures and the soil was saturated with countless coats of clotting blood. I was the strongest and gained all the victories. Stinging wounds covered my body: I pretended not to notice them. Earthly animals shunned me and I stayed alone in my resplendent grandeur. Great was my astonishment when, after swimming across a river in order to depart the countries my fury had depopulated and to reach other regions – there to instil my customs of murder and carnage – I tried to walk upon that flowery bank. My feet were paralysed; no movement came and betrayed the verity of that forced immobility. It was then, amid uncanny efforts to continue on my way, that I awoke and realized I had become a man again. Thus Providence made me understand, in a not inexplicable manner, that she did not wish my sublime plans to be fulfilled, even in dream. Resuming my pristine shape was for me so great a sorrow that at night I still weep over it. My sheets are constantly soaked as if they had been dipped in water, and every day I have them changed. If you do not believe it, come and see me; you will verify from your own experience, not the probability but the truth itself of my assertion.

How often, after that night spent on a clifftop under the stars, have I not mingled with herds of swine to resume, as my right, my ruined metamorphosis!

It is time to abandon these glorious memories, which leave in their wake only the pale Milky Way of everlasting regrets.

Translated by A. Lykiard

RIMBAUD

Deserts of Love

'Deserts of Love' was written in 1871, when the author, Arthur Rimbaud, one of the greatest poets of the nineteenth century, was only seventeen. It is one of his earliest attempts to write in the form of the prose poem. Although Rimbaud often complained in his letters of that year about the boredom and frustration he was feeling at home after his flight to Paris, 1871 was for him a time of intense creation: he wrote then *Le bateau ivre*, the most famous of his poems, and *La lettre d'un voyant* where he stated his poetics of 'a long, immense and reasoned upsetting of all senses' ('un long, immense et raisonné dérèglement de tous les sens').

This time, it is the Woman I saw in the City, and to whom I spoke and who speaks to me.

I was in a room without light. Someone came to tell me she was in my room: and I saw her in my bed, completely mine, without light! I was very moved, and especially so because it was the family house. And therefore I was distressed! I was in rags, and she, a worldly woman, was offering herself. She had to leave! A nameless anguish. I took her, and let her fall out of the bed, almost naked. In my unspeakable weakness, I fell on her and dragged myself with her over the rugs, without light! The family lamp reddened one after the other the neighbouring rooms. Then the woman disappeared. I shed more tears than God would ever have asked for.

I went into the endless city. O weariness! Drowned in the dark night and in this flight from happiness. It was like a winter night with snow precisely to stifle the world. The friends to whom I cried out: where is she? gave me the wrong answer. I went in front of the windows of the place she goes every evening: I ran to a buried garden. I was repulsed. I wept enormously over all that. Finally I went to a place full of dust, and, seated on some framework, I gave vent to all the tears of my body with that night. – And yet my exhaustion still returned.

I understood that She was occupied with her daily life, and that the circuit of kindness would be longer in returning than a star. She did not return, and will never return, that Adorable woman who came to my room – something I would never have supposed. In truth, this time I wept more than all the children in the world.

This is certainly the same countryside. The same rustic house of my parents: the same room where the frieze panels are russet-coloured sheep-folds, with arms and lions. At dinner, there is a parlour with candles and wines and ancient wainscoting. The dining table is very large. The servants! there were several, as far as I could remember. – There was one of my former young friends, a priest and dressed as a priest; now: it was in order to be freer. I remember his dark red room, with windowpanes of yellow paper: and his books, hidden, that had soaked in the ocean!

I was abandoned in this vast country house: reading in the kitchen, drying the mud of my clothes before my hosts, in the parlour conversations: deadly moved by the murmuring of the morning milk and the night of the last century.

I was in a very dark room: what was I doing? A servant girl came near me: I can say she was a little dog: although she was beautiful, of an inexpressible maternal nobility for me: pure, known, totally charming! She pinched my arm.

I do not even remember any longer her face: that is not in order to recall her arm whose flesh I rolled between my two fingers; nor her mouth, which mine seized like a small desperate wave, endlessly excavating something. I took her in a basket of cushions and ship canvases, in a dark corner. I remember only her white lace panties.

Then, O despair! the partition vaguely became the shadow from the trees, and I sank into the voluptuous sadness of night.

Translated by P. Schmidt

LE FANU

Mr Justice Harbottle

This is an extract from Joseph Sheridan Le Fanu's short story 'Mr Justice Harbottle', first published in the collection *In a Glass Darkly* in 1872.

Judge Harbottle went this night to the play at Drury Lane. He was one of the old fellows who care nothing for late hours, and occasional knocking about in pursuit of pleasure. He had appointed with two cronies of Lincoln's Inn to come home in his coach with him to sup after the play.

They were not in his box, but were to meet him near the entrance, and get into his carriage there; and Mr Justice Harbottle, who hated waiting, was looking a little impatiently from the window.

The Judge yawned.

He told the footman to watch for Counsellor Thavies and Counsellor Beller, who were coming; and, with another yawn, he laid his cocked hat on his knees, closed his eyes, leaned back in his corner, wrapped his mantle closer about him, and began to think of pretty Mrs Abington.

And being a man who could sleep like a sailor, at a moment's notice, he was thinking of taking a nap. Those fellows had no business to keep a judge waiting.

He heard their voices now. Those rake-hell counsellors were laughing, and bantering, and sparring after their wont. The carriage swayed and jerked, as one got in, and then again as the other followed. The door clapped, and the coach was now jogging and rumbling over the pavement. The Judge was a little bit sulky. He did not care to sit up and open his eyes. Let them suppose he was asleep. He heard them laugh with more malice than good-humour, he thought, as they observed it. He would give them a d—d hard knock or two when they got to his door, and till then he would counterfeit his nap.

The clocks were chiming twelve. Beller and Thavies were silent as tombstones. They were generally loquacious and merry rascals.

The Judge suddenly felt himself roughly seized and thrust from his corner into the middle of the seat, and opening his eyes, instantly found himself between his two companions.

Before he could blurt out the oath that was on his lips, he saw that they were two strangers — evil-looking fellows, each with a pistol in his hand, and dressed like Bow Street officers.

The Judge clutched at the check-string. The coach pulled up. He stared about him. They were not among houses; but through the windows, under a broad moonlight, he saw a black moor stretching lifelessly from right to left, with rotting trees, pointing fantastic branches in the air, standing here and there in groups, as if they held up their arms and twigs like fingers, in horrible glee at the Judge's coming.

A footman came to the window. He knew his long face and sunken eyes. He knew it was Dingly Chuff, fifteen years ago a footman in his service, whom he had turned off at a moment's notice, in a burst of jealousy, and indicted for a missing spoon. The man had died in prison of the jail-fever.

The Judge drew back in utter amazement. His armed companions signed mutely; and they were again gliding over this unknown moor.

The bloated and gouty old man in his horror considered the question of resistance. But his athletic days were long over. This moor was a desert. There was no help to be had. He was in the hands of strange servants, even if his recognition turned out to be a delusion, and they were under the command of his captors. There was nothing for it but submission, for the present.

Suddenly the coach was brought nearly to a standstill, so that the prisoner saw an ominous sight from the window.

It was a gigantic gallows beside the road; it stood three-sided, and from each of its three broad beams at top depended in chains some eight or ten bodies, from several of which the cere-clothes had dropped away, leaving the skeletons swinging lightly by their chains. A tall ladder reached to the summit of the structure, and on the peat beneath lay bones.

On top of the dark transverse beam facing the road, from which, as from the other two completing the triangle of death, dangled a row of these unfortunates in chains, a hangman, with a pipe in his mouth, much as we see him in the famous print of the 'Idle Apprentice,' though here his perch was ever so much higher, was reclining at his ease and listlessly shying bones, from a little heap at his elbow, at the skeletons that hung round, bringing down now a rib or two, now a hand, now half a leg. A long-sighted man could have discerned that he was a dark fellow, lean; and from continually looking down on the earth from the elevation over which, in another sense, he always hung, his nose, his lips, his chin were pendulous and loose, and drawn down into a monstrous grotesque.

This fellow took his pipe from his mouth on seeing the coach, stood up, and cut some solemn capers high on his beam, and shook a new rope in the air, crying with a voice high and distant as the caw of a raven hovering over a gibbet, 'A robe for Judge Harbottle!'

The coach was now driving on at its old swift pace.

So high a gallows as that, the Judge had never, even in his most hilarious moments, dreamed of. He thought he must be raving. And the dead footman! He shook his ears and strained his eyelids; but if he was dreaming, he was unable to awake himself.

There was no good in threatening these scoundrels. A *brutum fulmen* might bring a real one on his head.

Any submission to get out of their hands; and then heaven and earth he would move to unearth and hunt them down.

Suddenly they drove round a corner of a vast white building, and under a *porte-cochère*.

The Judge found himself in a corridor lighted with dingy oil lamps, the walls of bare stone; it looked like a passage in a prison. His guards placed him in the hands of other people. Here and there he saw bony and gigantic soldiers passing to and fro, with muskets over their shoulders. They looked straight before them, grinding their teeth, in bleak fury, with no noise but the clank of their shoes. He saw these by glimpses, round corners, and at the ends of passages, but he did not actually pass them by.

And now, passing under a narrow doorway, he found himself in the dock, confronting a judge in his scarlet robes, in a large courthouse. There was nothing to elevate this Temple of Themis above its vulgar kind elsewhere. Dingy enough it looked, in spite of candles lighted in decent abundance. A case had just closed, and the last juror's back was seen escaping through the door in the wall of the jury-box. There were some dozen barristers, some fiddling with pen and ink, others buried in briefs, some beckoning, with the plumes of their pens, to their attorneys, of whom there were no lack; there were clerks to-ing and fro-ing, and the officers of the court, and the registrar, who was handing up a paper to the judge; and the tipstaff, who was presenting a note at the end of his wand to a king's counsel over the heads of the crowd between. If this was the High Court of Appeal, which never rose day or night, it might account for the pale and jaded aspect of everybody in it. An air of indescribable gloom hung upon the pallid features of all the people here; no one ever smiled; all looked more or less secretly suffering.

'The King against Elijah Harbottle!' shouted the officer.

'Is the appellant Lewis Pyneweck in court?' asked Chief-Justice Twofold, in a voice of thunder, that shook the woodwork of the court, and boomed down the corridors.

Up stood Pyneweck from his place at the table.

'Arraign the prisoner!' roared the Chief: and Judge Harbottle felt the panels of the dock round him, and the floor, and the rails quiver in the vibrations of that tremendous voice.

The prisoner, *in limine*, objected to this pretended court, as being a sham, and non-existent in point of law; and then, that, even if it were a court constituted by law (the Judge was growing dazed), it had not and could not have any jurisdiction to try him for his conduct on the bench.

Whereupon the chief-justice laughed suddenly, and everyone in court, turning round upon the prisoner, laughed also, till the laugh grew and roared all round like a deafening acclamation; he saw nothing but glittering eyes and teeth, a universal stare and grin; but though all the voices laughed, not a single face of all those that concentrated their gaze upon him looked like a laughing face. The mirth subsided as suddenly as it began.

The indictment was read. Judge Harbottle actually pleaded! He pleaded 'Not Guilty.' A jury were sworn. The trial proceeded. Judge Harbottle was bewildered. This could not be real. He must be either mad, or *going* mad, he thought.

One thing could not fail to strike even him. This Chief-Justice Twofold, who was knocking him about at every turn with sneer and gibe, and roaring him down with his tremendous voice, was a dilated effigy of himself; an image of Mr Justice Harbottle, at least double his size, and with all his fierce colouring, and his ferocity of eye and visage, enhanced awfully.

Nothing the prisoner could argue, cite, or state, was permitted to retard for a moment the march of the case towards its catastrophe.

The chief-justice seemed to feel his power over the jury, and to exult and riot in the display of it. He glared at them, he nodded to them; he seemed to have established an understanding with them. The lights were faint in that part of the court. The jurors were mere shadows, sitting in rows; the prisoner could see a dozen pair of white eyes shining, coldly, out of the darkness; and whenever the judge in his charge, which was contemptuously brief, nodded and grinned and gibed, the prisoner could see, in the obscurity, by the dip of all these rows of eyes together, that the jury nodded in acquiescence.

And now the charge was over, the huge chief-justice leaned back panting and gloating on the prisoner. Everyone in the court turned about, and gazed with steadfast hatred on the man in the dock. From the jury-box where the twelve sworn brethren were whispering together, a sound in the general stillness like a prolonged 'hiss-s-s!' was heard; and then, in answer to the challenge of the officer. 'How say you, gentlemen of the jury, guilty or not guilty?' came in a melancholy voice the finding, 'Guilty.'

The place seemed to the eyes of the prisoner to grow gradually darker and darker, till he could discern nothing distinctly but the lumen of the eyes that were turned upon him from every bench and side and corner and gallery of the building. The prisoner doubtless thought that he had quite enough to say, and conclusive, why sentence of death should not be pronounced upon him; but the lord chief-justice puffed it contemptuously away, like so much smoke, and proceeded to pass sentence of death upon the prisoner, having named the tenth of the ensuing month for his execution.

Before he had recovered the stun of this ominous farce, in obedience to the mandate, 'Remove the prisoner,' he was led from the dock. The lamps seemed all to have gone out, and there were stoves and charcoal-fires here and there, that threw a faint crimson light on the walls of the corridors through which he passed. The stones that composed them looked now enormous, cracked and unhewn.

He came into a vaulted smithy, where two men, naked to the waist, with heads like bulls, round shoulders, and the arms of giants, were welding red-hot chains together with hammers that pelted like thunderbolts.

They looked on the prisoner with fierce red eyes, and rested on their hammers for a minute; and said the elder to his companion, 'Take out Elijah Harbottle's gyves;' and with a pincers he plucked the end which lay dazzling in the fire from the furnace.

'One end locks,' said he, taking the cool end of the iron in one hand, while with the grip of a vice he seized the leg of the Judge, and locked the ring round his ankle. 'The other,' he said with a grin, 'is welded.'

The iron band that was to form the ring for the other leg lay still red hot upon the stone floor, with brilliant sparks sporting up and down its surface.

His companion, in his gigantic hands, seized the old Judge's other leg, and pressed his foot immovably to the stone floor; while his senior, in a twinkling, with a masterly application of pincers and hammer, sped the glowing bar around his ankle so tight that the skin and sinews smoked and bubbled again, and old Judge Harbottle uttered a yell that seemed to chill the very stones, and make the iron chains quiver on the wall.

Chains, vaults, smiths, and smithy all vanished in a moment; but the pain continued. Mr Justice Harbottle was suffering torture all round the ankle on which the infernal smiths had just been operating.

His friends, Thavies and Beller, were startled by the Judge's roar in the midst of their elegant trifling about a marriage à-la-mode case which was going on. The Judge was in panic as well as pain. The street lamps and the light of his own hall door restored him.

'I'm very bad,' growled he between his set teeth; 'my foot's blazing. Who was he that hurt my foot? 'Tis the gout – 'tis the gout!' he said, awaking completely. 'How many hours have we been coming from the playhouse? 'Sblood, what has happened on the way? I've slept half the night!'

There had been no hitch or delay, and they had driven home at a good pace.

The Judge, however, was in gout; he was feverish too; and the attack, though very short, was sharp; and when, in about a fortnight, it subsided, his ferocious joviality did not return. He could not get this dream, as he chose to call it, out of his head.

HUCH

The Bowl

Friedrich Huch was a minor but extremely prolific German writer of the turn of the century. *Träume* ('Dreams'), written in 1904, is an attempt to reconstruct the dreams of three years of his life (for other dreams by Huch, see pages 193, 287, 354).

I am holding a goldfish-bowl-shaped glass vessel in my hands. It is full of water, in which a mass of strange, diaphanous soft creatures are swimming. I cannot resist the temptation of ever so slightly unscrewing the glass lid. But at the same moment there is the responding pressure of a force from within: the water fizzes and the creatures throng upwards. The lid opens further and further, and I can't close it any more. Sitting alongside of me is someone who knows how to close the lid. I cry out to him, but he doesn't hear, I cry again, but he doesn't hear, I shake him by the shoulders, but he doesn't hear; he's sleeping. Then the glass bowl is shattered. The water and the creatures are on the floor. I see them making hideous movements; disgust and fear take possession of me. Then I pick up a great big sharp knife and carefully cut each one of them through the middle, and then cut up the separate parts again, until finally all the death throes come to an end, and all that is left on the floor are formless little black lumps.

Translated by M. Hollington

Swapping Heads

I am standing in front of a pedestal and looking at a head that it supports. It is my own head, coloured reddish brown, with all its features very intense and alive. I say to my mother: well, yes, it is very statuesque, now I can see that myself. But I'm curious to find out how long it can stand the heat without spoiling! She is angry at what I've just said and tells me not to keep thinking such things: I should know how bad it is for me. At the same moment it enters my consciousness all of a sudden that what I see standing in front of me is my own real-life head, and the one I have on is artificial. I have the simultanous feeling of something unusual, heavy and padded lying on my shoulders; it shifts when I make a movement. My mother cries out: don't you see now how dangerous it is to think like that! But I am stifled by the fear that I might wake up in the morning after a restless night's sleep to find there's nothing more than a stump left where my head was before.

Translated by M. Hollington

PROUST

Swann's Dream

This text comes from Marcel Proust's *Swann's Way*, which was first published in 1913.

When Swann happened to alight, close at hand, upon something which proved that Forcheville had been Odette's lover, he discovered that it caused him no pain, that love was now utterly remote, and he regretted that he had had no warning of the moment in which he had emerged from it for ever. And just as, before kissing Odette for the first time, he had sought to imprint upon his memory the face that for so long had been familiar, before it was altered by the additional memory of their kiss, so he could have wished – in thought at least – to have been in a position to bid farewell, while she still existed, to that Odette who had inspired love in him and jealousy, to that Odette who had caused him so to suffer, and whom now he would never see again.

He was mistaken. He was destined to see her once again, a few weeks later. It was while he was asleep, in the twilight of a dream. He was walking with Mme Verdurin, Dr Cottard, a young man in a fez whom he failed to identify, the painter, Odette, Napoleon III and my grandfather, along a path which followed the line of the coast, and overhung the sea, now at a great height, now by a few feet only, so that they were continually going up and down; those of the party who had reached the downward slope were no longer visible to those who were still climbing; what little daylight yet remained was failing, and it seemed as though a black night was immediately to fall on them. Now and then the waves dashed against the cliff, and Swann could feel on his cheek a shower of freezing spray. Odette told him to wipe this off, but he could not, and felt confused and helpless in her company, as well as because he was in his nightshirt. He hoped that, in the darkness, this might pass unnoticed; Mme Verdurin, however, fixed her astonished gaze upon him for an endless moment, in which he saw her face change its shape, her nose grow longer, while beneath it there sprouted a heavy moustache. He turned away to examine Odette; her cheeks were pale, with little fiery spots, her features drawn and ringed with shadows; but she looked back at him with eyes welling with affection, ready to detach themselves like tears and to fall upon his face, and he felt that he loved her so much that he would have liked to carry her off with him at once. Suddenly Odette turned her wrist, glanced at a tiny watch, and said: 'I must go.' She took leave of everyone, in the same formal manner, without taking Swann aside, without telling him where they were to meet that evening, or next day. He dared not ask, he would have liked to follow her, he was obliged, without turning back in her direction, to answer with a smile some question by Mme Verdurin; but his heart was frantically beating, he felt that he now hated Odette, he would gladly have crushed those eyes which, a moment ago, he had loved so dearly, have torn the blood into those lifeless cheeks.

He continued to climb with Mme Verdurin, that is to say that each step took him farther from Odette, who was going downhill, and in the other direction. A second passed and it was many hours since she had left him. The painter remarked to Swann that Napoleon III had eclipsed himself immediately after Odette. 'They had obviously arranged it between them,' he added; 'they must have agreed to meet at the foot of the cliff, but they wouldn't say good-bye together; it might have looked odd. She is his mistress.' The strange young man burst into tears. Swann endeavoured to console him. 'After all, she is quite right,' he said to the young man, drying his eyes for him and taking off the fez to make him feel more at ease. 'I've advised her to do that, myself a dozen times. Why be so distressed? He was obviously the man to understand her.' So Swann reasoned with himself, for the young man whom he had failed, at first, to identify, was himself also; like certain novelists, he had distributed his own personality between two characters, him who was the 'first person' in the dream, and another whom he saw before him, capped with a fez.

As for Napoleon III, it was to Forcheville that some vague association of ideas, then a certain modification of the Baron's usual physiognomy, and lastly the broad ribbon of the Legion of Honour across his breast, had made Swann give that name; but actually, and in everything that the person who appeared in his dream represented and recalled to him, it was indeed Forcheville. For, from an incomplete and changing set of images, Swann in his sleep drew false deductions, enjoying, at the same time, such creative power that he was able to reproduce himself by a simple act of division, like certain lower organisms; with the warmth that he felt in his own palm he modelled the hollow of a strange hand which he thought that he was clasping, and out of feeling and impressions of which he was not yet conscious, he brought about sudden vicissitudes which, by a chain of logical sequences, would produce, at definite points in his dream, the person required to receive his love or to startle him awake. In an instant night grew black about him; an alarum rang, the inhabitants ran past him, escaping from their blazing houses; he could hear the thunder of the surging waves, and also of his own heart, which, with equal violence, was anxiously beating in his breast. Suddenly the speed of these palpitations redoubled, he felt a pain, a nausea that were inexplicable; a peasant, dreadfully burned, flung at him as he passed: 'Come and ask Charlus where Odette spent the night with her friend. He used to go about with her, and she tells him everything. It was they that started the fire.' It was his valet, come to awaken him, and saying:

'Sir, it is eight o'clock, and the barber is here. I have told him to call again in an hour.'

But these words, as they dived down through the waves of sleep in which Swann was submerged, did not reach his consciousness without undergoing that refraction which turns a ray of light, at the bottom of a bowl of water, into another sun; just as, a moment earlier, the sound of the door-bell, swelling in the depths of his abyss of sleep into the clangour of an alarum, had engendered the episode of the fire. Meanwhile the scenery of his dream-stage scattered in dust, he opened his eyes, heard for the last time the boom of a wave in the sea, grown very distant. He touched his cheek. It was dry. And yet he could feel the sting of the cold spray, and the taste of salt on his lips. He rose, and dressed himself.

Translated by C. K. M. Scott-Moncrieff

ARTAUD

The Bad Dreamer

This is the answer of the playwright and *metteur-en-scène* Antonin Artaud to an enquiry on dreams and psychoanalysis published in the French journal *Le Disque vert* in 1925. Artaud, the author of, among other things, the celebrated *The Theatre and its Double*, was later interned at Rodez, in a lunatic asylum, where he spent his last years.

My dreams are above all a liquor, a sort of nausea water into which I dive, with bleeding micas tossing in it. Neither in the life of my dreams, nor in the life of my life do I ever attain the height of certain images, or settle into the continuity of my self. My dreams are all without exit, without castle keep, without town plan. A musty stench of severed limbs.

Besides, I know too much about my mind to care much what happens in it; I ask only one thing, to be locked up for good in my thoughts.

And as for the physical appearance of my dreams, I've already told you: a liquor.

Translated by J. Romney

SCHNITZLER

Adulterous Dream

Arthur Schnitzler, from Vienna, is one of the major writers and playwrights of the century. *Rhapsody*, in the original *Traumnovelle* ('Dream-story'), was written in 1926. The novel starts with a quiet family scene. It is evening; a child is reading a fairy tale; the parents, Fridolin and Albertina, smile upon their offspring. Fridolin, a doctor, is then called away to visit a patient, who is already dead by the time the physician gets there. Fridolin wanders through the city, and is taken by an old friend to a house where a secret ball is being held and there he meets a naked woman who is wearing a mask. After several nocturnal adventures he walks home, determined to go back to the same mysterious house next day. He enters his wife's bedroom, and finds her asleep. When she wakes, she tells him of her adulterous dreams.

It was four o'clock in the morning when Fridolin walked up the steps of his home. Before doing anything else he went into his office and carefully locked the masquerade costume in a closet. As he wished not to wake Albertina, he took off his shoes and clothes before going into the bedroom, and very cautiously turned on the light on the little table beside his bed. Albertina was lying there quietly, with her arms folded under her head. Her lips were half open, and painful shadows surrounded them. It was a face that Fridolin did not know. He bent down over her, and at once her forehead became lined with furrows, as though someone had touched it, and her features seemed strangely distorted. Suddenly, still in her sleep, she laughed so shrilly that he became frightened. Involuntarily he called her name. She laughed again, as if in answer, in a strange, almost uncanny manner. Fridolin called her in a louder voice, and she opened her eyes, slowly and with difficulty. She stared at him, as though she did not recognize him.

'Albertina!' he cried for the third time. As she gained consciousness, an expression of fear, even of terror, came into her eyes. Half awake, and seemingly in despair, she raised her arms.

'What's the matter?' asked Fridolin with bated breath. As she still stared at him, terrified, he added, to reassure her: 'It is I, Albertina.' She breathed deeply, tried to smile, dropped her arms on the bed cover and said in a far-away voice: 'Is it morning yet?'

'It will be very soon,' replied Fridolin, 'it's past four o'clock. I've just come home.' She was silent and he continued: 'The Councillor is dead. He was dying when I arrived, and naturally I couldn't – leave immediately.'

She nodded, but hardly seemed to have heard or understood him. She stared into space, as though she could see through him. He felt that she must know of his recent experiences – and at the same time the idea seemed ridiculous. He bent down and touched her forehead. She shuddered slightly.

'What's the matter?' he asked again.

She shook her head slowly and he passed his hand gently over her hair. 'Albertina, what's the matter?'

'I've been dreaming,' she said distantly.

'What have you been dreaming?' he asked mildly.

'Oh, so much, I can't quite remember.'

'Perhaps if you try?'

'It was all so confused – and I'm tired. You must be tired, too.'

'Not in the least. I don't think I shall go to bed at all. You know, when I come home so late – it would really be best to sit right down to my desk – it's just in such morning hours –' He interrupted himself: 'Wouldn't it be better if you told me your dream?' He smiled a little unnaturally.

She replied: 'You really ought to lie down and take a little rest.'

He hesitated a moment, then he did as she suggested and stretched himself beside her, though he was careful not to touch her. There shall be a sword between us, he thought, remembering a remark he had once made, half joking, on a similar occasion. They lay there silently with open eyes, and they felt both their proximity and the distance that separated them. After a while he raised his head on his arm and looked at her for a long time, as though he could see much more than just the outlines of her face.

'Your dream!' he hinted, once more. She must just have been waiting for him to speak. She held out her hand to him, he took it and, more absent-mindedly than tenderly, clasped his hand about her slender fingers, as he had often done before. She began: 'Do you still remember the room in the little villa on Lake Wörther, where I lived with Mother and Father the summer we became engaged?'

He nodded.

'Well, it was there the dream began. I was entering this house, like an actress stepping on to the stage – I don't know where I came from. My parents seemed to have gone on a journey and left me alone. That surprised me, for our wedding was the next day. But my wedding-dress hadn't yet arrived. I thought I might be mistaken, and I opened the wardrobe to look. Instead of the wedding-dress a great many other clothes, like fancy dress costumes, were hanging there, opera-like, gorgeous, Oriental. Which shall I wear for the wedding? I thought. Then the wardrobe was suddenly closed again, or it disappeared, I don't remember. The room was brightly lighted, but outside the window it was pitch black ... Suddenly you were standing out there. Galley slaves had rowed you to the house. I had just seen them disappearing in the darkness. You were dressed in marvellous gold and silver clothes, and had a dagger in a silver sheath hanging by your side. You lifted me down from the window. I, too, was gorgeously dressed, like a princess. We stood outside in the twilight, and a fine grey mist reached up to our ankles. The countryside was perfectly familiar to us: there was the lake, the mountain rose above us and I could even see the villas which stood there like little toy houses. We were floating, no, flying, alone above the mist, and I thought: so this is our honeymoon trip. Soon, however, we stopped flying and were walking along a forest path, the one leading to Elizabeth Heights. Suddenly we came into a sort of clearing in the mountains enclosed on three sides by the forest, while a steep wall of rock towered up in the back. The sky was blue and starry, with an expanse far greater than it ever has in reality; it was the ceiling of our bridal-chamber. You took me in your arms and loved me very much.' 'I hope you loved me too,' remarked Fridolin with an invisible, malicious smile.

'Even more than you did me,' replied Albertina seriously, 'but, how can I explain it – in spite of the intensity of our happiness our love was also sad as if filled with some presentiment of sorrow. Suddenly, it was morning. The meadow was light and covered with flowers, the forest glistened with dew, and over the rocky wall the sun sent down quivering rays of light. It was now time to return to the world and go among people. But something terrible happened: our clothes were gone. I was seized with unheard-of terror and a shame so burning that it almost consumed me. At the same time I was angry with you, as though you were to blame for the misfortune. This sensation of terror, shame and anger was much more intense than anything I had ever felt when awake. Conscious of your guilt, you rushed away naked, to go and get clothes for us. When you had gone I was very gay. I neither felt sorry for you, nor worried about you. Delighted to be alone, I ran happily about in the meadow singing a tune we had heard at some dance. My voice had a wonderful ring and I wished that they could hear me down in the city, which I couldn't see but which nevertheless existed. It was far below me and was surrounded by a high wall, a very fantastic city which I can't describe. It was not Oriental and not exactly Old-German, and yet it seemed to be first one, and then the other. At any rate, it was a city buried a long time ago and for ever. Suddenly I was lying in the meadow, stretched out in the sunlight – far more beautiful than I ever was in reality, and while I lay there, a young man wearing a light-coloured fashionable suit of clothes walked out of the woods. I now realized that he looked like the Dane whom I mentioned yesterday. He walked up and spoke to me courteously as he passed, but otherwise paid no particular attention to me. He went straight to the wall of rock and looked it over carefully, as though considering how to master it. At the same time I could see you hurrying from house to house, from shop to shop in the buried city, now walking beneath arbours, then passing through a sort of Turkish bazaar. You were buying the most beautiful things you could find for me: clothes, linen, shoes, and jewellery. And then you put these things into a little hand-bag of yellow leather that held them all. You were being followed by a crowd of people whom I could not see, but I heard the sound of their threatening shouts. The Dane, who had stopped before the wall of rock a little while before, now reappeared from the woods – and apparently in the meantime he had encircled the whole globe. He looked different, but he was the same, nevertheless. He stopped before the wall of rock, vanished and came out of the woods again, appearing and disappearing two, or three, or a hundred times. It was always the same man and yet always different. He spoke to me every time he passed, and finally stopped in front of me and looked at me searchingly. I laughed seductively as I have never laughed in my life, and he held out his arms to me. I wished to escape but it was useless – and he sank down beside me on the meadow.'

She was silent. Fridolin's throat was parched. In the darkness of the room he could see she had concealed her face in her hands.

'A strange dream,' he said, 'but surely that isn't the end?' When she said 'no,' he asked: 'Then why don't you continue?'

'It's not easy,' she began again. 'Such things are difficult to express in words. Well, to go on – I seemed to live through countless days and nights; there was neither time nor space. I was no longer in the clearing, enclosed by the woods and rock. I was on a flower-covered plain, that stretched into infinite distance and, finally, into the horizon in all directions. And for a long time I had not been alone with this one man on the meadow. Whether there were three, or ten, or a thousand other couples I don't know. Whether I noticed them or not, whether I was united only with that particular man or also with others, I can't say. Just as that earlier feeling of terror and shame went beyond anything I have ever felt in the waking state, so nothing in our conscious existence can be compared with the feeling of release, of freedom, of happiness, which I now experienced. Yet I didn't for one moment forget you. In fact, I saw that you had been seized – by soldiers, I think – and there were also priests among them. Somebody, a gigantic person, tied your hands, and I knew that you were to be executed. I knew it, without feeling any sympathy for you, and without shuddering. I felt it, but as though I were far removed from you. They led you into a yard, a sort of castle-yard, and you stood there, naked, with your hands tied behind your back. Just as I saw you, though I was far away, you could also see me and the man who was holding me in his arms. All the other couples, too, were visible in this infinite sea of nakedness which foamed about me, and of which my companion and I were only a wave, so to speak. Then, while you were standing in the castle-yard, a young woman, with a diadem on her head and wearing a purple cloak, appeared at a high arched window between red curtains. It was the queen of the country, and she looked down at you with a stern questioning look. You were standing alone. All the others stood aside, pressed against the wall, and I heard them whispering and muttering in a malicious and threatening manner. Then the queen bent down over the railing. Silence reigned, and she signalled to you, commanding you to come up to her, and I knew that she had decided to pardon you. But you either didn't notice her, or else you didn't want to. Suddenly you were standing opposite her, with your hands still tied. You were wrapped in a black cloak, and you were not in a room, but in the open, somehow, floating, as it were. She held a piece of parchment in her hand, your death-sentence, which stated your crime and the reasons for your conviction. She asked you – I couldn't hear the words, but I knew it was so – whether you were willing to be her lover, for in that case the death-penalty would be remitted. You shook your head, refusing. I wasn't surprised, for it seemed natural and inevitable that you should be faithful to me, under all circumstances. The queen shrugged her shoulders, waved her hand, and suddenly you were in a subterranean cellar, and whips were whizzing down upon you, although I couldn't see the people who were swinging them. Blood flowed down you in streams. I saw it without feeling cruel, or even surprised. The queen now moved towards you, her loose hair flowing about her naked body, and held out her diadem to you with both hands. I realized that she was the girl at the seashore in Denmark, the one you had once seen nude, in the morning, on the ledge of a bathing-hut. She didn't say a word, but she was clearly there to learn if you would be her husband and the ruler of the land. When you refused again, she suddenly disappeared. At the same time I saw them erecting a cross for you – not down in the castle-yard, but on the meadow, where I was resting with my lover among all the other couples. I saw you walking alone through ancient streets without a guard, but I knew that your course was marked out for you and that it was impossible for you to turn aside. Next, you were coming up the forest path, where I anxiously awaited you, but I did not feel any sympathy for you, though your body was covered with the weals which had stopped bleeding. You went higher and higher, the path widened, the forest receded on both sides, and you stood at the edge of the meadow at an enormous, incomprehensible distance. Your eyes smiled at me as if to show that you had fulfilled my wish and had brought me everything I needed – clothing and shoes and jewels. But I thought your actions senseless beyond description, and I wanted to make fun of you, to laugh in your face – because you had refused the queen's hand out of faithfulness to me, and because you had been tortured and now came tottering up here to a horrible death. As I ran to meet you, you came near more and more quickly. We were floating in the air, and then I lost sight of you; and I realized we had flown past each other. I hoped that you would, at least, hear my laughter when they were nailing you to the cross. And so I laughed, as shrill and loud as I could – that was the laugh, Fridolin, that you heard when I awoke.'

Neither of them spoke or moved. Any remark at this moment would have seemed futile. The further her story progressed, the more ridiculous and insignificant did his own experiences become, at least up to date. He swore to himself that he would resume and conclude all of them. He would then faithfully report them and so take vengeance on this woman who had revealed herself as faithless, cruel and treacherous, and whom he now believed he hated more than he had ever loved her.

He realized that he was still clasping her fingers. Ready as he was to hate her, his feeling of tenderness for these slender, cool fingers was unchanged except that it was more acute. Involuntarily, in fact again his will, he gently pressed his lips on this familiar hand before he let it go.

Albertina still kept her eyes closed and Fridolin thought he could see a happy, innocent smile playing about her mouth. He felt an incomprehensible desire to bend over and kiss her pale forehead. But he checked himself. He realized that it was only the natural fatigue of the last few hours which disguised itself as tenderness in the familiarity of their mutual room.

But whatever his present state of mind – whatever decisions he might reach in the next few hours, the urgent demand of the moment was for sleep and forgetfulness. He had been able to sleep long and dreamlessly the night following the death of his mother, so why not now? He stretched himself out beside his wife who seemed already asleep. A sword between us, he thought, we are lying here like mortal enemies. But it was only an illusion.

Anonymous translation

JOUVE

Red

Pierre Jean Jouve, the French poet, published in 1932 a collection of short stories, *Histoires sanglantes* ('Bloody Stories'), from which we have selected the following dream.

I had purchased a black dress. Black is always my favourite. I had bought a black dress with a red trim, and a black hat adorned with a red flower. The hat matched the dress. The dress had a bolero and a long train, it gave me a wasp waist, and the hat projected over my eyes. The dress and the hat were almost the same black and exactly the same red. The trim on the dress was red, bright red. The flower on the hat was a rose. And so, dressed up to the nines, I went down into the street where there are always lots of people walking in front of the shops in the afternoon. Passing in front of one shop, I notice a mirror. I hurry to take a look at myself. That's practical, I think: a full-length mirror. I look at myself, turning around in every direction to see if everything is all right. Absolutely perfect! I think, but . . . What's this? Something was sticking out. It wasn't much, if you like, but nothing ought to be sticking out. Something was sticking out, and falling down, what was it? – my underpants. It would be too stupid just to stand there, so, as if there were nothing wrong, I bend down and pick my underpants up. Picking up this little item, with the least scandal possible, I folded them up like a handkerchief, and immediately put it to my face, seeing as my nose was bleeding. Just as the blood's soaked into my underpants, I can hear someone talking about me behind my back. I can hear someone saying: Well! she's got red all over her! What a thing to say! Quickly I turn around. I turn around and simply say, 'No, I've just forgotten to put on any red lipstick.'

Translated by J. Romney

ELUARD

I Dream I am not Sleeping

Paul Eluard was one of the founding members of the Surrealist movement, which relied to a great extent on automatic writing and transcription of dreams. He was one of the leading poets of political engagement during the last war. This dream comes from *Donner à voir*, 1938.

18 June 1937

I dream that I am in bed and it is late. Impossible to get to sleep. I am aching all over. I try to turn on the light. I cannot, so I get up and grope my way in the darkness towards my wife's room. In the corridor, I fall. Unable to get up, I crawl slowly forward. I can hardly breathe, I have a terrible pain in my chest. On the threshold of my wife's room, I fall asleep (I *dream* that I fall asleep).

Suddenly, I wake (I *dream* that I wake) with a start. My wife has coughed and I have taken fright. Now I realize I cannot move at all. I am flat on my belly, and my chest and face are weighing horribly on the ground. They seem to be sinking into it. I try to call out to my wife, to make her hear me as I call the word 'pa-ra-lysed'. In vain. In a horrifying moment of anguish, I realize I am blind, dumb, paralysed, that I will never again be able to communicate anything of myself. I will be alive, but the others will be left alone. Then, I see the image of a screen, hands pressing down on a window-pane, but without breaking it. My pains are gradually diminishing. Until it occurs to me to use my fingertips to check whether I am really on the floor. I pinch the sheets lightly, I am saved, I am in my bed.

Translated by J. Romney

BACHELARD

Flying

Gaston Bachelard was a French historian of science and a philosopher whose work on the 'material' basis of imagination was very influential in France in the nineteen fifties and sixties. He devoted a series of books to the presence of the four main elements (water, fire, earth and air) in human imagination (*Psychanalyse du feu*, *L'air et les songes*, *L'eau et les rêves*, etc.). The passages below belong to *L'air et les songes* ('Air and dreams'), 1944.

If in the course of the dream-flight we return to the ground, a new impulsion instantly gives us back our aerial liberty. We suffer no anxiety on this score. We know very well a force is within us, and we know the secret that unlocks it. A return to earth is not a fall, for we have the certainty of our *elasticity*. Every dreamer of oneiric flight possesses this knowledge of elasticity. He also has the impression of a *pure bound*, which knows no finality, no end to be attained. Returning to earth, the dreamer, a new *Antaeus*, rediscovers a facile, certain, intoxicating energy. But it is not the earth which really powers his bound. If the myth of Antaeus is often interpreted as a myth of the maternal earth, it is because our imagination of the terrestrial element is powerful and all pervasive. Our imagination of the aerial element, on the other hand, is often weak and masked. A psychologist of the material, dynamic imagination must therefore separate out the mythical traits which persist in our dreams. The dream-flight seems to prove that the myth of Antaeus is a *myth of sleep* rather than of life. Only in sleep is a kick sufficient to return us to our ethereal nature, to that life of rising up. As Nodier says, this movement is really the trace 'of an instinct' of flight which persists or which comes alive in our nocturnal life. We might well say it is the trace of a *lightness instinct*, one of the most deep-rooted instincts in life. The present essay devotes many pages to seeking out the phenomena associated with this lightness instinct. Dream-flight, in its extreme simplicity, is, we believe, a dream of instinctive life. That explains why it is so little differentiated.

In these conditions, when we want to rationalize *to the lowest common denominator* our memories of the nocturnal air journey, where then shall we place our wings? Nothing in our innermost experience of the night allows us to place wings on our shoulders. Unless there is some particular contamination of the imaginary, no dreamer ever dreams wings which flap. Often the dream of flapping wings is only a dream of falling. We ward off vertigo by moving our arms, and this dynamic can give rise to wings on the shoulder. But natural dream-flight, the positive flight that is our night work, is not a rhythmic flight, for it has the continuity and the history of a single bound, it is the rapid creation of a *dynamized instant*. Thus the only rationalization by the image of wings which can be in agreement with primitive dynamic experience is that of the *winged heel*, the pinions of Mercury the night voyager.

Conversely, the wings of Mercury are nothing but the heel dynamized. We would not hesitate to make these little wings – dynamically well placed to symbolize the aerial dream, and without real visual significance – the very sign of the dreamer's sincerity. When a poet in his images is able to suggest these minuscule wings, we can be fairly sure that his poem is in contact with a *lived dynamic experience*. Then we can frequently recognize in these poetic images a particular consistency which does not belong to images assembled by mere fancy. They are endowed with the greatest of all poetic realities: *oneiric reality*. They induce natural reveries. It is hardly surprising that the winged heel occurs in myths and tales the world over. Jules Duhem, in his thesis on the history of flight, points out that in Tibet, 'Buddhist saints travel through the air with the aid of certain shoes known as light-feet', and he refers to the tale of the flying slipper, so common in the folk literatures of Europe and Asia. This alone is the origin of the *seven-league boots* (in English, thousand-league boots). The writer will make the connection instinctively.

. . . It is in the foot that the dreamer's forces of flight are situated. To put it briefly, we will therefore permit ourselves in our metapoetic research, to call these wings on the heel *dream-wings*.

Translated by J. Romney

Air

Judging from our personal experience, in order to sleep well, one must find the base element of the unconscious. More exactly, we must sleep *in* our own element. A good slumber is a slumber cradled, a slumber carried, and the imagination knows that one is cradled and carried by something and not by someone. In sleep, we are the creatures of a Cosmos; we are cradled by water, carried on the wind, in the air, by the air we breathe, following the rhythm of our breath. These are the slumbers of childhood, or at least the peaceful sleep of youth, whose nocturnal life so often receives an invitation to travel on an infinite journey.

Translated by J. Romney

GENET

Harcamone

Jean Genet, who died in 1986, is the most successful combination in European letters, after François Villon in the fifteenth century, of the underworld thug and the man of letters. A novelist, a poet, a playwright, he has used all these literary media to exalt the beauty and vitality of criminal life. Jean-Paul Sartre, who discovered and launched him as a writer, attempted to make him the patron saint of rebellion against society and the culture of the establishment, but Genet's fantasy cannot be so easily pigeon-holed, as it appears from the text presented here. This is an extract from *Miracle of the Rose* (1946), a homosexual love story set in the death wing of a prison. It is situated towards the end of the novel, just before the execution of the hero, Harcamone.

Someone opened Harcamone's door. He was sleeping on his back. First, four men entered his dream. Then he awoke. Without getting up, without even raising his torso, he turned his head to the door. He saw the black men and understood immediately, but he also realized very quickly that, in order to die in his sleep, he must not disrupt or destroy the state of dreaming in which he was still entangled. He decided to maintain the dream. He therefore did not run his hand through his matted hair. He said 'yes' to himself, and he felt a need to smile – but the smile was barely perceptible to the others – to smile inwardly so that the virtue of the smile would be transmitted to his inner being and he would be stronger than the moment, for the smile would ward off, despite his sadness, the tremendous gloom of his abandonment which threatened to drive him to despair, with all the pain it entails. He therefore smiled, with the faint smile he was to retain until his death. Above all, let it not be thought that he was intent on anything but the guillotine. His eyes were focused on it, but he decided to live ten heroic, that is, joyous, minutes. He did not joke, as the newspapers dared report, for sarcasm is bitter and conceals ferments of despair. He stood up. And when he was on his feet, upright in the middle of the cell, his head, neck and entire body emerged from the lace and silk which are worn, in the most trying moments, only by the diabolical masters of the world, and with which he was suddenly adorned. Without growing an inch, he became huge, over-topping and splitting the cell, filling the universe, and the four black men shrank until they were no bigger than four bedbugs.

The reader has realized that Harcamone was invested with such majesty that his clothes themselves were ennobled and turned to silk and brocade. He was clad in patent-leather boots, breeches of soft blue silk and a shirt of old blond-lace, the collar of which was open on his splendid neck that supported the collar of the Order of the Golden Fleece. Truly, he came in a straight line, and by way of the sky, from between the legs of the captain of the galley. Perhaps because of the miracle of which he was the place and object, or for some other reason – to give thanks to God his Father – he put his right knee on the floor. The four men quickly took advantage and climbed up his leg and sloping thigh. They had great difficulty, for the silk was slippery. Halfway up the thigh, forgoing his inaccessible and tumultuous fly, they encountered his hand, which was lying in repose. They climbed on to it, and from there to the arm, and then to the lace sleeve. And finally to the right shoulder, the bowed neck, the left shoulder and, as lightly as possible, the face. Harcamone had not moved, except that he was breathing through his parted lips. The judge and the lawyer wormed their way into the ear and the chaplain and executioner dared enter his mouth. They moved forward a little along the edge of the lower lip and fell into the gulf. And then, almost as soon as they passed the gullet, they came to a lane of trees that descended into a gentle, almost voluptuous slope. All the foliage was very high and formed the sky of the landscape. They were unable to recognize the scents, for in states like theirs one can no longer distinguish particular features: one passes through forests, tramples down flowers, climbs over stones. What surprised them most was the silence. They nearly took each other by the hand, for in the interior of such a marvel the chaplain and the executioner became two lost schoolboys. They pressed onward, inspecting left and right, prospecting the silence, stumbling over moss, in order to get their bearings, but they found nothing. After a few hundred yards, it grew dark though nothing had changed in that skyless landscape. They kicked around rather gaily the remains of a country fair: a spangled jersey, the ashes of a camp-fire, a circus-whip. Then, upon turning their heads, they realized that they had unwittingly been following a succession of winding paths more complicated than those of a mine. There was no end to Harcamone's interior. It was more decked with black than a capital whose king has just been assassinated. A voice from the heart declared: 'The interior is grieving,' and they swelled with fear, which rose within them like a light wind above the sea. They moved ahead, more lightly, between rocks and dizzying cliffs, some of them very close together, where no eagle flew. These walls kept converging. The men were approaching the inhuman regions of Harcamone.

The judge and the lawyer, who had entered by the ear wandered at first through an extraordinary maze of narrow alleys where they suspected the houses (windows and doors were shut) of sheltering dangerous lovemaking punishable by law. The alleys were unpaved, for the sound of the men's shoes was inaudible; they seemed to be walking on elastic ground, where they lightly rebounded. They were skipping. The meandering alleys suggested a kind of Toulon, as if meant to contain the lurching walk of sailors. The men turned left, thinking that was the right way, then left, left. The streets were all alike. Behind them, a young sailor came out of a sinister-looking house. He looked about. In his mouth, between his teeth, was a blade of grass which he was chewing. The judge turned his head and saw him but was unable to make out his face, for the sailor was advancing in profile and turned away when he was looked at. The lawyer realized that the judge could not see. He turned around but was likewise unable to see the hiding face. I am still amazed at the privilege which allowed me to witness Harcamone's inner life and to be the invisible observer of the secret adventures of the four black men. The alleys were as complicated as the steep gorges and the mossy lanes. They had the same downward slope. Finally, all four met at a kind of crossroads which I cannot describe accurately. It led down, again to the left, into a luminous corridor lined with huge mirrors. They went in that direction. All four questioned each other at the same time in an anxious tone, almost ceasing to breathe:

'The heart – have you found the heart?'

And realizing at once that none of them had found it, they continued their way along the corridor, tapping and listening to the mirrors. They advanced slowly, cupping their ears and often flattening them against the wall. It was the executioner who first heard the beats. They quickened their pace. They were now so frightened that they sped along the elastic ground in leaps and bounds of several yards. They were breathing hard and talking to themselves without a stop, as one does in dreams, that is, so softly and indistinctly that the words merely ruffle the silence. The beats were nearer and louder. Finally, the four dark men came to a mirror on which was drawn (obviously carved with the diamond of a ring) a heart pierced by an arrow. No doubt it was the portal of the heart. I don't know what gesture the executioner made, but it made the heart open and we entered the first chamber. It was bare, white and cold, without an aperture. Alone, in the midst of that emptiness, upright on a wooden block, stood a young drummer of sixteen. His icy, impassive gaze looked at nothing in the world. His supple hands were beating the drum. The drumsticks rose and fell sharply and neatly. They were beating out Harcamone's highest life. Did he see us? Did he see the open, profaned heart? How could we not be seized with panic! And that chamber was only the first.

The mystery of the hidden chamber remained to be discovered. But no sooner did one of the four realize that they were not in the heart of the heart than a door opened by itself and we saw before us a red rose of monstrous size and beauty.

'The Mystic Rose,' murmured the chaplain.

The four men were staggered by the splendour. The rays of the rose dazzled them at first, but they quickly pulled themselves together, for such people never permit themselves to show signs of respect . . . Recovering from their agitation, they rushed in, pushing back the petals and crumpling them with their drunken hands, as a lecher who has been deprived of sex pushes back a whore's skirt. They were in the throes of drunken profanation. With their temples throbbing and their brows beaded with sweat, they reached the heart of the rose. It was a kind of dark well. At the very edge of this pit, which was as murky and deep as an eye, they leaned forward and were seized with a kind of dizziness. All four made the gestures of people losing their balance, and they toppled into that deep gaze.

Translated by B. Frechtman

MANDIARGUES

The Pink Bitch

André Pieyre de Mandiargues, novelist and art critic, particularly known for the extreme eroticism of some of his work, has written some forty books, and translated several poets, among others Yeats, Mishima and Octavio Paz. *Marbre*, from which this passage is taken, was published in 1953.

I dreamt that I was dreaming of a pink bitch, which insisted on following me despite all my efforts (cries and gestures) to send her back to her litter of pups, all as horribly hairless as their mother; but I knew it was only a dream.

Then I dreamt I was waking, and that I could see lying next to me, although I had no idea how she had got there, my old fiancée Carita, almost naked, and smiling at me with a look halfway between shame and the most imbecilic gratitude. I felt utterly disgusted, now I saw the multiple breasts on her bosom, like the bosom of the Ephesan Diana, or like grapes hanging in a bunch.

I woke up alone as usual, but turned on the light to look distrustfully at the bed, at the place where she had been lying in my dream.

Translated by J. Romney

LEIRIS

The Address

Michel Leiris, an ethnographer by profession, published his best known book, *L'âge d'homme*, in 1939. It was a sort of autobiography in which he was trying to note down, almost randomly and with as few stylistic interventions as possible, the memories of his childhood. The same kind of scientific purity in the art of transcription can be found in *Nuits sans nuit et quelques jours sans jour* ('Nights Without Night and Some Days Without Day') (1961), from which we have selected the passage below.

14–15 July 1958

'Poulet Vuillambert (or Vuillambeau, or Vuillambé)', the name and surname of a prostitute or hostess who gave me her telephone number when I met her in a nightclub. Someone's clumsy fingernail, perhaps my own, has torn the piece of paper or card on which I had written the number. How can I find it again, unless I go back to sleep, to plunge myself once more into dream and propel myself towards this woman with whom I passed some hours chatting so agreeably?

I go back to sleep, but to no avail: this adventure, barely begun, is now a thing of the past. Perhaps by writing this story, I might find another roundabout way to retrieve at least some of it, and if chance will have it, once more breathe her perfume?

Translated by J. Romney

GOMEZ DE LA SERNA

The Transference of Dreams

Born in Madrid in 1888, Ramon Gomez de la Serna is one of the most interesting figures of the Spanish literary avant-garde. He coined the word 'gregueria' (literally, gobbledygook), which he used for a very personal collection of humorous aphorisms, in the manner of Ambrose Bierce or Cioran. *Caprichos*, from which our text is taken, was published in 1962. It is a collection of pieces of various nature written at different times. About *Caprichos* Gomez de la Serna said that they represent 'a Goyesque carpet of former times . . .'

Suddenly he ceased to have nightmares and he felt relieved, since by then they had become an obsessive projection on the walls of his bedroom.

As he was sitting in his reading chair, rested and peaceful, his man-servant announced that the gentleman from upstairs wished to see him.

Since there should never be any valid reason for delay in seeing a neighbour, he had him shown in and listened to his concern:

'I'm here because you have transferred your dreams to me.'

'And how did you know it?'

'Being the old neighbours that we are, I know your habits, your whims, and above all I know your name, the call mark of the dreams which exhaust me, who never used to dream . . . Landscapes, ladies, children appear, with whom I have never had anything to do . . .'

'But how could this happen?'

'Undoubtedly, since dreams rise up like smoke, they have ascended into my bedroom, which is above yours . . .'

'And what do you think we can do?'

'Well, exchange flats for a few days and see if your dreams return to you.'

It seemed reasonable to him; they exchanged flats, and a few days later the dreams had returned to their rightful owner.

Translated by J. Lyons

MALERBA

The Serpent

Luigi Malerba, one of the foremost Italian novelists, published his best known novel, *Il serpente* ('The Serpent'), from which we have taken the following dream, in 1966. His next novel, *Salto Mortale*, (translated into English with the title 'What is this buzzing? Do you hear it too?') won the Prix Médicis in 1970. *The Serpent* tells the story of a philatelist who invents for himself imaginary lives, love-affairs, adventures and misadventures, so that at the end no one, and the reader least of all, is able to distinguish between reality and fantasy.

. . . After one day I waited for Miriam for many more days. Time seemed to be racing past outside the shop window, while the city also raced insensibly past on foot and by car, while the garage attendant opposite my place went on selling petrol, the newspaperman went on selling newspapers (what a lot of news, what a lot of headlines), and the old people came to sit at the foot of the

monument to Cairoli, who was also a Hero, while the boys from Trastevere
entered the city across the Garibaldi Bridge where little groups of Americans
were lurking and the girls ran to the Ideal Home shop in the Piazza Argentina.
My eye recorded, beyond the window, a movement in which Vaud 1849s have
never counted for anything, where a girl had become blended with another
thousand girls all unknown like the unknown soldier in the Piazza Venezia (a
bouquet and a wreath for Miriam, who had vanished). Other things could be
seen beyond the window, stray dogs running along sniffing the pavement, the
pavement which allowed itself to be sniffed by the stray dogs, rhomboids
cubes human forms human shadows.

I have always dreamed at night ever since I can remember. My mother
dreamed too. When she got out of bed her legs hurt and her knees because of
all the running she had done in her dreams. At table she would tell my father
the long stories of the night. In her dreams there was almost always a knight
on horseback who appeared on the scene at a certain point in the performance. My father hated this knight because he suspected there was something
between him and my mother. So my mother, when she told her dreams, began
leaving him out. Then the meadows remained, the dusty roads, the paths in
the woods, the river with its broad stony bed, and the bandits who pursued her
(on foot or on horseback? my father would ask), the stage-setting remained all
ready for the entrance of the rider who was to save my mother, but the rider
didn't enter. It was like telling the first act of the Opera when the chorus sings
Si, la vita s'addoppia al gioir and everybody waits for Alfredo to enter, and
instead Alfredo doesn't enter. Sometimes my father, who wasn't stupid, used
to put down his fork and leave the house.

On certain nights I succeed in steering my dreams (not the way you steer a
car or a bicycle, but the way you steer a boat that always veers a little and can't
take narrow curves). In theory it's a simple matter. First of all you have to start
your thoughts in a certain way before preparing to sleep, you have to arrange a
suitable terrain because it's from there (from your thoughts) that the dream
takes shape, on being born. When I feel sleep approaching I begin to imagine
a scene with the characters and everything. The chief character, the Protagonist is always me. I am always in the centre of the action in the first person. A
dream in the third person, an objective dream, can happen to anybody, and in
fact they do happen, but they are hard to steer because you're not on the
scene. Then there are the secondary characters, often there's the antagonist as
in plays in the theatre. This starting scene I have to imagine with my eyes
(which, however, are shut), that is to say visually, otherwise it's no use, I mean
it's no use in steering the dream. If it is carefully devised, according to the
rules of verisimilitude as Aristotle says, the dream naturally fits in and follows
the same line. You have to have talent for inventing these scenes, the characters have to be in their places in a situation that can be developed naturally, the
relationships have to be established promptly with the first speeches.

Sometimes I begin with a scene that interests me and the development takes place in a different direction from the one desired, but there also exists a subsequent control, the possibility of intervention or repeating a scene, as in a theatre during rehearsals. When the action takes a very dramatic turn, then this control becomes impossible, there's nothing to be done and the dream follows its own bent.

All dreams are always a bit mysterious and this is what is beautiful about them, but certain ones are very mysterious, I mean you don't understand a thing, they are like puzzles. Whereas puzzles have a solution, these dreams don't, you can give them a hundred different meanings and one is as likely as the other.

Now I will tell a mysterious dream which involves Miriam though she isn't seen (she is barely mentioned) and where I think Baldasseroni is also involved though he isn't seen and isn't even mentioned. I dreamed this dream all in one night even if the action is divided into various scenes. In these scenes I am always on stage, I move, I speak, I do things but I don't know why I do them.

It moved in spirals, it became knotted in the air, it twisted around upon itself. It formed little eddies and currents. It was dense and yellow. I am speaking about the fog. In the vicinity of the Railway Station I stumbled over a cement bench. In the Strada Garibaldi I bumped against a pregnant woman. People ran into each other on the pavements and you could hear both sides apologizing. Some people cursed. Cars and bicycles drove around with their headlights on at midday and the city's Administration had turned on the street-lamps. It was hard to walk, hard to move. Fog-lights, din of crazed car-horns, voices of infuriated people. I made a little cut on one finger, a mark to stop me from being confused with the others.

I had to reach the Hotel Carillon which is in the centre of the town, behind the City Hall, beyond the fountain and the statue of the Du brassè which is dialect for the Two Embracers. I was walking in the dark, in the fog, I always found the right direction thanks to my instinct which said to me turn right, turn left. I recognized the streets. But I know these places by heart, I said to myself, I must have already seen these places somewhere.

In the lobby if you want to call it that, there was only a man with a newspaper in his hand, but he wasn't reading. And an old woman behind a kind of schoolmaster's desk who asked me if I had a tail.

'Why?' I asked.

'I see you haven't shut the door after you.'

I shut the door and went to sit in the easy chair opposite the man with the paper in his hand, who wasn't reading. He had to be the informer who was to inform me about I couldn't remember what.

'For those who want to be thinner.' It was the old woman behind the desk who spoke.

'Diet,' the man said promptly.

The woman bent over a crossword puzzle magazine and wrote 'diet'.

'Are you in a trade? Are you a tradesman? Or are you a professor of something?' This time it was the man who spoke.

'I'm here by chance,' I said. I was lying.

'May I say something?'

'Say it.'

'No, for the moment I won't say it,' the man said. 'Have you seen the fog? Continental climate, too cold in the winter, too hot in the summer. In the summer you can swim on the asphalt, the streets melt, the cars blow up like bombs. I am exaggerating, obviously.'

The man raised his eyes, stared at me for a long time.

'Well then?'

I was sitting there and I was waiting for him to speak, I was there to listen to him, I had come a long way purposely for this.

'Anthropophagi,' the woman said.

'Cannibals,' the man answered.

The woman wrote 'cannibals'.

'If you want to know the story of the Fiat 600,' the man said, 'you mustn't apply to me. I mean it's no use coming to me especially. Everybody knows about it, even the *Gazzetta* spoke of it. It blew up. Like a bomb. Get somebody to tell you, it's quite a story. You can stop somebody in the street, they all know it. There's no need to come to me. No, look here, I won't tell anything. Terrible, a terrible story. It had sat in the sun for quite a while, the Fiat 600. Cars made of tin. Look here, though, I won't tell you the whole story. The ring, get somebody to tell you the business of the ring, that's a part of the story. Remember the ring. Now I really must leave.'

The man slipped on his overcoat and wrapped a scarf around his neck. He opened the door and disappeared into the fog.

'We've become famous,' the woman behind the desk said, 'because of this Fiat. There's a great coming-and-going of foreigners here, I mean a lot of tourists. We have the Duomo the Baptistry the Palazzo della Pilotta and the Art Gallery, nobody pays any attention. They come here because of the Fiat. From everywhere you know. Even from abroad. Especially from France because the wife of the petroleum Engineer was French, do you know we have petroleum here just fifteen miles out of town? It's being depleted though. His wife had left for France and he hadn't bothered about putting it in the garage, the car that is. Apparently somebody was asleep inside it, you understand?'

'But the explosion . . . ?' I asked.

'What? Don't you understand? The heat? Doesn't that tell you anything?'

I couldn't understand.

'Then try to imagine what happens to a corpse, shall we say, with the summer's heat, inside a locked car. What happens?'

I looked at the woman in bewilderment.

'Putrefaction,' the woman exclaimed. 'Right? You can imagine the rest, there's no need for me to tell you about it. Then there's the part that's still unfinished, so to speak. When you tell a story, first of all you have to know who's the Protagonist. I go to the Opera, for example, suppose they show me the whole thing but they don't show me the Protagonist. That spoils the plot completely. Giving examples is a speciality of mine, but still I often get them wrong. This one with the Opera wasn't right either, do forgive me.'

'No, please go ahead,' I said.

'I've told you too much as it is. You can work out the rest for yourself. It was a big story in all the papers, like the one about the bath-soap. Maybe you can find somebody who'll tell it to you from the beginning. There's the newspaper-seller at the Barriera Solferino, go and see him. The newspaper-seller has the advantage of having read all the newspapers when it happened. I only read the *Gazetta*, but he reads the paper from Milan as well, the *Giorno*, the *Corriere*. But there are some things that even he doesn't know, they simply aren't known.'

I approached the door and I looked outside, through the glass. The fog was still thick, no longer yellow but almost black, the air cold and heavy. Difficult to go out along the street. Taking flight was unthinkable, and yet I thought about it anyway. No lights could be seen any more, no more voices could be heard, but in the black and in the darkness you could still make out the writhing, rolling, twisting fog like a crazed serpent.

I had to hurry, the next scene took place at the Barriera Solferino, at the newspaper-seller's. The newspaper-seller was waiting for me, I had plunged into the fog and was running like a man running after the plot of a film, who has to jump from one scene to the next and the scenes all take place in different localities and if he arrives late he finds it's already begun. I had climbed on to a tram that was proceeding slowly, clanging its bell, and I said 'Hurry, please hurry,' to the driver, but he didn't answer because it's forbidden for the driver to speak to the passengers. 'Hurry,' I said, 'because the scene is about to begin.'

'Don't give that story any more thought,' the newspaper-seller at the Barriera Solferino said, 'it's best for you to forget it. That's the way we are around here, we like to joke about everything. You're a foreigner, that's obvious immediately, and you mustn't listen to all the things you hear around this town. We're all big talkers in these parts, you mind what I say. The car on the street by the river? They wrote about it even in the provincial papers but that doesn't prove anything. Do you believe the newspapers? I don't. Take it from somebody who's been handling them for fifteen years. The Fiat really did blow up, that's true. But there are all sorts of ways of blowing up and the truth has a hundred thousand faces, like falsehood. You know what was inside that car? Inside there were some pumpkins. They fermented with the heat, that's what it was. Pumpkins are like dynamite, did you know that? Take it from me. They heard an explosion at three in the afternoon, one afternoon last summer. At that hour people are asleep or in the shade, indoors, so there aren't any witnesses. They began by saying that inside the car there was a bomb, that the windows of the houses were broken and so on. It takes more than that to break windows. Then I came along and I told them the business of the girl, they've probably told you about it. The girl without a home who goes and sleeps every night in the car parked along the river. What do you think of that? The story of the girl appealed to everybody, the papers began to talk about it. We're big talkers around these parts, you understand? I say one thing, you say another and a whole novel comes out and ends up in the papers. The ring? That's another tale. Who ever saw this ring? Does anybody say he saw it?' He's saying something wrong. The name written inside it was one I made up out of the whole cloth. A commonplace name, the first that came into my head, Miriam.

In the street beside the river there was still the hulk of the Fiat opposite the Social Security Building, just beyond the Ponte Caprazucca. The hulk was there, abandoned and rusty, without tyres, without the seats any more, the headlights shattered, a wreck. The metal was misshapen, as if an explosion had burst it from inside. One of the doors was missing and this reinforced the explosion thesis but it left unsolved the problem of the nature of the explosive.

The fact is that the newspaper-seller had lied, I mean he had told the truth saying that it was all a lie. For what reason? To hide what? I climbed up the few steps to the Social Security building. Many window-panes had been replaced recently, you could tell because the stucco was still fresh. So the car had exploded, the window-panes had been broken. Let's hope so, I said to myself, but what should I hope for? And yet something had to happen, it couldn't end like this, this was no finale not even for a dream.

What an ugly mixed-up dream you're having, I said to myself, what an ugly dream that doesn't mean anything, it fills you with strange fears and nothing else. I jumped from one scene to the next, I boarded moving trams, I also ran on foot and now I was tired of running back and forth through that city I don't want to name. Why run so much? I said to myself, and I went on running. What does all this running mean, all this rush? Do you at least know why you're running? Are you running after somebody or is somebody running after you? Is it pursuit or flight? The fog in the streets, the woman doing her crossword puzzle, the newspaper-seller at the Barriera Solferino, the whole story, true or false, of the Fiat 600: what sense do they have? According to the Book of Dreams fog is a bad sign, but now the fog was going away.

I had sat down on the steps of the Social Security building, it was three in the afternoon and the stereo hour was approaching as *The Radio Times* says, the hours of sounds and voices that pass from ear to ear and ricochet in the air on Marconi's waves. If dreams really do express hidden desires, probably I desired to go back. But then it's useless, I said to myself, if a person goes back it's in order to be at peace, not to hear all these noises, these voices. You should find another place for your dreams, I said to myself. What an ugly mixed-up dream you're having, but already I had to run off because another scene was about to begin.

The little airport of the Aero-club is to the North of the city, with its landing field of steel mesh set on the gravel, its low hangers, meadows all around, long natural hedges surrounding it on all sides. I arrived a few minutes late, the City Authorities were already there, the Editor of the *Gazetta* tall and thin, looking at me through his spectacles. The Commander signalled to me with his little flag, all clear. I began to run when I was on the taxi-way, I rose up from the mid-point of the runway in a perfect take-off.

The air was warm and inviting, I flew over the city hovering, borne by the warm air, I grazed the tops of the spires, the chimney-pots on the roofs, the electric pylons. You can be happy in dreams, I was happy or at least I believe it was happiness. The air entered my clothing, swelled my trousers, my jacket, my shirt. My tie flapped gaily. I flew straight forward and sideways, I also flew backwards, I did acrobatics plunging in a dive and then rising vertically like Stukas during the war, or else I went up very high and let myself drop headlong, head hands arms legs in the wind, at a hundred and fifty yards from the ground I resumed regular flight, I began again to veer gracefully as if a symphony were accompanying my movements. I passed beneath the arches of the bridge to the amazement of the populace who ran out to see the sight. The stream was dry otherwise I could have raised a cloud of spray and soaked all those curious bystanders who had crowded around to watch. Some waved handkerchiefs to greet me. Watch out for the high tension, I said to myself, if you touch the wires you die. But why don't swallows die then? Perhaps I could have perched on the wires like a swallow. But more than a swallow I was an aeroplane. I volplaned down over the Old City, I waved to the men seated outside the taverna, below me the straight line of the Via Emilia with its traffic of cars and bicycles, if I went higher I could take in with a single glance the whole city from the Barriera Vittorio to the Barriera Massimo D'Azeglio, from the Barriera Solferino to the Underpass and beyond, the roads that fan out towards the plains to the North and the hills to the South.

I wore a compass on my wrist tied there with a band. Perhaps I had other instruments built in, or perhaps not. In any case I navigated professionally. A few last traces of fog were going away, whipped off by the gusts of wind that blew down along the bed of the stream, there up above the air was warm and soft and down below you could see the roofs gleaming in the sun, the cables of the trams glistened and the window-panes. Many people had climbed up to the terraces and even the roof-tops to watch me, traffic jams had formed in the streets. The next day the whole city would be talking about the event, that is about me flying over the city, the *Gazetta* would publish an article and I would get Miriam to read it. I wheeled around the spire of the Duomo, over the smoke-stacks of the Barilla pasta factory, everybody had his nose in the air to watch me. It was outright madness. All gaping. The Book says about flight: good luck, great honours and wealth.

Translated by W. Weaver

BISHOP

Sleeping Standing Up

This poem by Elizabeth Bishop is taken from her *Complete Poems* published in New York in 1969. Another poem by Elizabeth Bishop is entitled 'Sleeping on the ceiling'.

As we lie down to sleep the world turns half away
    through ninety dark degrees;
      the bureau lies on the wall
and thoughts that were recumbent in the day
    rise as the others fall,
      stand up and make a forest of thick-set trees.

The armored cars of dreams, contrived to let us do
    so many a dangerous thing,
      are chugging at its edge
all camouflaged, and ready to go through
    the swiftest streams, or up a ledge
of crumbling shale, while plates and trappings ring.

—Through turret-slits we saw the crumbs or pebbles that lay
    below the riveted flanks
      on the green forest floor,
like those the clever children placed by day
    and followed to their door
      one night, at least; and in the ugly tanks

we tracked them all the night. Sometimes they disappeared,
    dissolving in the moss,
      sometimes we went too fast
and ground them underneath. How stupidly we steered
    until the night was past
      and never found out where the cottage was.

PEREC

The Arrest

This text belongs to the collection of dreams published in 1973 under the title *La Boutique Obscure* ('The Dark Shop') by Georges Pérec, who was one of the leaders of the *Ouvroir de Littérature Potentielle* ('Workshop of Potential Literature'), better known as OULIPO.

July 1970

I am in Tunis. The whole town is built on heights. I am taking a very long walk: a winding road, curtains of trees, views through clearings, panoramas. It was as if the landscape were revealing itself in its entirety like the background of an Italian painting.

The next day, the police come to arrest me. At some time in the past I have committed a minor misdemeanour. I have no memory of it, but I know that today it might cost me twenty years.

I am fleeing, armed with a revolver. The places I run through are unknown to me. There is no immediate danger, but I know in advance that running will solve nothing. I return to the familiar places where I was walking the day before. Three sailors ask me their way. Behind a line of trees, veiled women are washing linen.

A winding road takes me back into town. The police are everywhere, in their hundreds. They are stopping everyone and searching cars.

I pass through the police. As long as I don't catch their eye, I stand a chance of getting out of this.

I go into a café where I find Marcel B. I go and sit next to him.

Three guys walk into the café (police, obviously!); they walk around the room ever so casually. Perhaps they haven't seen me? I am almost breathing a sigh of relief, when one of them comes and sits at my table.

'I don't have my papers on me', I say.

He is about to get up and leave (which would mean I am safe), when he says to me under his breath:

'Copulate!'

I don't understand.

He writes the word down in the margin of a newspaper, in big hollowed-out letters:

COPULATE

then he goes over the first three letters again, shading in the interior:

COPULATE

At last I understand. It is extremely complicated: I am to go home and 'copulate with my wife'; so that when the police come and get me, the fact that I have 'copulated on a Saturday', being Jewish, will constitute a mitigating circumstance.

The fact that I am Jewish is indeed what lies behind this whole business, and complicates it considerably. My arrest is a consequence of the Jewish-Arab conflict and it would do me no good at all to affirm my pro-Palestinian sentiments.

I return to my villa (perhaps it is just a simple room). Most of all, I am anxious to know whether I will be a Tunisian prisoner in France or a French prisoner in Tunisia. In both cases, I am hoping for a pardon in the event of a visit by a head of state.

I feel innocent. What annoys me most is that I will have to keep my socks on for several more years, and they are dirty already.

Translated by J. Romney

BUTOR

Dream Matter

This is the beginning of a research on dreams and their use in writing which Butor is still pursuing. This text was published in 1975. Until now, four volumes of *Matière de Rêve* have come out. The title is usually translated as 'Dream Matter', but there is probably an allusion to Hamlet's 'stuff that dreams are made on'.

I am on a beach; it is evening. A line of hills slopes down towards the left. Above, a strip of orange, and the grey smoke trail of a jet plane rising. There must be an airport not far away; but I can hear no sound of a motor. The wind is pushing me. The waves are lapping gently at my feet. I am wearing black elongated town shoes. It is because I have just been giving a lecture. There was a cocktail party afterwards; congratulations and canapés. I slipped out by the service entrance, went down some steps, pushed open the white garden gate, and followed the path that led down through the flowering lilacs. The party must still be going on. They are no doubt waiting for my return. Later there will be a dinner at one of the other lecturers' houses; but I have several hours to spare before that. As I walk, my feet sink a little into the sand. Water seeps into every footprint, forming little pools. I turn around and see the house on the cliff. Behind me, my footprints have already been covered by the tide.

Long-legged greyish birds are running about in the foam, rummaging and letting out little cries.

A slightly stronger wave rushes in over my shoe. Now I will have to dry it. I can't go straight back to the cocktail party. First I must find some leaves and grass and wipe my shoe. I am going to climb the hill in front of me. A wave has just washed over my other shoe. The beach has shrunk considerably. Sheets of newspaper are floating on the sea. To my right, the rocks form a creek of dry sand. Several newspapers, still intact, which the wind is leafing through; the remains of a fire and a picnic. I sit down on a stool of granite. The bottoms of my trouser legs are also wet. The sun, about to set, emerges from the clouds and projects a great patch of red, but no heat at all. I unlace my shoes and place them on a table of dry stone. My socks are drenched, sand sticking to them; I take them off and lay them out next to the shoes, unbuckle my belt, remove my trousers and leave them to dry too, then take a sheet of newspaper to wipe my feet. The patch of setting sun is disappearing; the sound of the sea rising. The foam has reached the edges of the creek. No stairway at all is left for me to escape towards dry land. With the sheets of newspaper I wipe my trouser legs and my socks as best I can, mop off the excess water, make them into a packet, with the shoes on top, then I start to walk in the water, try to get back to the house, where they must be wondering where I am, but the sea-bed suddenly drops away; so I head off on the other side, and wander even further away. The sky is green. I see Atala . . .

. . . The sky is green. On the path, at the top of the cliff, embracing, I can see two students, who had been at my lecture, they can't see me now, they are pointing out a cargo ship passing in the distance. Now I am in the second, wider creek. Here the ground is covered with black stains which I am doing my best to avoid. A cry behind me; it is the girl, who must have recognized me despite the thickening shadow. I stumble and find myself floundering in the middle of an oil slick. The main thing is not to dirty my only town clothes. I put them down on a rock. Now to remove this clinging substance. But in this creek, there's not a sheet of newspaper to be seen, no grass or seaweed. Pebbles, springs, old tin cans in various degrees of rustiness. I clamber over the rocks to get back to the first creek, slip, and graze my knee. It seems the sea has already engulfed it completely. The sheets of paper are now floating. Some are carried on top of others, as if on rafts. I go to pick them, trip over a sea-urchin and fall flat in the water; the sheets move away. This time my jacket sleeves are soaked, my shirt cuffs too.

The first priority is to undo my wristwatch; it might well be waterproof, but better to be on the safe side; I slip it into my inside jacket pocket, between my wallet and my passport, and retrace my steps once more. The breeze is blowing up. The waves are breaking on the rocks. I arrive just in time to save trousers, shoes and socks. Now the big creek is also closed off by water. I take advantage of the shingles that remain uncovered to remove and fold my jacket and shirt, and roll up my tie. Now I only have on a vest and underpants. My feet are black with oil. Atala signals to me. Sighs . . . My feet are black with oil. I make up my packet again, place it on my head, holding it there with my left hand, while I use my right to hold on to the rocks, and I lower myself into the water. Another aeroplane takes off, all its lights ablaze. This time the noise is deafening. Pebbles fall from the cliff. I pull Atala to one side. Tears. There was a time when France owned a vast empire in North America, stretching from Labrador to the Floridas, from the Atlantic shores to the remotest lakes of upper Canada . . .

. . . Pebbles fall from the cliff. A whole face of the ridge is beginning to fall away; I move aside just in time; the flying debris knocks me backwards. I let go of my clothes and a wave carries them away. My shoes are floating like two little boats. I dive in and swim to retrieve them. My watch, my money, my passport, the jacket is much more important. I am chest-deep in water and can barely move forward. Night has fallen, I can hardly see any more, searching blindly, I catch hold of one sleeve, manage to pull myself up on to a rock, I have completely lost my bearings. I must clamber up. I put on the soaked jacket to free my hands, grip the roots, causing pebbles to fall under my feet, and clumps of grass, and I reach the top. A little moonlight is filtering through the clouds. In the distance, car headlights. I shiver, caress Atala. Gasping. Four great rivers, with their sources in the same mountains, divided these immense regions: the Saint-Lawrence River that vanishes in the East into the gulf that bears its name, the West River that carries its water into unknown seas, the Bourbon River that rushes from South to North into Hudson Bay, and the Meschacebé that falls from North to South, into the Gulf of Mexico. Hazy . . .

I shiver. Where can I go? Where can I get dry? Where can I get warm? I can hardly go back to the cocktail party dressed like this. Perhaps there might be barns around here, with straw I could hide in? I am on a waste ground, where the vegetation is rather thorny, I step barefoot on to the ground with the greatest care, cutting myself at every step, and finally I take off my soaked pants and vest, and fashion myself slippers of a sort, which allow me to walk on. Behind me the sea is still lapping. I make love with Atala. Pain. This last river, coursing over more than a thousand leagues, waters a delightful region which the inhabitants of the United States call New Eden, and to which the French have left the fair name of Louisiana. Blurring. In the room an edition of *Atala* and *René*, texts on the course . . .

Translated by J. Romney

HANDKE

'Who has ever...'

This passage is taken from the first few pages of *A Moment of True Feeling*, by Peter Handke, the Austrian novelist, first published in 1975.

Who has ever dreamed that he has become a murderer and from then on has only been carrying on with his usual life for the sake of appearances? At that time, which is still going on, Gregor Keuschnig had been living in Paris for some months, serving as press attaché at the Austrian embassy. He, his wife, and their four-year-old daughter Agnes occupied a dark apartment in the sixteenth arrondissement. The building, which dated from the turn of the century and reflected the bourgeois comfort of the period, had a stone balcony on the second floor and a cast-iron balcony on the fifth floor. It was situated, side by side with similar apartment houses, on a quiet boulevard sloping gently downward to the Porte d'Auteuil, one of the western exits from the city. Every five minutes or so, in the daytime hours, the glasses and dishes in the dining-room cupboard rattled when a train passed in the railway cutting that ran parallel to the boulevard, carrying passengers from the periphery of Paris to the Gare Saint-Lazare in the centre of the city, where if they wished they could change to trains that would take them northwestward to the Channel, to Deauville or Le Havre, for instance. (Some of the older people in this neighbourhood, which as late as a hundred years ago consisted partly of vineyards, chose this mode of travel when they went to the seaside with their dogs for the weekend.) But after nine o'clock at night the trains stopped running, and then it was so quiet on the boulevard that the leaves of the plane trees outside the windows could be heard rustling from time to time in the breeze that is frequent in Auteuil. On such a night at the end of July, Gregor Keuschnig had a long dream, which began with his having killed someone.

All at once he had ceased to belong. He tried to change, as an applicant for a job undertakes to change; but for fear of being found out he had to go on living exactly as before and, above all, remain exactly as he had been. Even to sit down as usual to a meal with other people was to dissemble; and if he suddenly began to talk so much about himself and his 'past life,' it was only to divert attention from himself. Oh the disgrace to my parents, he thought, while the victim, an old woman, lay in an inadequately buried wooden box: a murderer in the family! But what oppressed him most was that he had become someone else, yet had to keep behaving as if he were still himself. The dream ended with a passer-by opening the wooden box, which in the meantime seemed to have moved to the pavement outside his house.

Formerly when Keuschnig found something unbearable, he had tended to lie down somewhere by himself and go to sleep. This night the opposite happened: his dream was so intolerable that he woke up. But waking was as impossible as sleeping – only more absurd, more tedious, as though he had begun an endless term of imprisonment. Something had been done that could never be undone. He folded his hands under his head, but this habitual action had no remedial effect. Dead calm outside his bedroom window; and when after a long while a branch of the evergreen tree in the courtyard stirred, he had the impression that it had been moved, not by a gust of wind, but by the accumulated inner tension of the branch itself. It occurred to Keuschnig that there were six more stories above his ground-floor apartment, one on top of another! – probably packed full of heavy furniture, of dark-stained cupboards. He did not remove his hands from under his head, but only puffed up his cheeks as though for self-protection. He tried to imagine how his life would go on. Because everything had lost its validity, he could imagine nothing. He rolled up in a ball and tried to get back to sleep. Falling asleep had ceased to be possible. When finally, with the passing of the first train at about six, the water glass on the bedside table tinkled, he mechanically got out of bed.

Keuschnig's apartment was large and intricate. In it two people could take different itineraries and suddenly meet. The long hallway seemed to stop at a wall, but then after a bend it continued on – you wondered if you were still in the same apartment – to the back room, where his wife sometimes did her homework for her audio-visual French course and stayed the night when, as she said, she was too tired to face the spooky corridor with its abrupt twists and turns. The apartment was so intricate that, though the child couldn't actually get lost, they were forever calling: 'Where are you?' The child's room could be entered from three sides: from the hallway, from the back room, which his wife called her 'study', and from the 'parents' bedroom', so called only in the presence of visitors they didn't know very well. The 'front' of the apartment consisted of the dining room, the kitchen, the 'servants' entrance' – they had no servants – and a special servants' toilet (the bolt of which, strange to say, was *outside* the door), and directly on the street, the two *salons*, which his wife spoke of as 'livings', while in the lease one of them was termed 'library' because of a niche in the wall. The small vestibule opening out on the street was called *antichambre* in the lease. The rent came to three thousand francs a month, the sole income of an elderly Frenchwoman, whose husband had once owned plantations in Indochina. Two thirds of this sum was paid by the Austrian Foreign Ministry.

Keuschnig looked at his sleeping wife through the half-open door to the back room. He wished that the moment she woke up she would ask him what he was thinking about. He would reply: 'I'm looking for a way of thinking you out of my life.' Suddenly he wished he would never see her or hear of her again. He wished she would be shipped away somewhere. Her eyes were closed; from time to time her wrinkled lids stretched smooth. That told him she was beginning to wake up. Now and then there were gurglings from her belly; the chirping of two sparrows outside the window, a remark, then an answer, always a few notes higher; separate sounds became distinguishable in what had been the even murmur of the city during the night. There was already traffic enough that the screeching of brakes could be heard and farther away the blowing of a horn. His wife still had her earphones on, and a language record was still turning on the record player. He switched off the machine and she opened her eyes. With open eyes she looked younger. Her name was Stefanie, and only yesterday she had aroused feeling in him, at least occasionally. Why didn't she notice anything peculiar about him? 'You're already dressed,' she said, and took off the earphones. In that moment he felt capable of kneeling down and telling her everything, everything. Where should he begin? Once or twice in the past he had placed his thumb on her throat, not as a threat but as one kind of contact among many others. Only if she were dead, he thought, would I be able to feel something for her again. Standing still and straight, he turned his head to one side as in a rogues' gallery photograph, and said only, as though repeating something he had often said before: 'You don't mean a thing to me. The thought of growing old with you is more than I can bear. Your mere existence drives me to despair.' 'That rhymes,' she said. True enough. His last two sentences rhymed – he hadn't noticed it in time – and therefore couldn't be taken seriously. Closing her eyes, she asked: 'What's the weather like today?' and he replied, without looking out: 'High clouds.' She smiled and dropped off to sleep. I'm coming away empty-handed, he thought. Strange. Everything he did struck him as strange that morning.

In the child's room he felt as though he were taking leave of something; not only of the child, but of the kind of life that had been right for him up until then. Now no kind of life was right for him. He stood there amid the scattered toys, and suddenly in his helplessness one of his knees gave way. He crouched down. I have to busy myself with something, he thought, already exhausted by the short time spent without imagination, and busied himself putting the laces, which the child had taken out of her shoes the night before, back in again. As Agnes slept, he could see nothing of her face; her hair had tumbled over it. He put his hand on her back to see how she was breathing. She was breathing so peacefully and smelt so warm that he remembered certain of the old days when everything seemed to be gathered under a wide dome and to belong together, when for instance he had involuntarily said 'Agnes' to his wife and involuntarily said 'Stefanie' to Agnes. Now that was gone; he couldn't even remember it any longer.

Translated by R. Manheim

LOBEL

The Dream

Arnold Lobel is one of the foremost writers and illustrators of children's stories in English. 'The Dream' is taken from *Frog and Toad Together*, of 1979.

Toad was asleep, and he was having a dream. He was on a stage, and he was wearing a costume. Toad looked out into the dark. Frog was sitting in the theatre.

A strange voice from far away said, 'PRESENTING THE GREATEST TOAD IN ALL THE WORLD!'

Toad took a deep bow. Frog looked smaller as he shouted, 'Hooray for Toad!'

'TOAD WILL NOW PLAY THE PIANO VERY WELL,' said the strange voice.

Toad played the piano and he did not miss a note.

'Frog,' cried Toad, 'can you play the piano like this?'

'No,' said Frog.

It seemed to Toad that Frog looked even smaller.

'TOAD WILL NOW WALK ON A HIGH WIRE AND HE WILL NOT FALL DOWN,' said the voice.

Toad walked on the high wire.

'Frog,' cried Toad, 'can you do tricks like this?'

'No,' peeped Frog, who looked very, very small.

'TOAD WILL NOW DANCE, AND HE WILL BE WONDERFUL,' said the voice.

'Frog, can you be as wonderful as this?' said Toad as he danced all over the stage.

There was no answer.

Toad looked out into the theatre. Frog was so small that he could not be seen or heard.

'Frog,' said Toad, 'where are you?'

There was still no answer.

'Frog, what have I done?' cried Toad.

Then the voice said, 'THE GREATEST TOAD WILL NOW . . .'

'Shut up!' screamed Toad.

'Frog, Frog, where have you gone?'

Toad was spinning in the dark.

'Come back, Frog,' he shouted. 'I will be lonely!'

'I am right here,' said Frog.

Frog was standing near Toad's bed. 'Wake up, Toad,' he said.

'Frog, is that really you?' said Toad.

'Of course it is me,' said Frog.

'And are you your own right size?' asked Toad.

'Yes, I think so,' said Frog.

Toad looked at the sunshine coming through the window. 'Frog,' he said, 'I am so glad that you came over.'

'I always do,' said Frog.

Then Frog and Toad ate a big breakfast. And after that they spent a fine, long day together.

STEINER

Before Language

These are the opening pages of George Steiner's lecture on *The Historicity of Dreams*, delivered in French at a Congress on *I linguaggi del sogno* ('The Languages of Dreams') held at the Fondazione Cini in Venice in 1982. The English version of this lecture was published by the American journal *Salmagundi*.

Anyone who has lived near animals, with his dog or his cat, knows of their dreams. Vivid, often clearly tempestuous, currents of agitation or pleasure will set in unmistakable motion the body of a sleeping dog or cat. In fact, this banal phenomenon is our most direct (our only direct?) behavioural evidence for the frequency and force of dreams. All human reports on dreams come to us via the screen of language.

Animals dream. Am I altogether in error in thinking that the philosophical and historical implications of this platitude are momentous, and that they have received remarkably little attention? For if animals dream, as they manifestly do, such 'dreams' are generated and experienced outside any linguistic matrix. Their content, their sensory dynamics, precede, are external to, any linguistic code. They unfold in a semantic world closed to our perceptions, except in its superficial aspects of bodily tremor or content. We know this world to be temporally far more ancient and 'statistically' far larger and more various than our own (i.e. animals precede man in the history of the planet and vastly outnumber the human species). But only rare artists, a Rilke, a Dürer or a Picasso, have *seemed* to penetrate (this too may be anthropomorphic illusion) into the outward penumbra of the pulsing and manifold consciousness of animals. The tiger does not answer Blake's question.

What can we say of these dreams before language?

The hermeneutic trap is all too obvious. Our intimations of that which lies prior to and outside verbalization are nothing but translations into further metaphor and analogy. The concept of the pre- or non-linguistic is itself inescapably verbal. We can imagine, in a fiction of abstractive isolation, the deployment of images, sounds, tactile and olfactory data without conceptual paraphrase, without a verbalizable signification. But not only can we have no proof that the dreams of animals occur in some such 'imagistic-sensory' mode, but we cannot ourselves even 'think' any such mode without adulterating it into verbal discourse. Man can almost be defined as a species with only exceedingly limited and falsifying access to the universe (for it is nothing less) of silence.

One speculates, of course – and in its etymology of mirroring the verb at least edges just past speech. Biology, genetics, our rudimentary intuitions do affirm that there are primordial continuities between ourselves and animals. Could it be that the cardinal *myths* (what current structural anthropology calls *les mythologèmes*), those archetypal configurations of immediate, seemingly remembered recognition, whereby we order and give general echo to our individual and inward existence, are related to, are a modulation from, the unspoken dreams of animals? Did hominid species, in their intimate co-existence not only with primates but with the whole animal kingdom, dream *zoo-logically*? It is, since Vico at least, a commonplace to suppose that the evolution of mythology and of human speech are concomitant and dialectically interactive. But perhaps we can take a step further. The archetypes, the *ur*-myths which we sense as arising from the no-man's land (because everyman's) just outside daylit consciousness and will, are vestigial, atavistic forms of *dreams before language.* Language is, in a sense, an attempt to interpret, to narrate dreams older than itself. But as he narrates his dreams, *homo sapiens* advances into contradiction: the animal no longer understands him, and with each narrative-linguistic act, individuation, the break between the ego and the communion of shared images, deepens. Narrated, interpreted, dreams have passed from truth into history. Two things alone remind us of their organic source: that resonance and meaning beyond conceptualization which inheres in myths, and that mystery of psycho-somatic affinity with animals which can be observed in many young children, in the 'untutored' and in the saint. (It is when he meets with the eyes of a beaten horse, that Nietzsche steps from the cruel summit of articulate intelligence into the second childhood, innocence and ascetic sanctity of his *Umnachtung*.)

DAMIAN

Sara

François Damian's *L'autre rive* (The other shore), came out at the beginning of 1985. The author states that his book is not a fiction but a faithful recording, 'day by night', of his dreams over a period of three years. But soon the random succession of dreams is replaced in this novel by a story – perhaps connected with the waking life of the narrator, who seems to be attracted by two different women. It was impossible in our anthology to give an impression of the main story-line, so we have chosen a few autonomous and significant dreams (for the other dreams by Damian, see page 221).

November 1
One of my daughters – Sara perhaps? – walks by, carrying quarters of human flesh in a transparent plastic bag. I want her very badly.

I wake up disturbed and fall straight back to sleep. Together, we make a meal out of the meat.

I wake again, just as briefly. I desire my daughter more than ever. I try to persuade her: No one will know you're my daughter . . . or: Considering your age . . . In the end, I leave to take a suburban train, but just as I reach the platform, my ticket, which is made of onion-skin paper, turns out to be too soft to punch. I have to go back to the counter to buy another. When I get back to the platform entrance, the train leaves before I can punch my ticket.

Translated by J. Romney

The Community Centre

December 1
The scene is a big community centre, where I am taking part in several activities. I am flicking through a magazine containing a feature on the centre. The cinema section is about a film from before the war: stars and juvenile leads with slicked-back glossy hair, gazing romantically at the camera. The pages dealing with the house we are in are handwritten in beautiful manuscript style. The magazine's dustcover, made out of the same paper, but rather sturdier, is printed in green. It is an international review, which does in fact have a readership in several countries.

I have come down into a part of the house devoted to everyday activities. I have just done some washing: a pair of socks and some light green underpants. I ask a friend standing next to me where the nearest toilets are. 'You'll find them on your left as you go up (the laundry-room is in the basement).' The left-hand side of the staircase is taken up with a metal lattice-work structure built on several levels. In one of the unpartitioned cubes formed by this structure, up on the highest level, I can see a toilet seat. It overlooks a landing where several passages intersect. When I get to it, it has turned into a seatless, Turkish-style bowl, and at its side is a rubber suction cup with a handle, rather like a chorister's handbell. I squat down and put the green underpants by my side. At that moment, people pass by down below. I can see them, and they can see me. In their midst, the one who directed me to this curious place is chanting under his breath: 'FRANÇOIS CABIN, EMPEROR OF THE ROMANS, IS SOWING HIS SHIT UP ABOVE THE HUMANS.'

Translated by J. Romney

Realistic dreams

The currents connecting the day world and the night world flow in two opposite directions, as the waters of the mythical Euripus. The day produces a continuous harvest of emotions and experiences, perceptions and feelings, preoccupations and anxieties, desires and fears, which are channelled into the night world, feeding the secret sources of our dreams. The dreams in turn recycle monsters and bogeys, tortures and delights, suspicions and revelations, manufactured – or shall we say mente-factured? – in their smithy, and address them towards waking life. The sleep of reason generates two kinds of monsters: day-monsters who emigrate into our night dreams; nightmares who cross back over the border of waking. Whoever ignores this traffic out of positivist short-sightedness is almost by definition a fool. Whoever thinks he is able to monitor or explain it is, almost by necessity, another kind of fool. When writing about dreams, one must beware of those two types of foolishness.

The world of dreaming and the world of waking have a common tract of border country where traffic, exchanges, smugglings, transpositions, double passports, are rife. This boundary area is the operative basis of the dreams we have decided to call 'realistic'. This category does not rest on aesthetic or stylistic criteria, nor does it indicate a particular school of dream-writing (though such schools do exist), but it witnesses a marked proximity of the two worlds. Some dreams in this section may seem ethereally fantastic, enigmatically symbolic or murkily instinctive; but they all share a particularly narrow connection – sometimes disturbingly narrow – between dreaming and waking. Life is like a dream, but it is slightly less inconsequent than a dream, says Pascal in one of his *Pensées* quoted here. The traffic therefore tends to scatter in the dreamward direction, and to concentrate again on the way back. The analogies between the two worlds are striking and awesome, and traffic accidents are all too frequent.

Let us take *The Dream of the Last Judgement* by Quevedo, which is apparently a fantasy; yet there are clear traces of a two-way traffic. In the evening, the author reads 'a discourse concerning the end of the world' and falls asleep; the dreamer picks up the scoria of this day-experience and turns it into a representation of the Last Judgement in which he is author, judge, director, bawd, usher, propman, prosecutor, stage manager, choreographer and spectator. But whence did that otherwise unspecified 'discourse concerning the end of the world' come if not from the dream world? Who else could have invented such a horrible, crazy and perverse legend if not the Dream God or one of his famuli? In turn Quevedo's reader, or Quevedo himself transcribing his dream – it does not matter at this point whether this is the protocol of a real dream or a literary invention, hence the fiction of a fiction, as seems more likely – pours the dream material back into reality. And maybe the reader, having read the *Dream of the Last Judgement*, will choose this theme for his next dream; and so on. This continuous to-ing and fro-ing between the two worlds cannot be denied, and makes it extremely difficult to give a static picture of dream-processes.

Dreams are fancies, this is granted; but they keep an incestuous connection with reality. According to Dickens's letter the author is unable to evoke in his dreams these typical dream-figures, the characters of his novels, and to converse with them. This is an interesting observation, even if it is contradicted by some of the examples we include in our selection. Kerouac claims he always encounters his characters in his dreams, but they were friends and acquaintances who, from a literary viewpoint, were mere husks; as to Grillparzer, Medea appears in a dream as the character in the play he is in the process of writing, not as an established character emerging from his literary past. All in all, the case of Dickens seems the most convincing. Dreams cannot be cheated so easily, and they insist on eliciting and deforming real people, not fictional characters. To illustrate this point: we may dream that we meet Hamlet, or Leopold Bloom, Aeneas or Emma Bovary, because we are not their creator, and somehow we half believe in their existence. But though the waking author can claim: 'Madame Bovary, c'est moi', he will never say in his dreams: 'Madame Bovary, I presume.' Dream, the reign of inconsequence and inconsistency, needs to feed daily on consequent and consistent reality.

Yet the relation between night-world and day-life is eminently ambiguous. Reality may be the efficient cause of the dream, but the dream, as a symptom of reality, helps us understand it. The *mauvais coucheur* in Groussac suffers from heartburn, hence he dreams that he is drawn into a brawl in which he is knifed in the upper stomach: the real indigestion has caused the dreamed wound. On the other hand, the duplication of the marriage of Cana in Dostoevsky, where the corpse of Zossima rises from the bier to exalt the merits of a festive religion, is a symptom of Aliosha's faith in that Christ who says 'He who loves men loves their gladness'; the dream clarifies the past and future religious behaviour of the young man.

In *The Shout* by Robert Graves the strength and suspense of the tale depends precisely on the uncertainty of the status of the shoe-buckle, lost in the dream and found again in the pocket of the mysterious but probably real visitor. But the key metaphor is Shakespeare's: 'We are of such stuff as dreams are made on'; and several dreamers/authors in this section insist on the weaving, plaiting and composing aspect of the dreams. 'We weave our dreams from our own substance' says Groussac. For Machado, dreams are spun of a double thread of hope and fear; elsewhere, he says that dreams 'untie the bundles of our designs so as to mix them with memories and fears'. Dreams weave elements from reality, and vice-versa; thus, along these gossamer threads, the crossing from one to the other can be quiet and sudden. Threatened by the enemy, Borges chooses the easy solution: 'To wake up', escaping into reality where the man who wants to kill him cannot follow him. He is safe – at least until the next dream the following night. When he goes to bed Lynkeus' rational dreamer takes the dream omnibus, trusting on a safe journey, and tells his servant he shall be back as usual at dawn: 'You can expect me at about six in the morning'. Men are commuters who take every night the green line coaches to the outskirts (unless our day-life be the outskirts, and our dreams the city centre: this is an eccentric opinion, but it is difficult to prove that it is unreal).

In some cases, dreams are like a photocopying machine which duplicates reality: the occupations of the day are reproduced faithfully in the nocturnal world (Lucretius); the memory of the loved woman elicits a perfect image of her face and of her voice (Petrarch and Froissart); the true burning of Dresden in the Second World War is projected into the imaginary burning of Indianapolis (Vonnegut); the misery of an unemployed hippy's daily life becomes the misery of the same hippy's night life, which retraces a similar path of emargination and refusal (Bob Dylan); the marriage of Cana is re-enacted (Dostoevsky); the sound of the Civil War guns re-echoes in the artilleryman's dream (Whitman). In some cases it is reality that copies the dream: Gradiva, the woman of the Roman bas-relief, comes alive in Hanold's dream, but the dream-Gradiva is projected on to the woman the hero of Jensen's novel meets in Pompei, Zoe, who turns out to be a childhood friend he would not have noticed without the dream; the man bitten in his dream by a serpent must be cured on awakening (Frazer).

There is no motion of the human mind and body that dreams cannot imitate. Dream is a minute *bricoleur*, crouching within us, who puts together thoughts, ideas, feelings and emotions: perfect forgeries which duplicate the feigned normality of waking life. This forger can almost imitate death: but Hervey Saint Denis, in the passage reproduced here, can only carry out his suicide-in-dream experiment up to the point where he jumps from a top-floor window. After that, there is a blank, and he is forced to abandon the character of the would-be suicide and take the role of a neutral bystander.

The dream is also a stranger, a shameless pedlar who sells us only imitation products which might be better than reality. Or perhaps this pedlar is Old Nick himself who tempts us with the apple of false knowledge. W. H. Auden was wrong: for him, '...the serpent on the poisonous tree/was *l'esprit de géométrie*'; but in fact the serpent could actually be the spirit of chaos, the dream that tempts us to be different from what we are. Because, like all photocopying machines, the dream sometimes goes wrong; it mischievously delights in transforming, polluting, falsifying, soiling, defiling, blackening: in short, mucking up the works. The residues of the day before, the *Tagesreste* which, according to Freud, form the basis of our oneiric imagination, are often metamorphosed into an unrecognizable or parodic version by the *Traumarbeit*, the dream-work: 'The dream is less a comment on the day than a digestive process of it, a breakdown and assimilation of the day-world within the labyrinthine tracts of the psyche' that assimilate it for their own use and consumption (James Hillman).

The exhausted soldier in Mérimée's tale gently slides into sleep, and there his wishful thinking draws out the experience of the day before in a duel, in seeming death, in a love adventure. Freud apparently did not know this short story, which would have made a nice example for his theory, according to which the remembered fragments of the day before, elaborated and manipulated by the dream, are used in order to satisfy the unconscious will of the dreamer: in this case love-desires and death-wishes.

Wishful thinking is also evidenced in Bierce's story, where the soldier on the threshold of death in his lightning-quick dream ('Sensations are rapid dreams', says Santayana) simultaneously retraces the stages of his being strangled and of his imaginary escape; or in Pirandello where the woman, prevented by her education from satisfying her passion in life, finds ample and tragic comfort in her unbridled sexual dream-behaviour. Visions are the thoughts of the day, according to Herodotus; they project on to the night screen what waking life, in spite of its infinite generosity, was not able to materialize fully. The other side of wishful thinking might be *fearful thinking*, when dreams actualize not what we want but what we fear: as in Machado's legend, where Avergonzález's fears of his sons' homicidal intentions are made explicit in his dream, and later realized by what actually occurs. We cannot escape from the 'realistic dreams' since there is no way of avoiding our 'latent' and 'patent' hopes and fears, to borrow Freud's terminology. The intercourse with these dreams is too close for comfort. Being unable to forget them, the only alternative is to put them in an anthology.

THE BIBLE

Solomon's Wish

This dream of Solomon is told in *I Kings iii, 3–15*. The *Books of Kings*, sometimes attributed to Jeremiah, were written around 550 BC.

And Solomon loved the LORD, walking in the statutes of David his father: only he sacrificed and burnt incense in high places.

And the king went to Gibeon to sacrifice there; for that *was* the great high place: a thousand burnt offerings did Solomon offer upon that altar.

In Gibeon the LORD appeared to Solomon in a dream by night: and God said, Ask what I shall give thee.

And Solomon said, Thou hast shewed unto thy servant David my father great mercy, according as he walked before thee in truth, and in righteousness, and in uprightness of heart with thee; and thou hast kept for him this great kindness, that thou hast given him a son to sit on his throne, as *it is* this day.

And now, O LORD my God, thou hast made thy servant king instead of David my father: and I *am but* a little child: I know not *how* to go out or come in.

And thy servant *is* in the midst of thy people which thou hast chosen, a great people, that cannot be numbered nor counted for multitude.

Give therefore thy servant an understanding heart to judge thy people, that I may discern between good and bad: for who is able to judge this thy so great a people?

And the speech pleased the Lord, that Solomon had asked this thing.

And God said unto him, Because thou hast asked this thing, and hast not asked for thyself long life; neither hast asked riches for thyself, nor has asked the life of thine enemies; but hast asked for thyself understanding to discern judgement;

Behold, I have done according to thy words: lo, I have given thee a wise and an understanding heart; so that there was none like thee before thee, neither after thee shall any arise like unto thee.

And I have also given thee that which thou has not asked, both riches, and honour: so that there shall not be any among the kings like unto thee all thy days.

And if thou wilt walk in my ways, to keep my statutes and my commandments, as thy father David did walk, then I will lengthen thy days.

And Solomon awoke; and, behold, *it was* a dream. And he came to Jerusalem, and stood before the ark of the covenant of the LORD, and offered up burnt offerings, and offered peace offerings, and made a feast to all his servants.

King James's Version

HERODOTUS

Xerxes and Artabanus

The *Histories* of Herodotus were written in the fifth century BC.
Xerxes came to power at the death of his father Darius in 486 BC,
and started preparing for a second war against the Greeks in 484
BC which must be the approximate date of this dream.

So far discourse went; and presently came the night-time, and Xerxes was
pricked by the counsel of Artabanus; and taking counsel of night, he saw
clearly that to send an army against Hellas was none of his business. Having
made this second resolve he fell asleep; then it would appear (for so the
Persians say) that in the night he saw this vision: It seemed to Xerxes that a tall
and goodly man stood over him and said, 'Art thou then changing thy counsel,
Persian, and wilt thou not lead thine army against Hellas, albeit thou hast
proclaimed the mustering of thy host? thou dost not well to change thy
counsel, nor will he that thou seest pardon thee for it; nay, let thy course be
according to thy design of yesterday.'

Thus the vision spake, and seemed to Xerxes to vanish away; but when day
dawned the king took no account of this dream, but assembling the Persians
whom he had before gathered together, he thus addressed them: 'Forgive me,
Persians! for that I turn and twist in my purpose; for I am not yet come to the
fulness of my wisdom, and they are ever with me who exhort me to do as I
said. 'Tis true that when I heard Artabanus' opinion my youthful spirit did for
the nonce take fire, whereby there brake from me an unseemly and wrongful
answer to one older than myself; yet now I see my fault and will follow his
judgement. Know therefore that my purpose of marching against Hellas is
changed, and abide in peace.'

When the Persians heard that, they rejoiced, and did obeisance. But when
night came on, the same vision stood again over Xerxes as he slept, and said,
'Son of Darius, hast thou then plainly renounced thine army's march before
the Persians, and made my words of no account, as though thou hadst not
heard them? Know then this for a surety: if thou leadest not thine army
forthwith, this shall be the outcome of it, that as a little while made thee great
and mighty, so in a moment shalt thou be brought low again.'

Greatly affrighted by the vision, Xerxes leapt up from his bed, and sent a
messenger to Artabanus to call him; and when he came, 'Artabanus,' said
Xerxes, 'for the moment my right judgement forsook me, and I answered your
good counsel with foolish words; but after no long time I repented and saw
that it was right for me to follow your advice. Yet, though I desire, I cannot do
it; for since I have turned me and repented, a vision comes haunting my sight,

that will in no wise consent that I should do as you counsel; and even now it has gone with a threat. Now if it be a god that sends the vision, and it be his full pleasure that there be this expedition against Hellas, that same dream will hover about you and lay on you the same charge as on me; and I am persuaded that this is likeliest to be, if you take all my attire and sit so clothed upon my throne, and presently lie down to sleep in my bed.'

Thus said Xerxes; Artabanus would not obey the first command, thinking it was not for him to sit on the royal throne; at last he was compelled, and did as he was bidden, saying first: 'O king, I judge it of equal worth whether a man be wise, or be willing to obey good counsel; to both of these you have attained, but evil communications are your bane; even as the sea, who is of all creatures the most serviceable to men, is hindered (they say) from following his natural bent by the blasts of winds that fall upon him. But for myself – it was not the hard words I had from you that stung me so much as this, that when two opinions were laid before the Persians, the one tending to increase of pride, and the other to its abatement, showing how evil a thing it is to teach the heart continual desire of more than it has, of these two opinions you preferred that one which was most fraught with danger to yourself and the Persians. Now, therefore, since you are turned to the better opinion, you say that while you would renounce your expedition against the Greeks you are haunted by a dream sent by some god, which forbids you to leave off from the expedition. But you err again, my son; this is none of heaven's working. The roving dreams that visit men are of such nature as you shall learn of me, that am many years older than you. Those visions that rove about us in dreams are for the most part the thoughts of the day; and in these latter days we have been very earnestly busied about this expedition. But if nevertheless this be not such as I determine, and have in it somewhat of heaven's will, then you have spoken the conclusion of the matter; let it appear to me even as it has to you, and utter its command; but if it has ever a mind to appear, I must needs see it none the more by virtue of wearing your dress instead of mine, and sleeping in your bed rather than my own. Whatever be this that appears to spirit; for I knew how evil a thing it was to have many desires, remembering the end of Cyrus's expedition against the Massagetae and Cambyses's against the Ethiopians, and having myself marched with Darius against the Scythians. Knowing this, I judged that you had but to abide in peace for all men to deem you fortunate. But since heaven impels, and the gods, as it seems, mark Hellas for destruction, I myself do change and correct my judgement; and do you now declare the god's message to the Persians, and bid them obey your first command for all due preparation: so act, that nought on your part be lacking to the fulfilment of heaven's commission.' After this discourse, the vision giving them courage, Xerxes when daylight came imparted all this to the Persians, and Artabanus now openly persuaded to that course from which he alone had before openly dissuaded.

After this Xerxes, being now intent on the expedition, saw yet a third vision in his sleep, which the Magians interpreted to have regard to the whole earth and to signify that all men should be his slaves. This was the vision: Xerxes thought that he was crowned with an olive bough, the shoots of which spread over the whole earth, and presently the crown vanished from off his head where it was set. This the Magians interpreted; and of the Persians who had been assembled, every man forthwith rode away to his own governorship and there used all zeal to fulfil the king's behest, each desiring to receive the promised gifts; and thus it was that Xerxes dealt with the mustering of his army, searching out every part of the continent.

Translated by A. D. Godley

PLATO

The Illusion of the Senses

This passage is taken from Plato's *Theaetetus or Of the Soul*, which was probably written between 370 and 365 BC.

Socrates Let us not leave the argument unfinished, then; as there still remains to be considered an objection which may be raised about dreams and diseases, in particular about madness, and the various illusions of hearing and sight, or of other senses. For you know that in all these cases the theory of the truth of perception appears to be unmistakably refuted, as in dreams and illusions we certainly have false perceptions; and far from saying that everything is which appears, we should rather say that nothing is which appears.

Theaetetus Very true, Socrates.

Soc. But then, my boy, how can anyone contend that knowledge is perception, or that things are to each one as they appear?

Theaet. I am afraid to say, Socrates, that I have nothing to answer, because you rebuked me just now for saying so; but I certainly cannot undertake to argue that madmen or dreamers think truly, when they imagine some of them that they are gods, and others that they can fly, and are flying in their sleep.

Soc. Do you know a question which is raised about these illusions, and especially about waking and sleeping?

Theaet. What question?

Soc. A question which I think that you must often have heard persons ask: How can you determine whether at this moment we are sleeping, and all our thoughts are a dream; or whether we are awake, and talking to one another in the waking state?

Theaet. Indeed, Socrates, I do not know how you can prove that the one is any more true than the other, for all the phenomena correspond; and there is no difficulty in supposing that during all this discussion we have been talking to one another in a dream; and when we are actually dreaming and talk in our dreams, the resemblance of the two states is quite astonishing.

Soc. You see, then, that a doubt about the reality of sense is easily raised, since there may even be a doubt whether we are awake or in a dream. And as the time is equally divided in which we are asleep or awake, in either sphere of existence the soul contends that the thoughts which are present to our minds at the time are true; and during one half of our lives we affirm the truth of the one, and, during the other half, of the other; and are equally confident of both.

Translated by B. Jowett

ARISTOTLE

Are Dreams Prophetic?

This passage is taken from Aristotle's *De Divinatione per Somnum* ('On Divination through Sleep'), written around 330 BC.

As to the divination which takes place in sleep, and is said to be based on dreams, we cannot lightly either dismiss it with contempt or give it implicit confidence. The fact that all persons, or many, suppose dreams to possess a special significance, tends to inspire us with belief in it [such divination], as founded on the testimony of experience; and indeed that divination in dreams should, as regards some subjects, be genuine, is not incredible, for it has a show of reason; from which one might form a like opinion also respecting all other dreams. Yet the fact of our seeing no probable cause to account for such divination tends to inspire us with distrust. For, in addition to its further unreasonableness, it is absurd to combine the idea that the sender of such dreams should be God with the fact that those to whom he sends them are not the best and wisest, but merely commonplace persons. If, however, we abstract from the causality of God, none of the other causes assigned appears probable. For that certain persons should have foresight in dreams concerning things destined to take place at the Pillars of Hercules, or on the banks of the Borysthenes, seems to be something to discover the explanation of which surpasses the wit of man. Well then, the dreams in question must be regarded either as *causes*, or as *tokens*, of the events, or else as *coincidences*; either as all, or some, of these, or as one only. I use the word 'cause' in the sense in which the moon is the cause of an eclipse of the sun, or in which fatigue is a cause of fever; 'token' in the sense in which the entrance of a star into the shadow is a token of the eclipse, or in which roughness of the tongue is a token of fever; while by 'coincidence' I mean, for example, the occurrence of an eclipse of the sun while someone is taking a walk; for the walking is neither a token nor a cause of the eclipse, nor the eclipse a cause or token of the walking. For this reason no coincidence takes place according to a universal or general rule. Are we then to say that some dreams are causes, others tokens, e.g. of events taking place in the bodily organism? At all events, even scientific physicians tell us that one should pay diligent attention to dreams, and to hold this view is reasonable also for those who are not practitioners, but speculative philosophers. For the movements which occur in the daytime within the body are, unless very great and violent, lost sight of in contrast with the waking movements, which are more impressive. In sleep the opposite takes place, for then even trifling movements seem considerable. This is plain in what often happens during sleep; for example, dreamers fancy that they are affected by thunder and lightning, when in fact there are only faint ringings in their ears; or that they are enjoying honey or other sweet savours, when only a tiny drop of phlegm is flowing down the oesophagus; or that they are walking through fire, and feeling intense heat, when there is only a slight warmth affecting certain parts of the body. When they are awakened, these things appear to them in this their true character. But since the beginnings of all events are small, so, it is clear, are those also of the diseases or other affections about to occur in our bodies. In conclusion, it is manifest that these beginnings must be more evident in sleeping than in waking moments.

Nay, indeed, it is not improbable that some of the presentations which come before the mind in sleep may even be causes of the actions cognate to each of them. For as when we are about to act in waking hours, or are engaged in any course of action, or have already performed certain actions, we often find ourselves concerned with these actions, or performing them, in a vivid dream; the cause whereof is that the dream-movement has had a way paved for it from the original movements set up in the daytime; exactly so, but conversely, it must happen that the movements set up first in sleep should also prove to be starting-points of actions to be performed in the daytime, since the recurrence by day of the thought of these actions also has had its way paved for it in the images before the mind at night. Thus then it is quite conceivable that some dreams may be tokens and causes of future events.

Most so-called prophetic dreams are, however, to be classed as mere coincidences, especially all such as are extravagant, and those in the fulfilment of which the dreamers have no initiative, such as in the case of a sea-fight, or of things taking place far away. As regards these it is natural that the fact should stand as it does whenever a person, on mentioning something, finds the very thing mentioned come to pass. Why, indeed, should this not happen also in sleep? The probability is, rather, that many such things should happen. As, then, one's mentioning a particular person is neither token nor cause of this person's presenting himself, so, in the parallel instance, the dream is, to him who has seen it, neither token nor cause of its so-called fulfilment, but a mere coincidence. Hence the fact that many dreams have no 'fulfilment', for coincidences do not occur according to any universal or general law.

Translated by J. I. Beare

THEOCRITUS

The Fishermen

This idyll, whose attribution to Theocritus is dubious, is one of the most ancient documents of the rich literary theme of the Poor Fisherman, which runs from antiquity to Andersen.

It is poverty alone, Diophantus, that awakes the crafts; she it is from whom men learn to toil, for carking cares forbid the labouring man even to sleep, and if for some fraction of the night he close his eyes, anxieties beset him on a sudden and disturb his rest.

Two old fishermen had made themselves a couch of dried seaweed in their wattled cabin, and lay there together, leaning against the leafy wall. Near by them lay the instruments of their toilsome craft – baskets and rods, hooks and weedy baits, lines and weels and pots of woven rush, cords and oars and aged skiff upon its props, a bit of matting beneath the head, their clothes, their caps – such was their sole resource, such their wealth. No key they had, no door, no watch-dog; all these they counted superfluity, for poverty watched over them, no neighbour was near, and by their very cabin the sea confined and lapped the land.

Not yet was the chariot of the Moon traversing her midmost course, yet their accustomed toil roused the fishermen, and, clearing their eyes of sleep, from thought they fell to speech.

Asphalion

They lied, my friend, all such as said the nights grew short in summer when the days they bring are long. Already I have had a thousand dreams, and dawn is not yet. How long the nights are.

The Other

Asphalion, do you blame the fair summertime? It is not that the season has unaccountably strayed from its own course, but that anxiety cuts short your sleep and makes the night seem long.

Asphalion

Have you ever learnt to interpret dreams? I have had fine ones, and I would not have you without your share in my vision.

The Other

We share our catch, and so share all your dreams with me. For even if I must trust my native wit and guess, he is your best interpreter of dreams who learns from his own wits. Besides, there's time on hand, for what is there to do as one lies on one's leafy bed by the sea and cannot sleep? The ass in the thorn bush, the lamp in the town hall – these, they say, are sleepless. Come, tell me your dream.

Asphalion

After our labours on the sea I fell asleep ere dark, and had not overeaten either, for we dined, you may remember, betimes and did not tax our stomachs. And I saw myself planted on a rock, and seated there watched for fish, dangling from my rod the treacherous bait. And a fat one nibbled at it – dogs in their sleep dream of their quarry and I of fish. Then he was hooked, and bled; and in my hand the rod curved with his struggles. I bent over with outstretched arms and was hard put to it how to raise that great fish on my weak irons. Then I pricked him lightly to remind him of the wound, and thereat gave him slack, but tightened when he did not run. Anyhow I was successful in the struggle and landed a golden fish, a fish set thick with gold all over. Then terror seized me lest it should be some favourite fish of Poseidon or a treasure of sea-green Amphitrite; and gently I loosed him from the hook lest the barbs should tear the gold from his mouth . . . and swore never to set foot upon the sea again, but to stay ashore and lord it over my gold. That woke me; and now, my friend, apply your mind to the matter, for I am frightened at the oath I swore.

The Other

Nay, never fear. You no more swore the oath than took the golden fish you saw. The vision was all lies. But if in your waking hours and not asleep you will search for these marvellous fish, then there's hope in your dreams; hunt the fish of flesh and blood, lest starvation and your golden dreams prove the death of you.

Translated by A. E. S. Gow

LUCRETIUS

On Dreams

De Natura Rerum, from which this dream is taken, was written by
the Latin Poet Lucretius in the first century BC.

Whatever have been our habitual occupations,
Whatever the things on which we have spent most time
And whatever we have most exerted our minds on
– These are the things we usually see in dreams.
The lawyer finds himself pleading or drafting documents;
The general is engulfed in imaginary battles;
The sailor has a bad time with the weather;
I am working on this, examining natural processes
And writing down the results in my native language.
Other pursuits and interests in like manner
Appear to us in the deception of dreams.

When people have spent day after day at the games
They go on seeing them after they are away from them;
For in their minds the ways are still left open
Through which the images of such things may come.
For many days the same objects present themselves
Before their eyes and, even awake, they seem
To see the dancers moving their supple limbs
And to hear the liquid music of stringed instruments.
They see the flocks of people and still admire
The splendour and variegation of the scenery.
Such is the power of things which take our attention
And give us pleasure, and things we are always engaged on;
It is so not only with men but with all living creatures.

And often hunting dogs, although sound asleep,
Will suddenly throw out their legs and utter cries,
Sniffing about as if they were on the scent
And really following the track of some wild animal.
They may when they wake up still follow the image
Of the stags they imagine they see, until it fades
And they once more become their reasonable selves.

The same with the little pet dogs about the house:
They will shake themselves and suddenly stand up
As if they were seeing new faces in the room.
The fiercer the breed of animal, the more he exhibits
Fury in his dreams, his nature requires it.
But various kinds of birds take flight and the noise of their wings
Breaks in the night-time on the sacred groves
If once in their dreams they think they see the hawk
Offering them violence and pursuing their flight.

What powerful movements the human mind may have:
Often in sleep the same things harry us still.
Men throw down kings; themselves are taken in battle;
They raise a shout as if their throats were cut.
Many will struggle, emitting horrible groans
And just as if a panther or lion had bitten them
Fill the place with the loudest possible cries.
Many will talk in sleep of important affairs;
It is not unknown for a man to speak of his crimes;
Many encounter death: and from high mountains
Have the impression of falling to sea-level;
They are terrified, and when they awake their minds
Are still so caught they hardly know what they are doing.
A man may feel thirsty and stop at the bank of a river
Or at a spring and offer to drink the lot.
Children often, when they are fast asleep,
Think they are on their pots or in the lavatory
And lift up their clothes and let out a whole bladderful,
Making a mess on a fine Babylonian carpet.

The adolescent, boiling for the first time
With seed inside him, ripened that very day,
Is met by images from some body or other
Suggesting a lovely face and a beautiful colour.
They rouse the parts which are swollen already with seed
Until, as if the whole thing was really happening,
He pours out a river which spills all over his tunic.

Translated by C. H. Sisson

CICERO

Friends

Marcus Tullius Cicero's *De Divinatione* was written c. 44 BC. It is a refutation of divination, all the more curious since Cicero himself was an augur. Anticipating the well-known joke about psycho-analysts, Cicero says of his colleagues: 'How can two augurs meet without laughing?' In Book I, from which we have taken all our quotations, Cicero puts a defence of the augural arts in the mouth of his brother Quintus, which he then refutes in Book II.

Two friends from Arcadia who were taking a journey together came to Megara, and one traveller put up at an inn and the second went to the home of a friend. After they had eaten supper and retired, the second traveller, in the dead of the night, dreamed that his companion was imploring him to come to his aid, as the innkeeper was planning to kill him. Greatly frightened at first by the dream he arose, and later, regaining his composure, decided that there was nothing to worry about and went back to bed. When he had gone to sleep the same person appeared to him and said: 'Since you would not help me when I was alive, I beg that you will not allow my dead body to remain unburied. I have been killed by the innkeeper, who has thrown my body into a cart and covered it with dung. I pray you to be at the city gate in the morning before the cart leaves the town.' Thoroughly convinced by the second dream he met the cart-driver at the gate in the morning, and, when he asked what he had in the cart, the driver fled in terror. The Arcadian then removed his friend's dead body from the cart, made complaint of the crime to the authorities, and the innkeeper was punished. What stronger proof of a divinely inspired dream than this can be given?

Translated by W. A. Falconer

Dreams and Diet

Now Plato's advice to us is to set out for the land of dreams with bodies so prepared that no error or confusion may assail the soul. For this reason, it is thought, the Pythagoreans were forbidden to indulge in beans; for that food produces great flatulence and induces a condition at war with a soul in search of truth. When, therefore, the soul has been withdrawn by sleep from contact with sensual ties, then does it recall the past, comprehend the present, and foresee the future. For though the sleeping body then lies as if it were dead, yet the soul is alive and strong, and will be much more so after death when it is wholly free of the body. Hence its power to divine is much enhanced by the approach of death.

Translated by W. A. Falconer

VIRGIL

Hector

This dream is taken from the second canto of Virgil's *Aeneid*, written between 30 and 19 BC. The Trojans are happily sleeping: the Greeks have left their shores, abandoning the great wooden horse. Aeneas is visited by a dream.

It was the hour when divinely-given rest first comes to poor human creatures, and creeps over them deliciously. In my sleep I dreamed that Hector stood there before my eyes. He looked most sorrowful, and was weeping plenteous tears. He was filthy with dust and blood, as he had been that day when he was dragged behind the chariot, and his feet were swollen where they had been pierced by the thongs. And, oh, how harrowing was the sight of him; how changed he was from the old Hector, back from battle wearing the spoils of Achilles, or that time when he had just flung Trojan firebrands on to the Greek ships! Now his beard was ragged and his hair clotted with blood, and all those wounds which he had sustained fighting to defend the walls of his homeland could still be seen. I dreamed that I spoke first, weeping and forcing myself to find words for this sad meeting: 'Light of the Dardan Land, Troy's surest hope, what held you from us so long? How we have waited for you, Hector! From what bourne do you come? We are weary now, and many of your folk are dead. We and our city have had many adventures, many trials. To think that we may look on you again! But what can have so shamefully disfigured your princely countenance? And why these wounds which I see?' He made no reply and gave no attention to my vain questions, but with a deep, choking sob he said: 'Son of the Goddess, make your escape quickly from the fires around you. Your walls are captured, and all Troy from her highest tower is falling; Priam and our dear land have had their day. If any strong arm could have defended our fortress, surely mine would have defended it. But now Troy entrusts to you her sanctities and her Guardians of the Home. Take them with you to face your destiny, and find for them the walled city which one day after ocean-wandering you shall build to be great, like them.' As he spoke, with his own hands he fetched out from the inner shrine the holy headbands, Vesta in whom dwells power, and her hearth-fire which burns for ever.

'Confused cries of anguish now began to reach me from inside our city. The house of my father Anchises lay back, secluded behind a screen of trees; but even there the battle-noise grew louder and louder, till the air was thick with its terror. I was startled out of my sleep, and climbing to the highest point of the roof stood listening keenly. It was like fire catching a cornfield when wild winds are blowing, or like the sweep of a mountain torrent in flood, flattening smiling crops for which oxen had toiled, and bringing whole forests down, while some shepherd standing high on a crag of rock hears the roar in helpless wonder. There was no doubt now as to the truth; it was at once clear how the Greeks had outwitted us. Already the fire had vanquished the broad mansion owned by Deiphobus, and down it crashed. Ucalegon's, closest to it, was already ablaze. The wide Straits of Sigeum were lit up by the burning. Shouts arose and trumpets rang. Out of my senses, I grasped my arms; not that I had any plan for battle, but simply a burning desire to muster a band for fighting, and rally with my comrades at some position of defence. Frantic in my fury I had no time for decisions; I only remembered that death in battle is glorious.

Translated by W. F. Jackson Knight

EGYPT

The Translator's Dream

This dream is written on a papyrus of the second century AD.

... King Nektanébo read Asklepios's book, and was so delighted by the divine nature of the story that, after discovering there had been twenty-six priests to carry the statue of the god in procession from Heliopolis to Memphis, he gave the prophetic appointment which belonged to them to all their descendants. Moreover, having re-read the book from end to end, he granted Asklepios a new gift of three hundred and thirty rich corn fields, following the example of Menecheres who had honoured the god with magnificent offerings as a sign of worship.

As to myself, although I had often vouched to translate the book into Greek, without feelings of envy, but to make it publicly known to my contemporaries, and even if I was already wading through the central part of the story, I was held up in my zeal by the loftiness of the tale, thinking that I would have to bring it to light: for it is only granted to gods, and not to mortals, to tell the marks of the gods' greatness. I was spellbound by what was expected from me: if I should fail, not only did I fear to be put to shame in front of mankind, but I was afraid of the wrath of the god, even if its immortal virtue would be enough to compensate for the inferiority of my work. On the other hand, if I should prove useful, it meant a happy life and immortal fame. For the god is willing to be benevolent, if it be true at least that he has saved those who were inspired by pious zeal when medicine was powerless against their illnesses. Therefore, recoiling from temerity, I bided the propitious time for a year: I postponed the fulfilling of my oath. For it is mainly in the force of age that man is presumptuous, for youth is rash, and its impetus pushes men to undertake things above their zeal.

But when three years had gone by without any more strivings on my part, and my mother was struck by a torturing quartan fever sent by the divine wrath, we belatedly understood and presented ourselves as suppliants to the god, conjuring him to heal my mother's illness. Being good towards all people, he appeared to her in a dream and freed her with inexpensive cures; so we accomplished the usual thanksgiving sacrifices. But then it was my turn to be overpowered by a sudden illness on my right side, and I ran immediately to the god, succourer of mankind; and again he condescended, with a willing ear, to an even more active pity, and proved his benevolent nature, whose authenticity I witness here with the aim of broadcasting the awesome signs of his power.

It was at night, when everything, save those afflicted by physical pain, is asleep, that the divinity revealed itself in all its power. I was burning with a violent fever, struggling convulsively with asthma and wrecked by coughing fits caused by the pain on my right side. My head was heavy, I was exhausted by the struggle when I eventually dropped to sleep. My mother, who was greatly worried by my torments – because I am her child and her heart is tender by nature – was sitting by my side without sleeping. And then she had a sudden vision – not as in dream or sleep, for her eyes were open, though they could not see quite clearly, for the divine phantasm entering into her filled her with terror and troubled her sight – she then saw either the god or his servant. At any rate there was a being much taller than any human being, dressed in a light, shining cloth, who was holding a book in his left hand. He just examined me from head to foot two or three times, and then disappeared. And when she saw that the fever had left me and that I was drenched with sweat, she thanked the visible manifestation of the god; then, after having wiped my body, she brought me to my senses. As we were talking, she wanted to tell me of the god's miracle, but I forestalled her: for indeed, everything she had seen in her vision had appeared to me as the images of a dream. In short, as the pains in my side had stopped – the god had also added a soothing medicine to his gifts – I started heralding his good deeds.

But after we had again propitiated the god with sacrifices congruous with our means, he, through the voice of the priest in charge of the purification, demanded the fulfillment of the oath I had given him long ago. Although we could not recall any debt in sacrifices or offerings, we renewed our supplications in similar guise. But he kept saying that none of these things were agreeable to him, and I was greatly embarrassed about this oath I had made. I was almost discouraged when I suddenly remembered my oath to the god concerning this text.

When I discovered, O Master, that I was neglecting the divine book, after invoking thy providence, filled with thy power, I gave myself with the greatest impetus to the arduous labour of the narration proposed by the god. I intend to make an offering to thee by revealing thy thought, like a prophet. Have I not already truthfully displayed, in another book, according to a physical method, the convincing myth of the creation of the world? In the whole of the text, have I not sometimes filled in the gaps, and at other times cut out superfluous details; either summarizing a dawdling discourse or saying complex things with one word? Therefore, Master, trusting thy benevolence more than my capacities, I believe I shall bring the book to perfection. Such a text is indeed fitting to thy divine nature. For thou hast written it, Asklepios, greatest of gods, preceptor: show it therefore to the grateful eyes of all. For if all offerings and sacrifices are only fresh when they are made, decaying already the next moment, writing on the other hand is an immortal gift which is renewed at all times by the memory of men.

Every Greek tongue shall repeat thy story, every Greek shall honour Imouthes, son of Phthah, come all you benevolent and good people, and leave, you denigrating and impious men . . .

Translated from the French by C. Béguin

PETRARCH

Sonnet

This poem comes from Petrarch's *Canzoniere*, written in the fourteenth century.

> Oh soul in bliss, that deignest to descend
>   And solace me through many a dreary night
>   With eyes, which death has rendered not less bright,
> But made all earthly glories to transcend;

How much I thank thee, that thou shouldest lend
  My weary days the comfort of thy sight,
  So that, as heretofore, thy beauty's light
In all thy noted haunts I apprehend!

Thou know'st that, where I walked and sang of thee
  So many years, I now must walk and grieve
Not for thy sake, but for the loss I dree.

One only comfort all my sorrows leave,
That clearly, when thou comest back to me,
  Thy walk, face, voice and vesture I perceive.

Translated by C. B. Cayley

BOCCACCIO

The Wolf

This is the seventh novella of the Ninth in Boccaccio's *Decameron*, written in the middle of the fourteenth century.

Panfilo's story being now at an end, the woman's presence of mind was applauded by one and all, after which the queen called upon Pampinea to tell hers, and she began as follows:

Delectable ladies, we have talked on previous occasions about the truths embodied in dreams, which many of us refuse to take seriously. But even though this topic has already been aired, I am determined to tell you a pithy little tale showing what happened not long ago to a neighbour of mine through ignoring a dream of her husband's in which she appeared.

I don't know whether you were ever acquainted with Talano d'Imolese, but he was a person of high repute, and was married to a young woman called Margarita, who, though exceedingly beautiful, was the most argumentative, disagreeable and self-willed creature on God's earth, for she would never heed other people's advice and regarded everyone but herself as an incompetent fool. This made life very difficult for Talano, but since he had no choice in the matter, he bore it all philosophically.

Now one night, when Talano happened to be staying with this wife of his at one of their country estates, he dreamt that he saw her wandering through some very beautiful woods, which were situated not far away from the house.

As he watched, an enormous and ferocious wolf seemed to emerge from a corner of the woods and hurl itself at Margarita's throat, dragging her to the ground. She struggled to free herself, screaming for help, and when at length she managed to escape from its clutches, the whole of her throat and face appeared to be torn to ribbons. So when Talano got up next morning, he said to his wife, 'Woman, your cussedness has been the bane of my life since the day we were married; but all the same I should be sorry if you came to any harm, and therefore, if you'll take my advice, you won't venture forth from the house today.'

When she asked him the reason, he told her about his dream, whereupon she tossed her head in the air and said, 'Evil wishes beget evil dreams. You pretend to be very anxious for my safety, but you only dream these horrid things about me because you'd like to see them happen. You may rest assured that I shall never give you the satisfaction of seeing me suffer any such fate as the one you describe, whether on this day or any other.'

'I knew you would say that,' said Talano. 'A mangy dog never thanks you for combing its pelt. But you may think whatever you like. I only mentioned it for your own good, and once again I advise you to stay at home today, or at any rate to keep well away from those woods of ours.'

'Very well,' said the woman, 'I'll do as you say.'

But then she began to think to herself: 'Here's a crafty fellow! Do you see how he tries to frighten me out of going near the woods today? He's doubtless made an appointment there with some strumpet or other, and doesn't want me to find him. Ah, he'd do well for himself at a supper for the blind, but knowing him as I do, I should be a great fool to take him at his word. He certainly won't get away with this. I shall find out what business takes him to those woods, even if I have to wait there the whole day.'

No sooner had she reached the end of these deliberations than her husband left the house, whereupon she too left the house by a separate door and made her way to the woods without a moment's delay, keeping out of sight as much as possible. On entering the woods, she concealed herself in the thickest part she could find, and kept a sharp lookout on all sides so that she could see if anyone was coming.

Nothing was further removed from her thoughts than the prospect of seeing any wolves, but all of a sudden, whilst she was standing there in the way we have described, a wolf of terrifying size leapt out from a nearby thicket; on seeing which, she scarcely had time to exclaim 'Lord, deliver me!' before the wolf hurled itself at her throat, seized her firmly in its jaws, and began to carry her off as though she were a new-born lamb.

So tightly was the wolf holding on to her throat that she was unable to scream for help, nor was there anything else she could do; and hence the wolf, as it bore her away, would assuredly have strangled her but for the fact that it ran towards some shepherds, who yelled at the beast and forced it to release her. The poor, unfortunate woman was recognized by the shepherds, who carried her back to her house, and after long and intensive treatment at the hands of various physicians, she recovered. Her recovery was not complete, however, for the whole of her throat and a part of her face were so badly disfigured that whereas she was formerly a beautiful woman, she was thenceforth deformed and utterly loathsome to look upon. Hence she was ashamed to show herself in public, and shed many a bitter tear for her petulant ways and her refusal to give credence, when it would have cost her nothing, to her husband's prophetic dream.

Translated by H. G. McWilliam

FROISSART

The Mirror

According to the French critic Sainte-Beuve, Jean Froissart's *Traité de l'Espinette Amoureuse*, from which this passage is taken, is a largely autobiographical poem. Written around 1370, its purported source was the impossible love of Froissart for a Lady, which forced him into exile. He was indeed attached for several years to the English court of Queen Philippa of Hainault, wife of Edward III. Froissart began to write both the *Espinette Amoureuse* and his lively *Chronicles* – which are better known than his poetry – after his return to France at the death of Queen Philippa in 1369.

I kept close to me the gift that the young lady had given me when she left; may God have mercy on her, for I loved looking at it: it was a beautiful mirror. It gave me joy and comfort, but also much to think about, for when I looked at the mirror I did not feel bitter about my lady but would rather say: 'She who has captured my heart and holds it in her power once gazed into this mirror. Alas, I can see her sweet face no more! She has looked into it many a time, but I am annoyed that I cannot even catch a glimpse of her. In truth, all that seems true in a reflection is but a shadow that overcomes light: here is light and then comes the shade making things dark and obscure. Why is it that when I contemplate the mirror I cannot see my dear love's form? If God help me, I would like to be like the artist in Rome who made the mirror in which one could see the reflection of those who rode in the vicinity. If I were as clever as he who made that mirror, by our Lord Jesus, I could see my lady clearly, here or anywhere else.'

Thus would I muse. Several times, by Saint Rémy, I felt such pleasure while talking to myself that it actually seemed as though I could see my lady in my mirror. I received great consolation from the reflection in the looking-glass where my lady had gazed at her face, and I held it very close to my heart and breast. Never would I be without it and I kept it by me wherever I went, for I derived great enjoyment from looking at it: it was my delight, my all.

Thus it happened that one night I lay in my bed, lost in thoughts of love; I had put it beneath my pillow and I fell asleep thinking about it. While I slept, I appeared to be all alone and enraptured in a lavishly decorated room lined with gold tapestry, and while I was in the room I came in this direction and had a look: I thought that in my mirror I could actually see the reflection of my lady, who was gazing into the mirror and she held an ivory comb with which she parted her beautiful long blonde hair. I was quite astonished, but I would not have wished to be elsewhere, not even for a hundred barrel-loads of good wheat. Then I left my mirror, for I believed she was near me: if a man is truly in love then he must look at what he desires. I was neither irritated nor angry, but said: 'Where are you my lady? Pardon me, oh tender, sweet heart, that I have stumbled upon you.'

Then I thought I could see her, without having to say one more word to her, but this was not the case, for I did not see her true form. I walked about the room several times and sought her everywhere, but I could not see her at all. Then I came back to the mirror and saw her again. So I declared: 'This must be magic! Indeed, my lady, I am very happy to see you combing your hair. If you are playing hide-and-seek, let me at least find you: I beg this of you in the name of love.' So I opened the windows and looked under all the rugs, but she was not there at all, even though I could really see her in the mirror. I murmured to myself: 'This must be some enchantment!' No it cannot be for something similar once happened to two lovers in Rome, so this is not all that improbable; Ovid tells the story thus:

Once upon a time in Rome there lived the son of a wise and noble man; his name was Papirus. He was well-known everywhere because his wisdom was held in great esteem. Naturally, he fell in love with a lady and was also loved by her. The maiden's name was Ydoree. The tale of Papirus and Ydoree is one of bliss, for they loved each other truly and never wavered in their loyalty; their hearts were as one.

It so happened that Papirus was chosen by the Romans for an important mission and they said to him: 'Papirus, you must go and talk to the king of Sicily. The distance is great and we want to send you because in Rome you are believed to be very wise and you are sure to carry out the mission well.' Papirus did not dare say no, but his heart was filled with anguish, and when he told Ydoree about this she shed many a tear and said, 'My dear, sweet Papirus, are you going to leave me then? My heart has received such a blow, that I fear you will never see me again.' When Papirus, who was very wise, heard

Ydoree's words he spoke as follows: 'My love, all this has to be, but you shall always see my face and I yours. Now take comfort and banish sorrow from your heart, for I will return.' Papirus made two mirrors, on what anvil I do not know, but they were of the same size and made with great magic, and what was quite wonderful about this artifice was that when Ydoree desired to look into hers, she could see her dear love Papirus and console herself, while Papirus could see Ydoree equally well in his. It is said that the two mirrors lasted thus throughout the whole journey, and an exemplar may still be seen at the temple of Minerva in Rome.

So, if I could see my lady in my mirror, I must believe it and be happy, for I have the example and the proof that this actually happened. Moreover, my peerless lady, I feel great joy when I see you because this is much more of an enchantment than was Papirus's mirror, for I can see you moving about in this room. Oh, that you would at least deign to speak and open your mouth a little! I cannot touch you with my hand, nor reach you in any way, so speak, since I wish to go to bed right here and lie next to my mirror and gaze at your countenance, for I could not be in a better state. Then I sat by the window resting upon my quilt with my hand on my chin, and I listened and heard my lady's voice. I did not dare move for were I to have done so, I might have lost too great a pleasure; instead I kept quiet and looked into the mirror which I held tight. I saw the image touching me and opening its mouth a little, then above me I heard the voice that gave me great joy:

[The lady swears her love in perfect courtly jargon, with many mythological examples, in 240 conventional lines.]

Then the voice was silent and altered, and the image faded; I saw nothing more in the mirror for it had said all it had to say. As I lay there I appeared to be saying 'This is indeed some magic or some enchantment!' Whereupon I stopped sleeping and when I awoke I was quite astounded. As for my pillow, I immediately sought counsel there to see if I would find my mirror and see her in it. Yes indeed! I found it exactly where I had left it. Then I picked it up and kissed it very gently and mused for some time, thinking I had seen my lady and heard her speak. But, in faith, I had merely been deceived by all this dream.

Translated by Ch. Lee

MONTAIGNE

Horns

This passage comes from Montaigne's Essay I, 21. The first two books of the *Essays* appeared in 1580. We are giving here John Florio's translation, which came out in 1603.

We sweat, we shake, we grow pale, and we blush at the motions of our imaginations; and wallowing in our beds we feele our bodies agitated and turmoiled at their apprehensions, yea in such manner, as sometimes we are ready to yeeld up the spirit. And burning youth (although asleepe) is often therewith so possessed and enfolded, that dreaming it doth satisfie and enjoy her amorous desires.

> *Ut quasi transactis saepe omnibu' rebu' profundant*
> *Fluminis ingentes fluctus, vestemque cruentent.*
> —Lucr. iv, 1027.

> And if all things were done, they powre foorth streames,
> And bloodie their night-garment in their dreames.

And although it be not strange to see some men have hornes growing upon their head in one night, that had none when they went to bed: notwithstanding the fortune or successe of *Cyppus* King of *Italie* is memorable, who because the day before he had with earnest affection, assisted and beene attentive at a bul-baiting, and having all night long dreamed of hornes in his head, by the very force of imagination brought them forth the next morning in his forehead.

Translated by J. Florio

BACON

Of Prophecies

This is a passage from one of Sir Francis Bacon's *Essays or Counsels Civil and Moral*, first published in 1597.

The daughter of Polycrates dreamed, that Jupiter bathed her father, and Apollo anointed him: and it came to pass, that he was crucified in an open place, where the sun made his body run with sweat, and the rain washed it.

Philip of Macedon dreamed he sealed up his wife's belly, whereby he did expound it, that his wife should be barren; but Aristander the soothsayer told him his wife was with child: because men do not use to seal vessels that are empty. A phantasm that appeared to M. Brutus, in his tent, said to him, *Philippis iterum me videbis*. Tiberius said to Galba, *Tu quoque, Galba, degustabis imperium* ... Domitian dreamed, the night before he was slain, that a golden head was growing out of the nape of his neck: and indeed the succession that followed him, for many years, made golden times.

... As for Cleon's dream, I think it was a jest: it was, that he was devoured of a long dragon; and it was expounded of a maker of sausages, that troubled him exceedingly. There are numbers of the like kind; especially if you include dreams, and predictions of astrology. But I have set down these few only of certain credit, for example. My judgement is, that they ought all to be despised, and ought to serve but for winter talk by the fireside. Though when I say despised, I mean it as for belief: for otherwise, the spreading or publishing of them, is in no sort to be despised; for they have done much mischief. And I see many severe laws made to suppress them. That that hath given them grace, and some credit, consisteth in three things: first, that men mark when they hit, and never mark when they miss; as they do, generally, also of dreams. The second is, that probable conjectures, or obscure traditions, many times, turn themselves into prophecies: while the nature of man, which coveteth divination, thinks it no peril to foretel that, which indeed they do but collect; as that of Seneca's verse. For so much was then subject to demonstration, that the globe of the earth had great parts beyond the Atlantic, which might be probably conceived not to be all sea: and adding thereto, the tradition in Plato's *Timaeus*, and his *Atlanticus*, it might encourage one to turn it to a prediction. The third and last, which is the great one, is, that almost all of them, being infinite in number, have been impostures, and, by idle and crafty brains, merely contrived and feigned, after the event past.

QUEVEDO

The Last Judgement

'The Last Judgement', of which we give here a passage, belongs to Francisco Gomez de Quevedo y Villegas's *Sueños* ('Visions'). Quevedo first wanted to publish it in 1610, but the book was deemed too outrageous. A first version came out in 1627, and a second, censored one, in 1631. We are giving here the seventeenth-century English version by Robert L'Estrange.

Dreams, especially those of sovereigns and princes, are, by Homer, said to proceed from Jove, if the matter of them be pious and important: And it is likewise the judgement of the celebrated Propertius, that good dreams coming from above, have their weight and ought to be credited. And truly I agree with him in the case of a dream I had last night. As I was reading a discourse concerning the end of the world, I fell asleep over the book, and dreamed of the Last Judgement: A thing which, in the house of a poet, is scarce admitted, so much as in a dream. This fancy brought into my mind a passage in Claudian; That all creatures dream at night of what they have heard and seen in the day as the hound dreams of hunting the hare.

I thought I saw a very beautiful youth towering in the air, and sounding a trumpet; but the forcing of his breath did indeed take much from his beauty. The very marbles, I perceived, and the dead were obedient to his call; for, in the same moment the earth began to open and set the bones at liberty, to seek their fellows. The first that appeared were swordsmen; as generals of armies, captains, lieutenants and common soldiers; who, supposing that it had sounded a charge, sprang from their graves with such briskness and resolution, as if they had been going to an assault, or a combat. The misers peeped out, pale and trembling, for fear of being robbed; the cavaliers and good fellows imagined they had been going to a horse-race, or a hunting-match: And, in a word, though they all heard the trumpet, there was not any creature understood the meaning of it; for I could read their thoughts by their looks and gestures. After this, there appeared several souls, whereof some came up to their bodies, with much difficulty and horror; others stood watching at a distance, not daring to approach so horrid a spectacle: This wanted an arm, that an eye, and the other a head. Upon the whole, though I could not but smile at the prospect of so strange an olio of figures, yet was it not without just matter of admiration at the All-powerful Providence, to see order drawn out of confusion, and every part restored to the right owner. I then imagined myself in a churchyard, and there, methought, several that were unwilling to appear, were changing of heads; and an attorney would have demurred, upon pretence that he had got a soul which was none of his own, and that his body and soul were not fellows.

At length, when the whole assembly came to understand that this was the Day of Judgement, it is worth while to observe what shifting and shuffling there was among the wicked. The epicure and whoremaster would not own their eyes, nor the slanderer his tongue; because they would be sure to appear in evidence against them. The pick-pockets ran away as hard as they could drive from their own fingers. There was one that had been embalmed in Egypt; and staying for his guts, an old usurer asked him if the bags were to rise with the bodies? I could have laughed at this question, but I was presently taken up with a crowd of cutpurses, running full speed from their own ears, that were offered them again, for fear of the sad stories they expected to hear.

I saw all this from a convenient standing; and in the instant, there was an outcry at my feet, of Withdraw, Withdraw. As soon as I heard this , down I came, and immediately a great many beautiful ladies put forth their heads, and called me clown, for not paying them that respect and ceremony which is due to their quality. You must know that the women stand upon punctilios, even in hell itself. They seemed at first very gay and frolicsome; and well enough pleased to be seen naked, for they were clean skinned, and well made. But when they came to understand that this was the Great Day of Account their consciences took check, and all their jollity was dashed in a moment: Whereupon they retired to a valley, very much out of humour. There was one among the rest that had had seven husbands, and promised every one of them never to marry again, for she was certain she could never love anybody else: This lady was casting about for excuses, and what answer she should make to that point. Another that had been as common as Ratcliff Highway, would neither lead nor drive; and stood humming and hawing a good while, pretending she had forgotten her night-clothes, and such fooleries; but, notwithstanding all her excuses, she was brought at last within sight of the throne; where she found all her old acquaintance, that she had carried part of their way to hell; who no sooner beheld her, but they fell to pointing or hooting, so that she took to her heels, and herded herself in a troop of serjeants. After this I saw several people driving a physician along the bank of the river; and these were only such as he had unnecessarily despatched before their time. They followed him with the cries of Justice, Justice, and forced him on toward the Judgement Seat, where they arrived, in the end, with much ado. While this passed, I heard, methought, on my left hand, a paddling in the water, as if one had been swimming: And what should this be, but a judge, in the midst of a river, washing his hands. I asked him the meaning of it; and he told me, that in his lifetime he had been often daubed in the fist, to make the business slip the better; and he would willingly get out the grease before he came to hold up his hand at the bar. There followed next a multitude of vintners and tailors, under the guard of a legion of devils, armed with rods, whips, cudgels and other instruments of correction: And these counted themselves deaf, and were very unwilling to leave their graves, for fear of a worse lodging. As they were passing on, up started a little lawyer, and asked whither they were going? They replied, that they were going to give an account of their works. With that the lawyer threw himself flat upon his belly, in his hole again: If I am to go downwards at last, says he, I am thus much onward on my way. The vintner sweated as he walked, till one drop followed another: That is well done, cried a devil at his elbow, to purge out the water, that we may have none in our wine. There was a tailor wrapped up in sarcenets, crook-fingered and baker-legged, who was quite silent all the way he went, but, Alas! alas! how can any man be a thief that dies for want of bread? But his companions gave him a rebuke for discrediting his trade. The next that appeared were a band of highwaymen, following upon the heels of one another, in great distrust and jealousy of thieves among themselves. These were fetched up by a party of devils, in the turning of a hand, and lodged with the tailors: For, said one of the company, your highwayman is but a wild tailor. They were a little quarrelsome at first, but in the conclusion, they went down into the valley and kennelled quietly together. After these came Folly, with her gang of poets, fiddlers, lovers and fencers; the people of all the world that dream the least of a day of reckoning: These were disposed of among the hangmen, Jews, scribes, and philosophers. There were likewise several solicitors, wondering among themselves that they should have so much conscience when they were dead, and none at all while living.

Translated by R. L'Estrange

LA FONTAINE

The Two Friends

Jean de la Fontaine's fables, from which this poem is taken, were first published in 1668. We give here Marianne Moore's translation.

Two fast friends lived somewhere in Monomotapa,
And each regarded as both's anything of his own:
      True fantasists of a vanished day,
      Almost finer than some we have known!
It appears that the friends had been sleeping peacefully,
Utilizing the darkness appropriately,
When one of them woke terror-struck with concern
And sped to the other distractedly,
Where Sleep, that great master, had brought passivity.
The sleeping friend was stunned, seized sword and purse in turn,
Ran to the door and said, 'What has occurred
That you come at this hour to your weary fellow men
Who were constrained to sleep that they be restored again?
Have you wagered your funds and found fortune untoward?
Then take mine. Has some fool been irascible?
I have a sword. Join me. You've been lonely too long—
A monk in your cell, doomed to nights that were dull;
I'll part with a slave who really is beautiful.'
The friend replied, 'Nothing at all has gone wrong.
      God bless one so lovable.

I dreamt you were sad, looked less well than you do.
Afraid it might be so, I have therefore run to you;
     My bad dream disturbed your repose.'
Reader, which of these friends should you say loved the more?
Too hard to say, yet a true friend is, I suppose,
One of the very sweetest things one knows!
Discerning needs that are interior,
     He does his friend this favour—
     Interprets him by intuition.
     He'll dream, give a start or betray pallor,
     Merely on a supposition.

Translated by M. Moore

PASCAL

Life is only a Dream

This text belongs to Pascal's *Pensées*, which were left unfinished at
his death in 1662, and were published posthumously in 1669.

Again, no one is sure, apart from faith, whether he is awake or asleep, seeing
that during sleep we believe that we are awake as firmly as we do when we *are*
awake. We believe we see spaces, figures, movements; we experience the
passage of time, we measure it; and in fact we behave just as when we are
awake. We spend half of our life asleep, in which condition, as we ourselves
admit, we have no idea of truth, whatever we may imagine, since all our
perceptions are then illusory. Who knows, therefore, whether the other half of
life, in which we believe ourselves awake, is not another dream, slightly
different from the first, from which we awake when we suppose ourselves
asleep?

If we dreamt in company and the dreams, as often happens, chanced to
agree, and if we spent our waking hours in solitude, who doubts that in such a
case we should believe matters reversed? Finally, as we often dream that we
are dreaming, and thus add one dream to another, life itself is only a dream
upon which other dreams are grafted and from which we awake at death, a
dream during which we have as few principles of truth and goodness as during
natural sleep, these different thoughts which disturb us being perhaps mere
illusions, like the flight of time and the empty fancies of our dreams.

Translated by J. Warrington

King and Labourer

This text is also taken from Pascal's *Pensées*.

If we dreamt the same thing every night, it would affect us as much as do the objects that we see every day. If a labourer were sure to dream for twelve hours every night that he was a king, he would, I believe, be almost as happy as a king who dreamt for twelve hours every night that he was a labourer.

If we dreamt every night that we were pursued by enemies and troubled by these disturbing phantoms, or that we spent every day in different occupations, as one does on a journey, we would suffer almost as much as if the dream were reality, and we would fear to sleep, just as we fear to wake when we dread having actually to face such misfortunes. It would indeed cause nearly the same discomfort as the reality.

But because our dreams are all different, and each one itself contains variety, what is seen in them affects us much less than what we see in our waking hours, because of the latter's continuity. This, however, is not so continuous and uniform as to preclude all change; but the change is less abrupt, except on such rare occasions as a journey, when we say: 'It seems as if I were dreaming.' For life is a dream, though a little less inconstant.

Translated by J. Warrington

ADDISON

The Theatre of Dreams

This essay by J. Addison was published in *The Spectator* of 18 September 1712.

Thursday, 18 September

————*Cum prostrata sopore*
Urget membra quies, & mens sine pondere ludit.—Petr.

Tho' there are many Authors, who have written on Dreams, they have generally considered them only as Revelations of what has already happened in distant Parts of the World, or as Presages of what is to happen in future Periods of Time.

I shall consider this Subject in another Light, as Dreams may give us some Idea of the great Excellency of an Human Soul, and some Intimation of its Independency on Matter.

In the first Place, our Dreams are great Instances of that Activity which is natural to the Humane Soul, and which it is not in the Power of Sleep to deaden or abate. When the Man appears tired and worn out with the Labours of the Day, this active Part in his Composition is still busie and unwearied. When the Organs of Sense want their due Repose and necessary Reparations, and the Body is no longer able to keep Pace with that spiritual Substance to which it is united, the Soul exerts her self in her several Faculties, and continues in Action till her Partner is again qualified to bear her Company. In this Case Dreams look like the Relaxations and Amusements of the Soul, when she is disencumbered of her Machine, her Sports and Recreations, when she has laid her Charge asleep.

In the Second Place, Dreams are an Instance of that Agility and Perfection which is natural to the Faculties of the Mind, when they are disengaged from the Body. The Soul is clogged and retarded in her Operations, when she acts in Conjunction with a Companion that is so heavy and unwieldy in its Motions. But in Dreams it is wonderful, to observe with what a Sprightliness and Alacrity she exerts her self. The slow of Speech make unpremeditated Harangues, or converse readily in Languages that they are but little acquainted with. The Grave abound in Pleasantries, the Dull in Repartees, and Points of Wit. There is not a more painful Action of the Mind, than Invention; yet in Dreams it works with that Ease and Activity, that we are not sensible when the Faculty is employed. For Instance, I believe every one, some Time or other, dreams that he is reading Papers, Books or Letters, in which Case the Invention prompts so readily, that the Mind is imposed upon, and mistakes its own Suggestions for the Compositions of another.

I shall, under this Head, quote a Passage out of the *Religio Medici*, in which the ingenious Author gives an Account of himself in his dreaming, and his waking Thoughts. *We are somewhat more than our selves in our Sleeps, and the Slumber of the Body seems to be but the Waking of the Soul. It is the Ligation of Sense but the Liberty of Reason, and our waking Conceptions do not match the Fancies of our Sleeps. At my Nativity my Ascendant was the watery Sign of Scorpius. I was born in the Planetary Hour of Saturn, and, I think, I have a Piece of that leaden Planet in me. I am no way facetious, nor disposed for the Mirth and Galliardize of Company, yet in one Dram I can compose a whole Comedy, behold the Action, apprehend the Jests, and laugh my self awake at the Conceits thereof. Were my Memory as faithful as my Reason is then fruitful, I would never study but in my Dreams: and this Time also would I chuse for my Devotions: but our grosser Memories have then so little hold of our abstracted Understandings, that they forget the Story, and can only relate to our awaked Souls, a confused and broken Tale of that that has passed.— Thus it is observed that Men sometimes, upon the Hour of their Departure, do speak and reason above themselves, for then the Soul beginning to be freed from the Ligaments of the Body, begins to reason like her self, and to discourse in a Strain above Mortality.*

We may likewise observe in the third Place, that the Passions affect the

Mind with greater Strength when we are a-sleep, than when we are awake. Joy and Sorrow give us more vigorous Sensations of Pain or Pleasure at this time, than at any other. Devotion likewise, as the excellent Author above-mentioned has hinted, is in a very particular Manner heightned and inflamed, when it rises in the soul at a Time that the Body is thus laid at Rest. Every Man's Experience will inform him in this Matter, though it is very probable, that this may happen differently in different Constitutions. I shall conclude this Head with the two following Problems, which I shall leave to the Solution of my Reader. Supposing a Man always happy in his Dreams, and miserable in his waking Thoughts, and that his Life was equally divided between them, whether would he be more happy or miserable? Were a Man a King in his Dreams, and a Beggar awake, and dreamt as consequentially, and in as continued unbroken Schemes, as he thinks when awake, whether he would be in Reality a King or Beggar, or rather whether he wou'd not be both?

There is another Circumstance which methinks gives us a very high Idea of the Nature of the Soul, in regard to what passes in Dreams, I mean that innumerable Multitude and Variety of Ideas which then arise in her. Were that active watchful Being only conscious of her own Existence at such a time, what a painful Solitude would her Hours of Sleep be? Were the Soul sensible of her being alone in her sleeping Moments, after the same Manner that she is sensible of it while awake, the Time would hang very heavy on her, as it often actually does when she dreams that she is in such a Solitude.

> —*Semperque relinqui*
> *Sola sibi, semper longam incomitata videtur*
> *Ire viam!* —*Virg.*

But this Observation I only make by the Way. What I would here remark is that wonderful Power in the Soul, of producing her own Company on these Occasions. She converses with numberless Beings of her own Creation, and is transported into ten thousand Scenes of her own raising. She is herself the Theatre, the Actors, and the Beholder. This puts me in Mind of a Saying which I am infinitely pleased with, and which *Plutarch* ascribes to *Heraclitus, That all Men whilst they are awake are in one common World: but that each of them, when he is asleep, is in a World of his own.* The waking Man is conversant in the World of Nature, when he sleeps he retires to a private World that is particular to himself. There seems something in this Consideration that intimates to us a natural Grandeur and Perfection in the Soul, which is rather to be admired than explained.

I must not omit that Argument for the Excellency of the Soul, which I have seen quoted out of *Tertullian* namely, its Power of Divining in Dreams. That several such Divinations have been made, none can question who believes the Holy Writings, or who has but the least Degree of a common historical Faith, there being innumerable Instances of this Nature in several Authors, both

Ancient and Modern, Sacred and Prophane. Whether such dark Presages, such Visions of the Night proceed from any latent Power in the Soul, during this her State of Abstraction, or from any Communication with the Supreme Being, or from any Operation of Subordinate Spirits, has been a great Dispute among the Learned; the Matter of Fact is I think incontestable, and has been looked upon as such by the greatest Writers, who have been never suspected either of Supersition or Enthusiasm.

I do not suppose, that the Soul in these Instances is entirely loose and unfettered from the Body: It is sufficient, if she is not so far sunk, and immersed in Matter, nor intangled and perplexed in her Operations, with such Motions of Blood and Spirits, as when she actuates the Machine in its waking Hours. The corporeal Union is slackened enough to give the Mind more Play. The Soul seems gathered within her self, and recovers that Spring which is broke and weakned, when she operates more in concert with the Body.

The Speculations I have here made, if they are not Arguments, they are at least strong Intimations, not only of the Excellency of an Humane Soul, but of its Independance on the Body; and if they do not prove, do at least confirm these two great Points, which are established by many other Reasons that are altogether unanswerable.

GRILLPARZER

Medea

Franz Grillparzer, the German Romantic playwright wrote this entry in his diary in 1821, when he was working on his tragedy, Medea.

Last night I had a strange dream. I dreamt of a prologue to Medea, of which all I can remember now is that it was entirely allegorical, that Medea appeared in it lying on a carriage that was a sort of bed, and that she was drawn about on a rope that was held by a figure in female form. One other thing was that in the course of the play I was suddenly struck with surprise at the appropriateness with which at one point Medea made a movement with her hands as if she were flying, or swimming. I had been enchanted by it all and went on dreaming now that I was awake and in the company of Schreyvogel, the secretary at the theatre, telling him my dream and of my intentions of altering my play in accordance with it. I couldn't any longer remember the particular details of the visions I'd had in my dream and had to think hard to try to

summon it back to life, finally getting the whole thing together again and
experiencing the greatest joy that it could be so extremely poetic and pregnant
with meaning. I was able moreover, with what seemed a much sharper kind of
consciousness, to reflect upon my dream and upon dreams in general – all of
this within the dream itself. When I awoke from such an extremely vivid
dream I was seized with two feelings. First, it seemed to me that my waking
state, compared with what had gone before it, was like a sketch by the side of a
painting, or a foggy day against a sunlit one; and then moreover I had a
peculiar, unpleasant sensation of confinement in time, for hitherto so much
had happened to me, in such a rush and short space of time.

Translated by M. Hollington

HEBBEL

The Elusive Poem

Friedrich Hebbel wrote this entry in his diary on 19 March 1838.
At the time, he was working on his tragedy, *Judith*, first represented in 1840.

19 March

I had a dream in the night which I think worthy of remark because of its
frequent recurrence: I've had it before a number of times. This is what I
dreamt: I had the idea of a poem. I was very pleased with it; it made me pace
up and down in my room, as is my wont, stepping up every now and again to
my table to write down the lines as they came to me. As I got closer and closer
to waking (I could feel this clearly, without being directly conscious of it) I
grew less and less happy with what I'd written, until finally the idea came to
seem of no value whatever. I considered it one last time, and in the very
moment of being convinced of its worthlessness I woke up; but now I no
longer had the slightest inkling of what had occupied me so intently a moment
or so beforehand. To me (if what happens in dreams can ever be properly
analysed, which I doubt, because I think that none of these experiences can
ever enter consciousness in a pure state, either because they never reach it at
all or because the act of waking introduces some foreign element that distorts
everything) it has often seemed as if the psyche were equipped in dreams with
a new scale of measure for determining the importance of what is happening
in and about it; it carries on its work not merely with new materials and
elements but (if the expression be admitted) according to a new method.

Obstacles that the waking mind cannot face are dispersed in dreams by a breath; trifles that in waking life we would hardly deign to circumvent have in dreams the power to break our strength.

It is just the same with states of mind: I am convinced, for instance, that the reason I woke up in the night was not that I became aware that the poetic idea I had seized upon would really lead to nothing, nor that my psychic activity suddenly came to a standstill; no, I am certain that the strange stirrings of self-consciousness that always precede waking, and cause us to look mistrustfully at the dream-state we are in, were responsible for numbing the psyche's poetic working and killing off the very living germ of that precious idea, like a sudden blast of cold air, so that when I awoke the idea was paralysed. I don't believe anyone will understand me in this who hasn't experienced something similar: yet to me it is as clear and simple as ABC. Admittedly there are other kinds of dreams as well, mere revolts against life in its positive aspect, of a kind that all of us may have in the waking state, imagining things transformed without the slightest actual change taking place; there may even be people who only have this kind of dream, and who are therefore eternal Philistines.

If anyone were to set down in print all his dreams – fearlessly, indiscriminately, honestly, thoroughly, and with the addition of a commentary to explain as much as he could with the aid of memories from his life and reading – he would be rendering mankind a great service. Yet in the present state of humanity it is improbable that anyone will undertake the task; still, even to attempt it in private, for one's own contemplation, is worth something.

Translated by M. Hollington

DICKENS

The Toasting Fork

Cornelius Conway Fenton, professor of Greek at Harvard, was a close friend of Charles Dickens who sent him, in the words of his biographer John Forster, some of 'his most delightful letters'. Fenton accompanied Dickens to New York during the writer's tour of America in 1842–3.

1 September 1843

To Cornelius Conway Fenton

Apropos of dreams, is it not a strange thing that writers of fiction never dream of their own creations; recollecting, I suppose, even in their dreams, that they have no existence? I never dreamed of any of my own characters, and I feel it so impossible that I would wager Scott never did of his, real as they are. I had a good piece of absurdity in my head a night or two ago.

I dreamed that somebody was dead. I don't know who, but it's not to the purpose. It was a private gentleman, and a particular friend; and I was greatly overcome when the news was broken to me (very delicately) by a gentleman in a cocked hat, top boots, and a sheet. Nothing else. 'Good God!' I said, 'is he dead?' 'He is dead, sir,' rejoined the gentleman, 'as a door-nail. But we must all die, Mr Dickens, sooner or later, my dear sir.' 'Ah!' I said. 'Yes, to be sure. Very true. But what did he die of?' The gentleman burst into a flood of tears, and said, in a voice broken by emotion, 'He christened his youngest child, sir, with a toasting-fork.' I never in my life was so affected as at his having fallen a victim to this complaint. It carried a conviction to my mind that he never could have recovered. I knew that it was the most interesting and fatal malady in the world; and I wrung the gentleman's hand in a convulsion of respectful admiration, for I felt that this explanation did equal honour to his head and heart.

HERVEY SAINT-DENIS

The Monsters

Hervey Saint-Denis published his book *Les rêves et les moyens de les contrôler* ('Dreams and How to Direct them') in 1864. He had started writing down and drawing his dreams during his child-hood, and never stopped. Like other dream-addicts (Huch and Pérec, for instance), he found that the fact he was observing them influenced his dreams; on the other hand, being conscious of dreaming during his dreams, he could thus attempt to direct them.

I was not aware that I was dreaming, and I thought I was being pursued by abominable monsters. I fled through an endless series of adjoining rooms; I had great difficulty opening the separating doors, and no sooner had I closed one behind me than I would hear it opened again by that hideous crew, which came in hot pursuit, gibbering horribly. They seemed to be catching up with me; I woke up with a start, gasping and drenched in sweat.

What had given rise to this dream I did not know; it is probable that some pathological cause had engendered it the first time, but afterwards, and on several occasions in the course of six weeks, it was obviously recalled by the simple fact of the impression it had left on me, and by my instinctive fear of seeing it return. Whenever I dreamt that I was alone in some closed room, the memory of that odious dream would instantly come back to life; I would cast my eyes upon the door, and the thought of what I dreaded to see having precisely the effect of provoking its instant reappearance, the same spectacle and the same terrors would resurge once again. I was all the more affected on waking in that, by some curious chance, this awareness of my state, which I had so often had since then in my dreams, was always lacking when this one dream returned.

One night, however, on its fourth reappearance, and at the very moment when my persecutors were about to resume their chase, the yearning for truth suddenly rose up in me; the desire to combat these illusions gave me the strength to tame my instinctive terror. Instead of fleeing, and by an effort of will, certainly all the more marked under such circumstances, I stood firm against the wall and resolved to contemplate with fruitful attention the ghosts which I had till then glimpsed rather than observed. The initial shock was quite violent, I admit, so difficult is it for the mind, even when forewarned, to guard itself against a much-feared illusion. I turned my gaze on the principal assailant, which looked rather like one of those shaggy, leering demons sculpted on the porch of cathedrals, and with my desire for knowledge already triumphing over all other emotion, I was able to observe the following: the fantastic monster had stopped a few paces from me, snorting and prancing in a manner which was rather burlesque once it had ceased to be frightening. I noticed the claws of one of its hands or paws, as you might call them, which numbered seven, and were very clearly drawn. The hair of its brows, a wound it seemed to have on its shoulder, and a host of other details offered a precision that made this one of the clearest visions I had ever had. Was it the memory of some Gothic bas-relief? In any case my imagination had added movement and colour. The attention I had concentrated on this figure had caused its acolytes to vanish away, as if by magic. Its own movements soon seemed to slow down, it began to lose its clarity, to take on a cotton-like appearance, and finally to turn into a sort of floating rag, like one of those faded costumes you see used as signs on fancy-dress shops at carnival time. A few insignificant scenes followed, and then I awoke.

The dream never occurred again, at least not spontaneously; but it provided me with a chance to try out another experiment, perhaps an even more conclusive one, to do with the effects of will and concentration on the fabric of our dreams. One night as I slept, fully aware of my actual state, rather indifferently watching all the fantasmagoria of my sleep pass before me clearer than ever, I thought I might take advantage of this to try out some experiments on the power that I might or might not have to evoke certain images by willpower alone. As I wondered which subject I should concentrate my thought on, to this end, I remembered those monstrous apparitions which had formerly impressed me so vividly, thanks to the terror they inspired in me. I tried to summon them up, delving deep into my memory and willing myself, for all I was worth, to see them again. This first attempt was unsuccessful. All that stretched before me now was the pastoral image of a countryside bathed in lovely sunlight, with harvesters and carts laden with corn. Not a single spectre answered my call, and the association of ideas and images that formed my dream did not seem the least bit disposed to quit the peaceful track it had naturally taken.

Then, while I was still dreaming, I made the following reflections: since a dream is like a reflection of real life, the events which seem to take place in them generally follow, even in their very incoherence, certain laws of succession conforming to the ordinary sequence of events in real life. That is, for example, if I dream that my arm is broken, then in the dream I will be wearing it in a sling, or using it with great care; if I dream of the shutters of a room being closed, then as an immediate consequence, the light will go out in my mind too, and I will dream I am plunged into darkness. With this in mind, I then had the idea, in my dream, that if I put my hand over my eyes, I would first obtain an initial illusion in accordance with what would really happen if I did the same while awake; that is, the images of the objects I seemed to have in front of me would disappear. I then wondered if, once the pre-existing objects had been banished, my imagination would find it easier to evoke the new objects I tried to concentrate on. The experiment closely followed this line of reasoning. Placing a hand over my eyes in my dream did indeed result in destroying that vision of a countryside in harvest-time that I had been unable to change with the force of imagination alone. For a moment I saw nothing, just as I would in real life. Then I made another energetic appeal to the memory of the oft-mentioned onslaught of the monsters, and, as if by magic, this memory, clearly placed this time at the focal point of my thoughts, suddenly reappeared, bright, clear and riotous, without my even having any awareness, before I awoke, of the way the transition had taken place.

Translated by J. Romney

Suicide

It happens quite often that one observation elicits another. The idea that led me to the results you have just read, was based on the principle that the imaginary events of our dreams, incoherent though they may be as a whole, none the less follow in their concentration a certain logic borrowed from the reminiscences of real life. This same reasoning made me think that if I managed to put myself, while dreaming, in a situation where I could never have been in reality, my memory would be powerless to provide an image or a consequent sensation. No matter which way the imagination extricated itself from this impasse, a sudden interruption in the texture of the dream would necessarily follow. Jumping from a fifth-floor window, blowing my brains out, cutting my throat with a razor, obviously these are experiences that I have never had. By provoking them in a dream, I would therefore submit my mind to an interesting test.

I decided to be sure not to let slip the first opportunity that presented itself, that is to say the first lucid dream in the middle of which I would clearly possess a sense of my situation. I waited about a month; one needs to persevere. At last one night when I dreamt I was walking in the street and all the images of the dream were very clear and my sensations felt perfectly distinct even though I was not awake, I suddenly remembered the experiment I had to carry out and immediately climbed to the top floor of a house that seemed very high. I saw an open window and the pavement far below. I admired for a moment the perfection of this illusion of sleep, and before it could change, threw myself into the void, full of anxious curiosity. Now this is what happened, as I remembered it after I woke up, of course. Instantly losing the memory of everything that had gone before, I thought I was on a cathedral square, mixing with a group of bystanders who gathered around a dead man. Near me people were saying that the unknown man had thrown himself from the church tower, and I saw the corpse carried away on a stretcher. That was how my memory and my imagination got out of the trap I had set them. That was how the association of idea-images had proceeded.

As for the variants that I wanted to put to the test, such as cutting my throat with a razor, or putting pistols against my forehead, I must say that I was never able to complete the experiment with success. Once, when I had managed to get hold of a razor in my dream, I found the instinctive horror of what I wanted to simulate stronger than my conscious will. As far as pistols were concerned, it was necessary that some vision first spontaneously presented itself to my mind's eye. Had it been so, I would no doubt have completed the projected experiment. But the need to search for these weapons in my dream, and to prepare them, involved too many accessory ideas; because of the mobility of images in dreams, the first idea was constantly sidetracked before it could be carried out. As I was about to get my pistols, for example, my attention was caught by the little bunch of keys among which was the one for their box. At the same time I caught sight of the one for a drawer where I remembered I had locked up some photographs. One of them came back to my memory, appeared before my eyes, took hold of my thoughts and already my mind had wandered off the pistols.

Translated by R. Clarke

LINCOLN

Premonition

Abraham Lincoln told this dream to Ward Hill Lamon in early April 1865. He was assassinated on the fourteenth of that month.

'About ten days ago, I retired very late. I had been up waiting for important dispatches from the front. I could not have been long in bed when I fell into a slumber, for I was weary. I soon began to dream. There seemed to be death-like stillness about me. Then I heard subdued sobs, as if a number of people were weeping. I thought I left my bed and wandered downstairs. There the silence was broken by the same pitiful sobbing, but the mourners were invisible. I went from room to room; no living person was in sight, but the same mournful sounds of distress met me as I passed along. It was light in all the rooms; every object was familiar to me; but where were all the people who were grieving as if their hearts would break? I was puzzled and alarmed. What could be the meaning of all this? Determined to find the cause of a state of things so mysterious and so shocking, I kept on until I arrived at the East Room, which I entered. There I met with a sickening surprise. Before me was a catafalque, on which rested a corpse wrapped in funeral vestments. Around it were stationed soldiers who were acting as guards; and there was a throng of people, some gazing mournfully upon the corpse, whose face was covered, others weeping pitifully. "Who is dead in the White House?" I demanded of one of the soldiers. "The President," was his answer; "he was killed by an assassin!" Then came a loud burst of grief from the crowd, which awoke me from my dream. I slept no more that night; and although it was only a dream, I have been strangely annoyed by it ever since.'

'This is horrid!' said Mrs Lincoln [according to the biographer]. 'I wish you had not told it. I am glad I don't believe in dreams, or I should be in terror from this time forth.'

'Well,' responded Mr Lincoln, thoughtfully, 'it is only a dream, Mary. Let us say no more about it, and try to forget it . . .'

WHITMAN

The Artilleryman's Vision

This poem by Walt Whitman was first published with the title 'The Veteran's Vision' in a separate collection, *Drum Tabs*, in 1865. It was integrated in *Leaves of Grass* in 1871 with the title given above.

While my wife at my side lies slumbering, and the wars are over long,
And my head on the pillow rests at home, and the vacant midnight passes,
And through the stillness, through the dark, I hear, just hear, the breath of my infant,
There in the room as I wake from sleep this vision presses upon me;
The engagement opens there and then in fantasy unreal,
The skirmishers begin, they crawl cautiously ahead, I hear the irregular snap! snap!
I hear the sounds of the different missiles, the short *t-h-t! t-h-t!* of the rifle-balls,
I see the shells exploding leaving small white clouds, I hear the great shells shrieking as they pass,
The grape like the hum and whirr of wind through the trees, (tumultuous now the contest rages,)
All the scenes at the batteries rise in detail before me again,
The crashing and smoking, the pride of the men in their pieces,
The chief-gunner ranges and sights his piece and selects a fuse of the right time,
After firing I see him lean aside and look eagerly off to note the effect;
Elsewhere I hear the cry of a regiment charging, (the young colonel leads himself this time with brandish'd sword,)
I see the gaps cut by the enemy's volleys, (quickly fill'd up, no delay,)
I breathe the suffocating smoke, then the flat clouds hover low concealing all;
Now a strange lull for a few seconds, not a shot fired on either side,
Then resumed the chaos louder than ever, with eager calls and orders of officers,
While from some distant part of the field the wind wafts to my ears a shout of applause, (some special success,)
And ever the sound of the cannon far or near, (rousing even in dreams a devilish exultation and all the old mad joy in the depths of my soul,)
And ever the hastening of infantry shifting positions, batteries, cavalry, moving hither and thither,
(The falling, dying, I heed not, the wounded dripping and red I heed not, some to the rear are hobbling,)

Grime, heat, rush, aide-de-camps galloping by or on a full run,
With the patter of small arms, the warning *s-s-t* of the rifles, (these in my
    vision I hear or see,)
And bombs bursting in air, and at night the vari-color'd rockets.

MERIMEE

Djoûmane

Djoûmane was the last short story written by Prosper Mérimée, a
few months before his death in September 1870. It first came out
in the *Moniteur universel* in the issues of 9, 10 and 12 January 1873,
and was republished the same year in the collection *Dernières
nouvelles*.

On 21 May 18—, we returned to Tlemcen. The expedition had been a
fortunate one: we brought back oxen, sheep, goats, prisoners and hostages.

After a thirty-seven days' campaign, or rather of incessant hunt, our horses
were thin and lean-ribbed, but their eyes were still lively and full of fire; not
one was saddle-galled. We men were bronzed by the sun, our hair was long,
our cross-belts were dirty, and our waistcoats were worn to threads; we all
presented that appearance of indifference to danger and hardship which
characterizes the true soldier.

What general would not have chosen our light cavalry for a battle-charge
rather than the smartest of squadrons all decked out in new clothes?

Since morning I had thought of all the little pleasures that awaited me.

Now I should sleep in my iron bedstead, after having slept for thirty-seven
nights on a square of oilcloth. I should sit on a chair to take my dinner, and
should have as much soft bread and salt as I liked. Next I wondered to myself
whether Mademoiselle Coucha would wear a pomegranate flower or jessa-
mine in her hair, and if she had kept the vows made when I left; but, faithful or
inconstant, I knew she could reckon on the great depth of tenderness that a
man brings home from the wilds. There was not anyone in our squadron who
had not made plans for the evening.

The colonel received us in a most fatherly manner, and even told us he was
satisfied with us; then he took our commanding officer aside and for five
minutes, and in low tones, communicated to him some not very agreeable
intelligence, so far as we could judge from their expressions.

We noticed the movements of the colonel's moustaches, which rose up to
his eyebrows, whilst those of the commandant fell, piteously out of curl,

almost on to his breast. A young trooper, whom I pretended not to hear, maintained that the commandant's nose stretched as far as one could see; but very soon ours lengthened too, for the commandant came to tell us to 'Go and feed your horses, and be ready to set off at sunset! The officers will dine with the colonel at five o'clock, in the open; the horses must be mounted after the coffee . . . Is it possible that you are not pleased at this, gentlemen . . . ?

It did not suit us, and we saluted in silence, inwardly sending him to all the devils we could think of, and the colonel into the bargain.

We had very little time in which to make our small preparations. I hurried to change my dress, and, when I had done this, I was wise enough not to sit in my easy-chair, for fear I should fall asleep.

At five o'clock I went to the colonel's. He lived in a large Moorish house. I found the open court filled wtih French and natives, all crowding round a band of pilgrims or mountebanks who had come from the South.

An old man conducted the performance; he was as ugly as a monkey and half naked, under his burnous, which was full of holes. His skin was the colour of chocolate made of water; he was tattooed all over with scars; his hair was frizzy and so matted that from a distance one might have thought he had a bearskin cap on his head; and his beard was white and bristly.

He was reputed to be a great saint and a great wizard.

In front of him an orchestra, composed of two flutes and three tambourines, made an infernal din, worthy of the performance about to be played. He said that he had received complete sway over demons and wild beasts from a famous Mahomedan priest, and, after some compliments addressed to the colonel and the élite audience, he went off into a sort of prayer or incantation, accompanied by his orchestra, whilst the actors danced to his command, turned on one foot, and struck their breasts heavy blows with their fists.

Meanwhile the tambourines and flutes increased their din and played faster and faster.

When exhaustion and giddiness had made these people lose what few brains they had, the chief sorcerer drew several scorpions and serpents from some baskets round him, and, after showing that they were full of life, he threw them to his jesters, who fell upon them like dogs on a bone, and tore them to pieces with their teeth, if you please!

We looked down on this extraordinary spectacle from a high gallery; no doubt the colonel treated us to it to give us a good appetite for our dinner. As for myself, I turned my eyes away from these beasts, who disgusted me, and amused myself by staring at a pretty girl of thirteen or fourteen years of age, who had threaded through the crowd to get nearer to the performance.

She had the most beautiful eyes imaginable, and her hair fell on her shoulders in fine tresses; these ended in small pieces of silver, which made a tinkling sound as she moved her head gracefully about. She was dressed with more taste than most of the girls of that country; she had a kerchief of silk and gold on her head, a bodice of embroidered velvet, and short pantaloons of blue satin, showing her bare legs encircled with silver anklets. There was not a vestige of a veil over her face. Was she a Jewess or a heathen? or did she perhaps belong to those wandering tribes of unknown origin who never trouble themselves with religious prejudice?

Whilst I followed her every movement with so much interest, she had arrived at the first row of the circle where the fanatics carried on their exercises.

While she was trying to get still nearer she knocked over a narrow-bottomed basket that had not been opened. Almost at the same time the sorcerer and the child both uttered a terrible cry, and there was a great commotion in the ring, everyone recoiling with horror.

A very big snake had escaped from the basket and the little girl had trodden on it. In an instant the reptile had curled itself round her leg and I saw several drops of blood ooze from under the ring that she wore round her ankle. She fell down backwards, crying, and grinding her teeth, while her lips were covered with a white foam, and she rolled in the dust.

'Run! run, doctor!' I cried out to our surgeon-major; 'for the love of Heaven save the poor child.'

'Greenhorn!' the major replied, shrugging his shoulders. 'Do you not see that it is part of the programme? Moreover, my trade is to cut off your arms and legs. It is the business of my *confrère* down below there to cure girls who are bitten by snakes.'

In the meantime the old wizard had run up, and his first care was to possess himself of the snake.

'Djoûmane! Djoûmane!' he said to it in a tone of friendly reproach. The serpent uncoiled itself, quitted its prey, and started to crawl away. The sorcerer nimbly seized it by the end of its tail, and, holding it at arm's length, he went round the circle exhibiting the reptile, which bit and hissed without being able to stand erect.

You know that a snake held by his tail does not know in the least what to do with himself. He can only raise himself a quarter of his length, and cannot therefore bite the hand of the person who seizes him.

The next minute the serpent was put back in his basket and the lid firmly tied down. The magician then turned his attention to the little girl, who shrieked and kicked about all the time. He put a pinch of white powder, which he drew from his girdle, on the wound, and whispered an incantation in the child's ear, with unexpected results. The convulsions ceased; the little girl wiped her mouth, picked up her silk handkerchief, shook the dust off it, put it on her head again, rose up, and soon after went away.

Shortly after she came up to our gallery to collect money, and we fastened on her forehead and shoulders many fifty-centime coins.

This ended the performance, and we sat down to dinner.

I was very hungry, and was preparing to do justice to a splendid Tartary eel, when our doctor, by whom I sat, said that he recognized the snake of the preceding moment. That made it quite impossible for me to touch a mouthful.

After first making great fun of my fastidiousness the doctor annexed my share of the eel, and declared that snake tasted delicious.

'Those brutes you saw just now,' he said to me, 'are connoisseurs. They live in caverns with their serpents as the Troglodytes do; their girls are pretty – witness the little girl in blue knickerbockers. No one knows what their religion is, but they are a cunning lot, and I should like to make the acquaintance of their sheik.'

We learnt during dinner why we were to recommence the campaign. Sidi-Lala, hotly pursued by Colonel R—, was trying to reach the mountains of Morocco.

There was choice of two routes: one to the south of Tlemcen, fording the Moulaïa, at the only place not rendered inaccessible by rocks; the other by the plain, to the north of our cantonment, where we should find our colonel and the bulk of the regiment.

Our squadron was ordered to stop him at the river crossing if he attempted it, but this was scarcely likely.

You know that the Moulaïa flows between two walls of rock, and there is but a single point like a kind of very narrow breach, where horses can ford it. I knew the place well, and I did not understand why a blockhouse had not been raised there before. At all events, the colonel had every chance of encountering the enemy, and we of making a useless journey.

Before the conclusion of dinner several orderlies from Maghzen had brought despatches from Colonel R—. The enemy had made a stand, and seemed to want to fight. They had lost time. Colonel R—'s infantry had come up and routed them.

But where had they escaped to? We knew nothing at all, and must decide which of the two routes to take. I have not mentioned the last resource that could be taken, viz. to drive them into the desert, where his herds and camp would very soon die of hunger and thirst. Signals were agreed upon to warn us of the enemy's movements.

Three cannon shots from Tlemcen would tell us that Sidi-Lala was visible in the plain, and we should carry rockets with us in case we had to let them know that we needed reinforcements. In all probability the enemy could not show itself before daybreak, and our two columns had several hours' start. Night had fallen by the time we got to horse. I commanded the advance guard platoon. I felt tired and cold; I put on my cloak, turned up the collar, thrust my feet far into my stirrups, and rode quietly to my mare's long-striding walk, listening absently to quartermaster Wagner's stories about his love affairs, which unluckily ended by the flight of an infidel, who had run off with not only his heart, but a silver watch and a pair of new boots. I had heard this history before, and it appeared even longer than usual.

The moon rose as we started on our way. The sky was clear, but a light, white mist had come up since sundown, and skimmed the ground, which looked as though it were covered with down. On this white background, the moon threw long shadows, and everything took on a fantastic air. Very soon I though I saw Arab mounted sentries. As I came nearer I found they were tamarisks in flower. Presently I stopped short, for I thought I heard the cannon-shot signal. Wagner told me it was the sound of a horse galloping.

We reached the fort and the commandant made his preparations.

The place was very easy to defend, and our squadron would have been sufficient to hold back a considerable force. Complete solitude reigned on the other side of the river.

After a pretty long wait, we heard the gallop of a horse, and soon an Arab came in sight mounted on a magnificent animal and riding towards us. By his straw hat crowned with ostrich plumes, and by his embroidered saddle from which hung a *gebira* ornamented with coral and chased with gold flowers, we recognized that he was a chief; our guide told us it was Sidi-Lala himself. He was a fine-looking and well-built young man, who managed his horse admirably. He put it at a gallop, threw his long gun up in the air and caught it again, shouting at us unintelligible terms of defiance.

The days of chivalry are over, and Wagner called for a gun to *take the marabout down a peg*, as he called it; but I objected, yet, so that it should not be said that the French refused to fight at close quarters with an Arab, I asked the commandant for leave to go through the ford and cross swords with Sidi-Lala. Permission was granted me, and I was soon over the river where the enemy's chief was trotting a little way off, and taking stock of things.

Directly he saw I was across he ran upon me and aimed with his gun.

'Take care!' cried Wagner.

I am rarely afraid of a horseman's shot, and, after the tricks he had just played with it, I thought that Sidi-Lala's gun could not be in a condition to fire. And in fact he pulled the trigger when he was only three paces from me, but the gun missed fire, as I had expected. Soon he turned his horse round so rapidly that instead of planting my sabre in his breast I only caught his floating burnous.

But I pressed him close, keeping him always on my right and beating him back, whether he was willing or not, towards the steep declivities which edged the river. He tried in vain to turn aside, but I pressed him closer and closer. After several moments of frantic effort, suddenly I saw his horse rear and the rider drew rein with both hands. Without stopping to ask myself why he made such a strange movement I was on him like a shot, and I pierced him with my blade, right in the centre of his back, my horse's hoof striking his left thigh at the same time. Man and horse disappeared, and my mare and I fell after them.

Without perceiving it we had reached the edge of a precipice and were hurled over it ... While I was yet in the air – so rapid is thought! – I remembered that the body of the Arab would break my fall. I could distinctly see under me a white burnous with a large red patch on it, and I should fall on it, head or tail.

It was not such a terrible leap as I feared, thanks to the water being high; I went in over head and ears and sputtered for an instant quite stunned, and I do not know quite how I found myself standing in the middle of the tall reeds at the river's edge.

I knew nothing of what had become of Sidi-Lala and the horses. I was dripping and shivering in the mud, between two walls of rock. I took a few steps forward, hoping to find a place where the declivity was less steep; but the further I advanced the more abrupt and inaccessible it looked.

Suddenly I heard above my head the sound of horses' hoofs and the jangling of sabres against stirrups and spurs; it was evidently our squadron. I wanted to cry out, but not a sound would come out of my throat; I must in my fall have broken in my ribs.

Imagine the situation I was in. I heard the voices of our men and recognized them, and I could not call them to my aid.

'If he had let me do that,' old Wagner was saying, 'he would have lived to be made colonel.'

The sound soon lessened and died away, and I heard it no more.

Above my head hung a great branch, and I hoped by seizing this to hoist myself up above the banks of the river. With a desperate effort I sprang up, and ... crack! ... the branch twisted and escaped from my hands with a frightful hissing ... It was an enormous snake ...

I fell back into the water; the serpent glided between my legs and shot into the river, where it seemed to leave a trail of fire ...

A moment later I had regained my sang-froid, and the fire-light had not disappeared: it still trembled on the water. I saw it was the reflection from a torch. A score of steps from me a woman was filling a pitcher at the river with one hand, and in the other she held a lighted piece of resined wood. She had no idea I was there; she placed the pitcher coolly upon her head and, torch in hand, disappeared among the rushes. I followed her and found I was at the entrance to a cave.

The woman advanced very quietly and mounted a very steep incline; it was a sort of staircase cut out of the face of an immense hall. By the torchlight I saw the threshold of this great hall, which did not quite reach the level of the river; but I could not judge of its full extent. Without quite knowing what I did, I entered the slope after the young woman who carried the torch, and followed her at a distance. Now and again her light disappeared behind some cavity of the rocks, but I soon found her again.

I thought I could make out, too, the gloomy openings of great galleries leading into the principal room. It looked like a subterranean town with streets and squares. I stopped short, deeming it dangerous to venture alone into that vast labyrinth.

Suddenly one of the galleries below me was lit up brilliantly, and I saw a great number of torches, which appeared to come out of the sides of the rocks as though they formed a great procession. At the same time a monotonous chanting rose up, which recalled the singing of the Arabs as they recited their prayers. Soon I could distinguish a vast multitude advancing slowly. At their head stepped a black man, almost naked, his head covered with an enormous mass of stubbly hair. His white beard fell on his breast, and contrasted with the brown colour of his chest, which was gashed with bluish-tinted tattooing. I quickly recognized the sorcerer of the previous evening, and, soon after, saw the little girl near him who had played the part of Eurydice, with her fine eyes, and her silk pantaloons, and the embroidered handkerchief on her head.

Women and children and men of all ages followed them, all holding torches, all dressed in strange costumes of vivid colour, with trailing skirts and high caps, some made of metal, which reflected the light from the torches on all sides.

The old sorcerer stopped exactly below me, and the whole procession with him. The silence was profound. I was twenty feet above him, protected by great stones, from behind which I hoped to see everything without being perceived. At the feet of the old man I noticed a large slab of stone, almost round, with an iron ring in the centre.

He pronounced some words in a tongue unknown to me, which I felt sure was neither Arabic nor Kabylic. A rope and pulleys, hung from somewhere, fell at his feet; several of the assistants attached it to the ring, and at a given signal twenty stalwart arms all pulled at the stone simultaneously. It seemed of great weight, but they raised it and put it to one side.

I then saw what looked like the opening down a well, the water of which was at least a yard from the top. Water, did I say? I do not know what the frightful liquid was; it was covered over with an iridescent film, disturbed and broken in places, and showing a hideous black mud beneath.

The sorcerer stood in the midst of the gathered crowd, near the kerbstone which surrounded the well, his left hand on the little girl's head; with his right he made strange gestures, whilst uttering a kind of incantation.

From time to time he raised his voice as though he were calling someone. 'Djoûmane! Djoûmane!' he cried; but no one came. None the less he went on making raucous cries which did not seem to come from a human throat, and rolled his eyes and ground his teeth. The mummeries of this old rascal incensed and filled me with indignation; I felt tempted to hurl a stone at his head that I had ready to hand. When he had yelled the name of Djoumâne for the thirtieth time or more, I saw the iridescent film over the well shake, and at this sign the whole crowd flung itself back; the old man and the little girl alone remained by the side of the hole.

Suddenly there was a great bubbling of the bluish mud from the well, and out of this mud came the head of an enormous snake, of livid grey colour, with phosphorescent eyes . . .

Involuntarily I leapt backwards. I heard a little cry and the sound of some heavy body falling into the water . . .

When perhaps a tenth of a second later I again looked below, I saw the sorcerer stood alone by the well-side; the water was still bubbling, and in the middle of what remained of the iridescent scum there floated the kerchief which had covered the little girl's hair . . .

Already the stone was being moved, and it glided into its place over the aperture of the horrible gulf. Then all the torches were simultaneously extinguished, and I remained in darkness in the midst of such a profound silence that I could distinctly hear my own heart beat . . .

When I had recovered a little from this ghastly scene I wanted to quit the cavern, vowing that if I succeeded in rejoining my comrades, I would return to exterminate the abominable denizens of those quarters, men and serpents.

But the pressing question was how to find my way out. I had come, I believed, a hundred feet into the cave, keeping the rock wall on my right.

I turned half round, but saw no light which might indicate the entrance to the cavern; furthermore, it did not extend in a straight line, and, besides, I had climbed up all the time from the river's edge. I groped along the rock with my left hand, and sounded the ground with the sword which I held in my right, advancing slowly and cautiously. For a quarter of an hour or twenty minutes . . . possibly for half an hour, I walked without being able to find the way I came in.

I was seized with apprehension. Had I entered unconsciously some side gallery instead of returning the way I had at first taken? . . .

I went on all the time groping along the rock, when in place of the cold stone I felt a curtain, which yielded to my touch and let out a ray of light. Redoubling my precaution, I drew the curtain noiselessly aside and found myself in a little passage which led to a well-lighted room. The door was open, and I saw that the room was hung with silk tapestry, embroidered with flowers and gold. I noticed a Turkey carpet and the end of a velvet-covered divan. On the carpet was a narghile of silver and several perfume-burners. In short, it was an apartment sumptuously furnished in Arabian taste.

I approached with stealthy tread till I reached the door; a young woman squatted on the divan, and near her was a little low table of inlaid wood, which held a large silver-gilt tray full of cups and flagons and bouquets of flowers.

On entering this subterranean boudoir I felt quite intoxicated by the most exquisite perfume.

Everything in this retreat breathed voluptuousness; on every side I saw the glitter of gold and sumptuous materials, and varied colourings and rare flowers. The young woman did not notice me at first; she held her head down and fingered the yellow amber beads of a long necklace, absorbed in meditation. She was divinely beautiful. Her features were like those of the unfortunate child I had seen below, but more finely formed, more regular and more voluptuous. She was as black as a raven's wing, and her hair was

'Long as are the robes of a king.'

It fell over her shoulders to the divan and almost to the carpet under her feet. A gown of transparent silk in broad stripes showed her splendid arms and neck. A bodice of velvet braided with gold enclosed her figure, and her short blue satin knickerbockers revealed a marvellously tiny foot, from which hung a gold-worked Turkish slipper which she danced up and down gracefully and whimsically.

My boots creaked, and she raised her head and saw me.

Without being disturbed or showing the least surprise at seeing a stranger with a sword in his hand in her room, she clapped her hands gleefully and beckoned me to come nearer. I saluted her by placing my hand first on my heart and then on my head to show her I was acquainted with Mahomedan etiquette. She smiled, and with both hands she put aside her hair which covered the divan – this was to tell me to take a seat by her side. I thought all the spices of Araby pervaded those beautiful locks.

I modestly seated myself at the extreme end of the divan, inwardly vowing I would very soon go much nearer to her. She took a cup from the tray, and holding it by the filigree saucer, she poured out some frothed coffee, and after touching it lightly with her lips she offered it to me.

'Ah, Roumi! Roumi! . . .' she said. 'Shall we not kill the vermin, lieutenant? . . .'

At these words I opened my eyes as wide as a carriage entrance. This young lady had enormous moustaches, and was the living image of Quartermaster Wagner . . . And it was indeed Wagner who stood over me with a cup of coffee, whilst, pillowed on my horse's neck, I stared at him wildly.

'It appears we have *pioncé*, all the same, lieutenant. We are at the ford, and the coffee is boiling.'

Translated by E. M. Waller

DOSTOEVSKY

Cana of Galilee

This passage comes from Fiodor Dostoevsky's *Brothers Karamazov* first published in 1879–80. This dream takes place just after the death of the staretz Zossima, the spiritual director of Alyosha, who is the youngest of the three brothers.

It was very late according to the monastery rules, when Alyosha arrived at the hermitage; the gate-keeper let him in by a special entrance. It had struck nine o'clock – the hour of general rest after such an anxious day for them all. Alyosha opened the door timidly and went into the elder's cell, in which his coffin was now standing.

There was no one in the cell except Father Paissy, who was reading the Gospel alone over the coffin, and the young novice Porfiry, who, exhausted after the discourse of the night before and by the disturbing events of the day, slept the sound sleep of youth, lying on the floor in the next room. Though he heard Alyosha come in, Father Paissy did not even look in his direction. Alyosha turned to the right of the door, knelt in the corner and began to pray. His heart was full of obscure feelings, and not one of them stood out clearly from the rest; on the contrary, one followed another in a sort of quiet and slow rotation. But his heart was at peace and, strange to say, Alyosha was not surprised at it. Again he saw the coffin before him, that covered-up dead man, so dear to him, but there was no weeping, gnawing, poignant compassion in his heart as in the morning. As he came in, he fell down before the coffin as before a holy shrine, but his mind and heart were full of gladness. One window of the cell was open, the air was fresh and cool. 'So the smell must have become stronger, if they decided to open the window,' thought Alyosha. But even this thought of the odour of corruption, which had seemed to him so dreadful and inglorious that morning, did not any longer arouse in him the former feeling of desolation and indignation. He began praying quietly, but soon he felt himself that he was praying almost mechanically. Fragments of thoughts flashed through his mind, caught fire like stars and died down again, to be succeeded by others. But his soul was full of something that was complete, firm, and satisfying, and he was conscious of it himself. Sometimes when he began praying ardently he felt a great desire to offer up thanks and to love ... But, having begun to pray, he suddenly passed to something else, or sank into thought, forgetting his prayer and what had interrupted it. He began listening to what Father Paissy was reading, but, feeling tired, he gradually began to doze ...

'*And the third day there was a marriage in Cana of Galilee,*' read Father Paissy, '*and the mother of Jesus was there: and both Jesus was called, and his disciples, to the marriage.*'

'Marriage? What's that – marriage –' the words swept through Alyosha's mind like a whirlwind. 'There's happiness for her, too – she's gone to the feast. No, she had not taken the knife – not taken the knife – it was just a melodramatic phrase – Well – one must forgive melodramatic phrases – Yes, one must, one must – melodramatic phrases comfort the soul – without them grief would be too heavy to bear – Rakitin has walked off into the side-street. As long as Rakitin goes on thinking about his wrongs, he will always walk off into back-alleys … And the road – the road is straight, bright, shining like crystal, and the sun is at the end of it. Eh? What is he reading?'

'*And when they wanted wine, the mother of Jesus saith unto him, They have no wine,*' Alyosha heard.

'Oh yes, I nearly missed that, and I didn't want to miss it. I love that passage: it is Cana of Galilee, it's the first miracle … Oh, that miracle, oh, that lovely miracle! It was not grief but men's gladness that Jesus extolled when he worked his first miracle – he helped people to be happy … 'He who loves men, loves their gladness' – that was what the dead man had kept repeating, that was one of his main ideas … Without gladness it is impossible to live, says Mitya … Yes, Mitya … Whatever is true and beautiful is always full of forgiveness – that also he used to say …'

'*Jesus saith unto her, Woman, what have I to do with thee? Mine hour is not yet come. His mother saith unto the servants, Whatever he saith unto you, do it.*'

'Do it … The gladness, the gladness of some poor, very poor people … Yes, poor, of course, if they hadn't enough wine even at a wedding … Historians write that the people living by the lake of Gennesaret and in all those places were the poorest that can possibly be imagined. … And another great heart of the other great being, his Mother, who was there at the time, knew that he had come down only for his great and terrible sacrifice, but that his heart was open also to the simple and artless joys of ignorant human beings, ignorant but not cunning, who had warmly bidden him to their poor wedding. "Mine hour is not yet come" – he said with a gentle smile (yes, he certainly smiled gently at her) … And, surely, it was not to increase the wine at poor weddings that he came down on earth. And yet he went and did as she asked him … Oh, he is reading again:'

'*Jesus saith unto them, Fill the waterpots with water. And they filled them up to the brim.*

'*And he saith unto them, Draw out now, and bear unto the governor of the feast. And they bare it.*

'*When the ruler of the feast had tasted the water that was made wine, and knew not whence it was: (but the servants which drew the water knew;) the governor of the feast called the bridegroom.*

'*And saith unto him, Every man at the beginning doth set forth good wine; and when men have well drunk, then that which is worse: but thou hast kept the good wine until now.'*

'But what's this? What's this? Why do the walls of the room move apart? O yes, it's a wedding – the marriage – yes, of course. And here are the wedding guests, and here are the bride and groom and the merry crowd and – where is the wise ruler of the feast? But who is that? Who is it? Again the room moved apart. Who is rising there at the great table? What? Is he here too? But he's in the coffin . . . But he is here too – he got up – he saw me – he's coming here – Lord!'

Yes, he went up to him, to him, the little dried-up old man, with little wrinkles on his face, joyful and smiling gently. The coffin was no longer there and he wore the same clothes as the day before, when he was sitting with them, when his visitors had gathered in his cell. His face was uncovered, his eyes were shining. So he, too, had been invited to the feast, to the wedding at Cana of Galilee. How was that?

'Yes, my dear boy, I too am invited, invited and bidden,' a soft voice was saying over him. 'Why have you hidden yourself here, so that no one can see you? Come and join us too!'

It was his voice, the elder Zossima's voice. And who else could it be, since he called? The elder raised Alyosha by the hand, and he rose from his knees.

'Let us make merry,' the dried-up old man went on. 'Let's drink new wine, the wine of new gladness, of great gladness. See how many guests there are here? And there's the bride and groom, and there's the ruler of the feast, tasting the new wine. Why are you wondering at me? I have given an onion, and here I am. And many here have given only an onion, only one little onion . . . What are our deeds? And you, my quiet one, and you, my gentle boy, you, too, have known how to give an onion today to a woman craving salvation. Begin your work, my dear one, begin your work, my gentle one! And do you see our Sun, do you see him?'

'I am afraid – I dare not look,' Alyosha whispered.

'Do not be afraid of him. He's terrible in his majesty, awful in his eminence, but infinitely merciful. He became like one of us from love and he makes merry with us, turns water into wine, so as not to cut short the gladness of the guests. He is expecting new guests, he is calling new ones unceasingly and for ever and ever. There they are bringing the new wine. You see, they are bringing the vessels . . .'

Something glowed in Alyosha's heart, something filled it suddenly till it ached, tears of ecstasy were welling up from his soul . . . He stretched out his hands, uttered a cry and woke up . . .

Again the coffin, the open window, and the soft, solemn, measured reading of the Gospel. But Alyosha no longer listened to the reading. It was strange, he had fallen asleep on his knees, and now he was standing up, and suddenly, as though torn from his place, he walked up right to the coffin with three firm, rapid steps. He even brushed against Father Paissy with his shoulder and did not notice it. Father Paissy raised his eyes from the book for an instant, but at once looked aside, realizing that something strange had happened to the boy. Alyosha gazed at the coffin for half a minute, at the covered, motionless stretched-out dead man in it, with the icon on his chest and the cowl with the eight-cornered cross on his head. Only a moment ago he had heard his voice, and that voice was still ringing in his ears. He was still listening, he was still expecting to hear it again – but suddenly, turning away abruptly, he went out of the cell.

He did not stop on the steps, but went down rapidly. His soul, over-flowing with rapture, was craving for freedom and unlimited space. The vault of heaven, studded with softly shining stars, stretched wide and vast over him. From the zenith to the horizon the Milky Way stretched its two arms dimly across the sky. The fresh, motionless, still night enfolded the earth. The white towers and golden domes of the cathedral gleamed against the sapphire sky. The gorgeous autumn flowers in the beds near the house went to sleep till morning. The silence of the earth seemed to merge into the silence of the heavens, the mystery of the earth came in contact with the mystery of the stars. . . . Alyosha stood, gazed, and suddenly he threw himself down flat upon the earth.

He did not know why he was embracing it. He could not have explained to himself why he longed so irresistibly to kiss it, to kiss it all, but he kissed it weeping, sobbing and drenching it with his tears, and vowed frenziedly to love it, to love it for ever and ever. 'Water the earth with the tears of your gladness and love those tears', it rang in his soul. What was the weeping over? Oh, he was weeping in his rapture even over those stars which were shining for him from the abyss of space and 'he was not ashamed of that ecstasy'. It was as though the threads from all those innumerable worlds of God met all at once in his soul, and it was trembling all over 'as it came in contact with other worlds'. He wanted to forgive everyone and for everything, and to beg forgiveness – oh! not for himself, but for all men, for all and for everything, 'and others are begging for me', it echoed in his soul again. But with every moment he felt clearly and almost palpably that something firm and immovable, like the firmament itself, was entering his soul. A sort of idea was gaining an ascendancy over his mind – and that for the rest of his life, for ever and ever. He had fallen upon the earth a weak youth, but he rose from it a resolute fighter for the rest of his life, and he realized and felt it suddenly, at the very moment of his rapture. And never, never for the rest of his life could Alyosha forget that moment. 'Someone visited my soul at that hour!' he used to say afterwards with firm faith in his words . . .

Three days later he left the monastery in accordance with the words of his late elder, who had bidden him 'sojourn in the world'.

Translated by D. Magarshack

BROWNING

Bad Dreams I

'Bad Dreams I' and 'Bad Dreams III' (see page 284) were published in the volume *Asolando* on 12 December 1889. Robert Browning died on the same day.

> Last night I saw you in my sleep:
>   And how your charm of face was changed!
> I asked 'Some love, some faith you keep?'
>   You answered 'Faith gone, love estranged.'
>
> Whereat I woke – a twofold bliss:
>   Waking was one, but next there came
> This other: 'Though I felt, for this,
>   My heart break, I loved on the same.'

FRAZER

The Snake-Bite

This is a passage from James George Frazer's *The Golden Bough*; it is taken from the first part of the work, 'Magic Art and the Evolution of Kingship'. *The Golden Bough* was first published between 1890 and 1915.

When a Cherokee has dreamed of being stung by a snake, he is treated just in the same way as if he had really been stung; otherwise the place would swell and ulcerate in the usual manner, though perhaps years might pass before it did so. It is the ghost of a snake that has bitten him in sleep. One night a Huron Indian dreamed that he had been taken and burned alive by his hereditary foes the Iroquois. Next morning a council was held on the affair, and the following measures were adopted to save the man's life. Twelve or thirteen fires were kindled in the large hut where they usually burned their prisoners to death. Every man seized a flaming brand and applied it to the naked body of the dreamer, who shrieked with pain. Thrice he ran round the hut, escaping from one fire only to fall into another. As each man thrust his blazing torch at the sufferer he said, 'Courage, my brother, it is thus that we have pity on you.' At last he was allowed to escape. Passing out of the hut he caught up a dog which was held ready for the purpose, and throwing it over his shoulder carried it through the wigwams as a sacred offering to the war-god, praying him to accept the animal instead of himself. Afterwards the dog was killed, roasted, and eaten, exactly as the Indians were wont to roast and eat their captives.

The Wandering Soul

This is a further passage from James George Frazer's *The Golden Bough*, taken from the second part, 'Taboo and the Perils of the Soul'.

The soul of a sleeper is supposed to wander away from his body and actually to visit the places, to see the persons, and to perform the acts of which he dreams. For example, when an Indian of Brazil or Guiana wakes up from a sound sleep, he is firmly convinced that his soul has really been away hunting, fishing, felling trees, or whatever else he has dreamed of doing, while all the time his body has been lying motionless in his hammock. A whole Bororo village has been thrown into a panic and nearly deserted because somebody had dreamed that he saw enemies stealthily approaching it. A Macusi Indian in weak health, who dreamed that his employer had made him haul the canoe up a series of difficult cataracts, bitterly reproached his master next morning for his want of consideration in thus making a poor invalid go out and toil during the night. The Indians of the Gran Chaco are often heard to relate the most incredible stories as things which they have themselves seen and heard; hence strangers who do not know them intimately say in their haste that these Indians are liars. In point of fact the Indians are firmly convinced of the truth of what they relate; for these wonderful adventures are simply their dreams, which they do not distinguish from waking realities.

BIERCE

An Occurrence at Owl Creek Bridge

This short story by Ambrose Bierce was first published in *Tales of Soldiers and Civilians* in 1892.

A man stood upon a railroad bridge in northern Alabama, looking down into the swift water twenty feet below. The man's hands were behind his back, the wrists bound with a cord. A rope closely encircled his neck. It was attached to a stout cross-timber above his head and the slack fell to the level of his knees. Some loose boards laid upon the sleepers supporting the metals of the railway supplied a footing for him and his executioners – two private soldiers of the Federal army, directed by a sergeant who in civil life may have been a deputy sheriff. At a short remove upon the same temporary platform was an officer in the uniform of his rank, armed. He was a captain. A sentinel at each end of the bridge stood with his rifle in the position known as 'support,' that is to say, vertical in front of the left shoulder, the hammer resting on the forearm thrown straight across the chest – a formal and unnatural position, enforcing an erect carriage of the body. It did not appear to be the duty of these two men to know what was occurring at the centre of the bridge; they merely blockaded the two ends of the foot planking that traversed it.

Beyond one of the sentinels nobody was in sight; the railroad ran straight away into a forest for a hundred yards, then, curving, was lost to view. Doubtless there was an outpost farther along. The other bank of the stream was open ground – a gentle acclivity topped with a stockade of vertical tree trunks, loop-holed for rifles, with a single embrasure through which protruded the muzzle of a brass cannon commanding the bridge. Midway of the slope between bridge and fort were the spectators – a single company of infantry in line, at 'parade rest', the butts of the rifles on the ground, the barrels inclining slightly backwards against the right shoulder, the hands crossed upon the stock. A lieutenant stood at the right of the line, the point of his sword upon the ground, his left hand resting upon his right. Excepting the group of four at the centre of the bridge, not a man moved. The company faced the bridge, staring stonily, motionless. The sentinels, facing the banks of the stream, might have been statues to adorn the bridge. The captain stood with folded arms, silent, observing the work of his subordinates, but making no sign. Death is a dignitary who when he comes announced is to be received with formal manifestations of respect, even by those most familiar with him. In the code of military etiquette silence and fixity are forms of deference.

The man who was engaged in being hanged was apparently about thirty-five years of age. He was a civilian, if one might judge from his habit, which was that of a planter. His features were good – a straight nose, firm mouth, broad forehead, from which his long, dark hair was combed straight back, falling behind his ears to the collar of his well-fitting frock coat. He wore a moustache and pointed beard, but no whiskers; his eyes were large and dark grey, and had a kindly expression which one would hardly have expected in one whose neck was in the hemp. Evidently this was no vulgar assassin. The liberal military code makes provision for hanging many kinds of persons, and gentlemen are not excluded.

The preparations being complete, the two private soldiers stepped aside and each drew away the plank upon which he had been standing. The sergeant turned to the captain, saluted and placed himself immediately behind that officer, who in turn moved apart one pace. These movements left the condemned man and the sergeant standing on the two ends of the same plank, which spanned three of the cross-ties of the bridge. The end upon which the civilian stood almost, but not quite, reached a fourth. This plank had been held in place by the weight of the captain; it was now held by that of the sergeant. At a signal from the former the latter would step aside, the plank would tilt and the condemned man go down between two ties. The arrangement commended itself to his judgement as simple and effective. His face had not been covered nor his eyes bandaged. He looked a moment at his 'unsteadfast footing', then let his gaze wander to the swirling water of the stream racing madly beneath his feet. A piece of dancing driftwood caught his attention and his eyes followed it down the current. How slowly it appeared to move! What a sluggish stream!

He closed his eyes in order to fix his last thoughts upon his wife and children. The water, touched to gold by the early sun, the brooding mists under the banks at some distance down the stream, the fort, the soldiers, the piece of drift – all had distracted him. And now he became conscious of a new disturbance. Striking through the thought of his dear ones was a sound which he could neither ignore nor understand, a sharp, distinct, metallic percussion like the stroke of a blacksmith's hammer upon the anvil; it had the same ringing quality. He wondered what it was, and whether immeasurably distant or nearby – it seemed both. Its recurrence was regular, but as slow as the tolling of a death knell. He awaited each stroke with impatience and – he knew not why – apprehension. The intervals of silence grew progressively longer; the delays became maddening. With their greater infrequency the sounds increased in strength and sharpness. They hurt his ear like the thrust of a knife; he feared he would shriek. What he heard was the ticking of his watch.

He unclosed his eyes and saw again the water below him. 'If I could free my hands,' he thought, 'I might throw off the noose and spring into the stream. By diving I could evade the bullets and, swimming vigorously, reach the bank, take to the woods and get away home. My home, thank God, is as yet outside their lines; my wife and little ones are still beyond the invader's farthest advance.'

As these thoughts, which have here to be set down in words, were flashed into the doomed man's brain rather than evolved from it the captain nodded to the sergeant. The sergeant stepped aside.

II

Peyton Farquhar was a well-to-do planter, of an old and highly respected Alabama family. Being a slave owner and like other slave owners a politician he was naturally an original secessionist and ardently devoted to the Southern cause. Circumstances of an imperious nature, which it is unnecessary to relate here, had prevented him from taking service with the gallant army that had fought the disastrous campaigns ending with the fall of Corinth, and he chafed under the inglorious restraint, longing for the release of his energies, the larger life of the soldier, the opportunity for distinction. That opportunity, he felt, would come, as it comes to all in war time. Meanwhile he did what he could. No service was too humble for him to perform in aid of the South, no adventure too perilous for him to undertake if consistent with the character of a civilian who was at heart a soldier, and who in good faith and without too much qualification assented to at least a part of the frankly villainous dictum that all is fair in love and war.

One evening while Farquhar and his wife were sitting on a rustic bench near the entrance to his grounds, a grey-clad soldier rode up to the gate and asked for a drink of water. Mrs Farquhar was only too happy to serve him with her own white hands. While she was fetching the water her husband approached the dusty horseman and inquired eagerly for news from the front.

'The Yanks are repairing the railroads,' said the man, 'and are getting ready for another advance. They have reached the Owl Creek bridge, put it in order and built a stockade on the north bank. The commandant has issued an order, which is posted everywhere, declaring that any civilian caught interfering with the railroad, its bridges, tunnels or trains will be summarily hanged. I saw the order.'

'How far is it to the Owl Creek bridge?' Farquhar asked.

'About thirty miles.'

'Is there no force on this side the creek?'

'Only a picket post half a mile out, on the railroad, and a single sentinel at this end of the bridge.'

'Suppose a man – a civilian and student of hanging – should elude the picket post and perhaps get the better of the sentinel,' said Farquhar, smiling, 'what could he accomplish?'

The soldier reflected. 'I was there a month ago,' he replied. 'I observed that the flood of last winter had lodged a great quantity of driftwood against the wooden pier at this end of the bridge. It is now dry and would burn like tow.'

The lady had now brought the water, which the soldier drank. He thanked her ceremoniously, bowed to her husband and rode away. An hour later, after nightfall, he repassed the plantation, going northward in the direction from which he had come. He was a Federal scout.

III

As Peyton Farquhar fell straight downward through the bridge he lost consciousness and was as one already dead. From this state he was awakened – ages later, it seemed to him – by the pain of a sharp pressure upon his throat, followed by a sense of suffocation. Keen, poignant agonies seemed to shoot from his neck downward through every fibre of his body and limbs. These pains appeared to flash along well-defined lines of ramification and to beat with an inconceivably rapid periodicity. They seemed like streams of pulsating fire heating him to an intolerable temperature. As to his head, he was conscious of nothing but a feeling of fulness – of congestion. These sensations were unaccompanied by thought. The intellectual part of his nature was already effaced; he had power only to feel, and feeling was torment. He was conscious of motion. Encompassed in a luminous cloud, of which he was now merely the fiery heart, without material substance, he swung through unthinkable arcs of oscillation, like a vast pendulum. Then all at once, with terrible suddenness, the light about him shot upward with the noise of a loud plash; a frightful roaring was in his ears, and all was cold and dark. The power of thought was restored; he knew that the rope had broken and he had fallen into the stream. There was no additional strangulation; the noose about his neck was already suffocating him and kept the water from his lungs. To die of hanging at the bottom of a river! – the idea seemed to him ludicrous. He opened his eyes in the darkness and saw above him a gleam of light, but how distant, how inaccessible! He was still sinking, for the light became fainter and fainter until it was a mere glimmer. Then it began to grow and brighten, and he knew that he was rising toward the surface – knew it with reluctance, for he was now very comfortable. 'To be hanged and drowned,' he thought, 'that is not so bad; but I do not wish to be shot. No; I will not be shot; that is not fair.'

He was not conscious of an effort, but a sharp pain in his wrist apprised him that he was trying to free his hands. He gave the struggle his attention, as an idler might observe the feat of a juggler, without interest in the outcome. What splendid effort! – what magnificent, what superhuman strength! Ah, that was a fine endeavour! Bravo! The cord fell away; his arms parted and floated upward, the hands dimly seen on each side in the growing light. He watched them with a new interest as first one and then the other pounced upon the noose at his neck. They tore it away and thrust it fiercely aside, its undulations resembling those of a water-snake. 'Put it back, put it back!' He thought he shouted these words to his hands, for the undoing of the noose had been succeeded by the direst pang that he had yet experienced. His neck ached horribly; his brain was on fire; his heart, which had been fluttering faintly, gave a great leap, trying to force itself out at his mouth. His whole body was racked and wrenched with an insupportable anguish! But his disobedient hands gave no heed to the command. They beat the water vigorously with quick, downward strokes, forcing him to the surface. He felt his head emerge; his eyes were blinded by the sunlight; his chest expanded convulsively, and with a supreme and crowning agony his lungs engulfed a great draught of air, which instantly he expelled in a shriek!

He was now in full possession of his physical senses. They were, indeed, preternaturally keen and alert. Something in the awful disturbance of his organic system had so exalted and refined them that they made record of things never before perceived. He felt the ripples upon his face and heard their separate sounds as they struck. He looked at the forest on the bank of the stream, saw the individual trees, the leaves and the veining of each leaf – saw the very insects upon them: the locusts, the brilliant-bodied flies, the grey spiders stretching their webs from twig to twig. He noted the prismatic colours in all the dewdrops upon a million blades of grass. The humming of the gnats that danced above the eddies of the stream, the beating of the dragon-flies' wings, the strokes of the water-spiders' legs, like oars which had lifted their boat – all these made audible music. A fish slid along beneath his eyes and he heard the rush of its body parting the water.

He had come to the surface facing down the stream; in a moment the visible world seemed to wheel slowly round, himself the pivotal point, and he saw the bridge, the fort, the soldiers upon the bridge, the captain, the sergeant, the two privates, his executioners. They were in silhouette against the blue sky. They shouted and gesticulated, pointing at him. The captain had drawn his pistol, but did not fire; the others were unarmed. Their movements were grotesque and horrible, their forms gigantic.

Suddenly he heard a sharp report and something struck the water smartly within a few inches of his head, spattering his face with spray. He heard a second report, and saw one of the sentinels with his rifle at his shoulder, a light cloud of blue smoke rising from the muzzle. The man in the water saw the eye of the man on the bridge gazing into his own through the sights of the rifle. He observed that it was a grey eye and remembered having read that grey eyes were keenest, and that all famous marksmen had them. Nevertheless, this one had missed.

A counter-swirl had caught Farquhar and turned him half round; he was again looking into the forest on the bank opposite the fort. The sound of a clear, high voice in a monotonous singsong now rang out behind him and came across the water with a distinctness that pierced and subdued all other sounds, even the beating of the ripples in his ears. Although no soldier, he had frequented camps enough to know the dread significance of that deliberate, drawling, aspirated chant; the lieutenant on shore was taking a part in the morning's work. How coldly and pitilessly – with what an even, calm inton-ation, presaging, and enforcing tranquillity in the men – with what accurately measured intervals fell those cruel words:

'Attention, company! . . . Shoulder arms! . . . Ready! . . . Aim! . . . Fire!'

Farquhar dived – dived as deeply as he could. The water roared in his ears like the voice of Niagara, yet he heard the dulled thunder of the volley and, rising again toward the surface, met shining bits of metal, singularly flattened, oscillating slowly downward. Some of them touched him on the face and hands, then fell away, continuing their descent. One lodged between his collar and neck; it was uncomfortably warm and he snatched it out.

As he rose to the surface, gasping for breath, he saw that he had been a long time under water; he was perceptibly farther down stream – nearer to safety. The soldiers had almost finished reloading; the metal ramrods flashed all at once in the sunshine as they were drawn from the barrels, turned in the air, and thrust into their sockets. The two sentinels fired again, independently and ineffectually.

The hunted man saw all this over his shoulder; he was now swimming vigorously with the current. His brain was an energetic as his arms and legs; he thought with the rapidity of lightning.

'The officer,' he reasoned, 'will not make that martinet's error a second time. It is as easy to dodge a volley as a single shot. He has probably already given the command to fire at will. God help me, I cannot dodge them all!'

An appalling plash within two yards of him was followed by a loud, rushing sound, *diminuendo*, which seemed to travel back through the air to the fort and died in an explosion which stirred the very river to its deeps! A rising sheet of water curved over him, fell down upon him, blinded him, strangled him! The cannon had taken a hand in the game. As he shook his head free from the commotion of the smitten water he heard the deflected shot humming through the air ahead, and in an instant it was cracking and smashing the branches in the forest beyond.

'They will not do that again,' he thought; 'the next time they will use a charge of grape. I must keep my eye upon the gun; the smoke will apprise me – the report arrives too late; it lags behind the missile. That is a good gun.'

Suddenly he felt himself whirled round and round – spinning like a top. The water, the banks, the forests, the now distant bridge, fort and men – all were commingled and blurred. Objects were represented by their colours only; circular horizontal streaks of colour – that was all he saw. He had been caught in a vortex and was being whirled on with a velocity of advance and gyration that made him giddy and sick. In a few moments he was flung upon the gravel at the foot of the left bank of the stream – the southern bank – and behind a projecting point which concealed him from his enemies. The sudden arrest of his motion, the abrasion of one of his hands on the gravel, restored him, and he wept with delight. He dug his fingers into the sand, threw it over himself in handfuls and audibly blessed it. It looked like diamonds, rubies, emeralds; he could think of nothing beautiful which it did not resemble. The trees upon the bank were giant garden plants; he noted a definite order in their arrangement, inhaled the fragrance of their blooms. A strange, roseate light shone through the spaces among their trunks and the wind made in their branches the music of æolian harps. He had no wish to perfect his escape – was content to remain in that enchanting spot until retaken.

A whiz and rattle of grapeshot among the branches high above his head roused him from his dream. The baffled cannoneer had fired him a random farewell. He sprang to his feet, rushed up the sloping bank, and plunged into the forest.

All that day he travelled, laying his course by the rounding sun. The forest seemed interminable; nowhere did he discover a break in it, not even a woodman's road. He had not known that he lived in so wild a region. There was something uncanny in the revelation.

By nightfall he was fatigued, footsore, famishing. The thought of his wife and children urged him on. At last he found a road which led him in what he knew to be the right direction. It was as wide and straight as a city street, yet it seemed untravelled. No fields bordered it, no dwelling anywhere. Not so much as the barking of a dog suggested human habitation. The black bodies of the trees formed a straight wall on both sides, terminating on the horizon in a point, like a diagram in a lesson in perspective. Overhead, as he looked up through this rift in the wood, shone great golden stars looking unfamiliar and grouped in strange constellations. He was sure they were arranged in some order which had a secret and malign significance. The wood on either side was full of singular noises, among which – once, twice, and again – he distinctly heard whispers in an unknown tongue.

His neck was in pain and lifting his hand to it he found it horribly swollen. He knew that it had a circle of black where the rope had bruised it. His eyes felt congested; he could no longer close them. His tongue was swollen with thirst; he relieved its fever by thrusting it forward between his teeth into the cold air. How softly the turf had carpeted the untravelled avenue – he could no longer feel the roadway beneath his feet!

Doubtless, despite his suffering, he had fallen asleep while walking, for now he sees another scene – perhaps he has merely recovered from a delirium. He stands at the gate of his own home. All is as he left it, and all bright and beautiful in the morning sunshine. He must have travelled the entire night. As he pushes open the gate and passes up the wide white walk, he sees a flutter of female garments; his wife, looking fresh and cool and sweet, steps down from the veranda to meet him. At the bottom of the steps she stands waiting, with a smile of ineffable joy, an attitude of matchless grace and dignity. Ah, how beautiful she is! He springs forward with extended arms. As he is about to clasp her he feels a stunning blow upon the back of the neck; a blinding white light blazes all about him with a sound like the shock of a cannon – then all is darkness and silence!

Peyton Farquhar was dead; his body, with a broken neck, swung gently from side to side beneath the timbers of the Owl Creek bridge.

LYNKEUS

The Rational Dreamer

This dream appears in the collection *Phantasien eines Realisten* ('Fantasies of a Realist') by Joseph Popper Lynkaeus, first published in 1899. Lynkeus is a pseudonym taken from a character in Goethe's *Faust*, where he is the watchman who, blinded by Helen's beauty, forgets to tell his master of her arrival. Lynkeus was also the pseudonym used by another writer, Max Wittenberg, a lawyer and economist. Our author's real name was Joseph Popper, and according to Carl Popper's *Autobiography*, he was a distant relative of his. A scientist by training, Lynkeus' interests ranged from the atom theory ('Physical principles of the electrical power conduction') to social philosophy ('The duty of universal feeding as a solution to the social problem').

This is the story of the only person who ever lived who could claim never to have dreamt an irrational dream. The man in question, a bachelor who lived a very modest existence, did nothing to distinguish himself in the world; his memory would sink without trace, and none would ever know of his existence, if I did not here recount the story of his remarkable peculiarity, never to have dreamt an irrational dream. It would be an eternal shame if mankind were never to learn that such a thing is possible, and that such a person once really existed.

This man, for example, never once dreamt (as the rest of us so often do) of being in several places at once, of someone long dead still alive, or the like. To be sure, he dreamt as others sometimes do that he could fly, or that he encountered creatures the like of which are not to be found in daylight; but in his case these things were not in such contradiction with everyday life that you could say for sure that they were impossible or patently absurd.

Furthermore, this man was not a little proud of this capacity of his. He felt himself at the same time so blessed in the possession of it that he held it responsible for his neverfailing cheerfulness. Now in this he was mistaken, for his cheerfulness and conviction of blessedness stemmed from a deeper source which, as we shall see, was the same source that fed his remarkable capacity never to dream an irrational dream.

Often he used to speak of the matter to friends. 'My whole being', he would say on such occasions, a light beaming in his eyes, 'my whole existence is untarnished. I am not on a par with the great geniuses of the world, but I believe I can claim never to have been besmirched with any kind of irr-ationality, either awake or asleep. My waking thoughts and my dreams are two branches of one common stem, supporting each other in the most delightful manner. I am whole and undivided; others are split into two, and their separate halves, their waking and dreaming selves, wage a more or less continual warfare with each other. Others must confine what they count as their life to their waking hours, in all about fourteen or at the most sixteen hours of the day, whereas I can include in mine the whole twenty-four. And they are all such peaceful hours! None of my sleeping hours is a blotting-out of waking existence, or vice-versa. But what is most particularly pleasant is the miraculous variety of the existence I enjoy, for I conduct my waking life as a loosely structured discourse and my dreaming life as a tightly controlled one . . .'

As one of the party did not immediately grasp these last remarks he continued on: 'I mean: I live in prose and in poetry. Waking and dreaming often convey the same message to me, but they use different forms or colours or whatever you care to name it. Now you must surely know what I mean. Oh, what a happy state it is to be in!'

One night, cheerful as ever, the man went to bed. 'I shall be back tomorrow morning', he said to his servant; 'you can expect me about six in the morning.' The tone was rather as if he were someone setting out on a journey. Thereupon he pounded his bolster into the right shape, settled himself down, and thought: 'Now I'm really curious to find out what new experience tonight will bring!'

A few moments later he found himself on quite unfamiliar terrain. He stood in the middle of newly ploughed farmland; furthermore, the landscape was quite flat, with a few low hills and friendly villages to be seen only on the far horizon. Over the whole scene the sun was just rising.

There stood beside him a lovely creature with a somewhat sickly-sweet countenance and as it were rather tiresome long blond hair flowing down over his shoulders, from whence two great white wings jutted out. At once the dreamer recognized him as the same man who had accompanied him the night before on a long journey and pointed out all kinds of marvellous sights on the way. At the sight of the man he cried out: 'Oh, it's my guardian angel again!'

This travelling companion had laid great store yesterday by the marvellous sights, and had wanted them to make a big impression on the man and provoke lively expressions of astonishment. But none of the things he showed him could summon forth the enthusiastic outbursts that the guardian angel expected and desired. Every time he showed him something meant to be quite extraordinary he would look quizzically at the man the moment afterwards to try to determine whether he was unmistakably aroused to enthusiasm, and as this was never the case he would try to lend him a hand and ask: 'What do you think of that now? Or that? Or this other?'

But he always got the same answer: 'fine', and immediately thereupon, 'it reminds me of such-and-such.' This made the guardian angel angry, and a heated dispute arose between the two. The guardian angel reproached the man with ingratitude. Whereupon the latter replied in a rather impatient manner: 'I've never clapped eyes on such an importunate tour guide before! Did you make all these beautiful things, then? You're only showing me them! I'm indeed grateful to you for that; but the way I look at things and the opinions I form is my business, not yours!' At which the guardian angel retreated with a very pained expression and resolved to return the next night and renew the assault with augmented forces. And that was precisely the reason that the guardian angel was with the man again on this night as he stood in the middle of the ploughed field at sunrise. 'I find these furrows very deep, much deeper than furrows usually are,' said the dreamer. 'So they are!' said the guardian angel. 'But let's just see now, what this is coming along.' And as he said that a bird came hopping up. It was not a bird of very beautiful or brilliant feather, but rather of a uniform grey colour, shaped like a skylark, but of enormous dimensions; it was in fact as big as the largest species of eagle.

The bird came nearer and nearer and finally settled in one of the furrows.

'It seems like an enormous lark', said the man to his guide, 'that is, if this bird can sing.' The guardian angel laughed at these words, and in the same instant the creature started to run a few steps, executing them in a rather awkward manner that made it seem a real old pedant of a bird; then it flew aloft, higher and higher, and sang down from on high a song of such beauty and power that it seemed as if the whole landscape were bathed in music. The whole earth, the valleys and distant mountains trembled with joy as the giant lark's piercing song resounded from the firmament; and the guardian angel, perceiving that the man was enraptured, seized the moment to say: 'Now then? Have you ever seen such a union of beauty and power, of tenderness and greatness?'

Whereupon the man answered: 'Fine! fine! but remember there's Johann Sebastian Bach as well . . .' At that point he woke up and carried on talking as he sat up straight in bed and felt about him for his clothes: 'and maybe he did even better.'

Having transacted the business in this manner, he set off that morning on his usual round of activity and carried on through the day in the cheerfulest possible mood.

Translated by M. Hollington

JENSEN

Gradiva

W. H. Jensen was a very prolific writer, publishing an average of two books, mainly novels, every year from 1866 till his death in 1911. *Gradiva*, from which this passage is taken, came out in 1903. The reputation of this novel comes from the essay Freud devoted to it in 1906.

Soon after his pedestrian investigations had yielded him this knowledge, he had, one night, a dream which caused him great anguish of mind. In it he was in old Pompeii, and on the twenty-fourth of August of the year 79, which witnessed the eruption of Vesuvius. The heavens held the doomed city wrapped in a black mantle of smoke; only here and there the flaring masses of flame from the crater made distinguishable, through a rift, something steeped in blood-red light; all the inhabitants, either individually or in confused crowd, stunned out of their senses by the unusual horror, sought safety in flight; the pebbles and the rain of ashes fell down on Norbert also, but, after the strange manner of dreams, they did not hurt him, and in the same way, he smelt the deadly sulphur fumes of the air without having his breathing impeded by them.

As he stood thus at the edge of the Forum near the Jupiter temple, he suddenly saw Gradiva a short distance in front of him. Until then no thought of her presence there had moved him, but now suddenly it seemed natural to him, as she was, of course, a Pompeiian girl, that she was living in her native city and, without his having any suspicion of it, was his contemporary. He recognized her at first glance; the stone model of her was splendidly striking in every detail, even to her gait; involuntarily he designated this as *lente festinans*. So with buoyant composure and the calm unmindfulness of her surroundings peculiar to her, she walked across the flagstones of the Forum to the Temple of Apollo. She seemed not to notice the impending fate of the city, but to be given up to her thoughts; on that account he also forgot the frightful occurrence, for at least a few moments, and because of a feeling that the living reality would quickly disappear from him again, he tried to impress it accurately on his mind. Then, however, he became suddenly aware that if she did not quickly save herself, she must perish in the general destruction, and violent fear forced from him a cry of warning. She heard it, too, for her head turned toward him so that her face now appeared for a moment in full view, yet with an utterly uncomprehending expression; and, without paying any more attention to him, she continued in the same direction as before. At the same time, her face became paler as if it were changing to white marble; she stepped up to the portico of the Temple, and then, between the pillars, she sat down on a step and slowly laid her head upon it.

Now the pebbles were falling in such masses that they condensed into a completely opaque curtain; hastening quickly after her, however, he found his way to the place where she had disappeared from his view, and there she lay, protected by the projecting roof, stretched out on the broad step, as if for sleep, but no longer breathing, apparently stifled by the sulphur fumes. From Vesuvius the red glow flared over her countenance, which, with closed eyes, was exactly like that of a beautiful statue. No fear nor distortion was apparent, but a strange equanimity, calmly submitting to the inevitable, was manifest in her features. Yet they quickly became more indistinct as the wind drove to the place the rain of ashes, which spread over them, first like a grey gauze veil, then extinguished the last glimpse of her face, and soon, like a Northern winter snowfall, buried the whole figure under a smooth cover. Outside, the pillars of the Temple of Apollo rose, now, however, only half of them, for the grey fall of ashes heaped itself likewise against them.

When Norbert Hanold awoke, he still heard the confused cries of the Pompeiians who were seeking safety, and the dully resounding boom of the surf of the turbulent sea. Then he came to his senses; the sun cast a golden gleam of light across his bed; it was an April morning and outside sounded the various noises of the city, cries of venders, and the rumbling of vehicles. Yet the dream picture still stood most distinctly in every detail before his open eyes, and some time was necessary before he could get rid of a feeling that he had really been present at the destruction on the bay of Naples, that night nearly two thousand years ago. While he was dressing, he first became gradually free from it, yet he did not succeed, even by the use of critical thought, in breaking away from the idea that Gradiva had lived in Pompeii and had been buried there in 79. Rather, the former conjecture had now become to him an established certainty, and now the second also was added. With woeful feeling he now viewed in his living-room the old relief which had assumed new significance for him. It was, in a way, a tombstone by which the artist had preserved for posterity the likeness of the girl who had so early departed this life. Yet if one looked at her with enlightened understanding, the expression of her whole being left no doubt that, on that fateful night, she had actually lain down to die with just such calm as the dream had showed. An old proverb says that the darlings of the gods are taken from the earth in the full vigour of youth.

Without having yet put on a collar, in morning array, with slippers on his feet, Norbert leaned on the open window and gazed out. The spring, which had finally arrived in the north also, was without, but announced itself in the great quarry of the city only by the blue sky and the soft air, yet a foreboding of it reached the senses, and awoke in remote, sunny places a desire for leaf-green, fragrance and bird song; a breath of it came as far as this place; the market women on the street had their baskets adorned with a few, bright wild flowers, and at an open window, a canary in a cage warbled his song. Norbert felt sorry for the poor fellow for, beneath the clear tone, in spite of the joyful note, he heard the longing for freedom and the open.

Yet the thoughts of the young archæologist dallied but briefly there, for something else had crowded into them. Not until then had he become aware that in the dream he had not noticed exactly whether the living Gradiva had really walked as the piece of sculputre represented her, and as the women of today, at any rate, did not walk. That was remarkable because it was the basis of his scientific interest in the relief; on the other hand, it could be explained by his excitement over the danger to her life. He tried, in vain, however, to recall her gait.

Then suddenly something like a thrill passed through him; in the first moment he could not say whence. But then he realized; down in the street, with her back toward him, a female, from figure and dress undoubtedly a young lady, was walking along with easy, elastic step. Her dress, which reached only to her ankles, she held lifted a little in her left hand, and he saw that in walking the sole of her slender foot, as it followed, rose for a moment vertically on the tips of the toes. It appeared so, but the distance and the fact that he was looking down did not admit of certainty.

Quickly Norbert Hanold was in the street without yet knowing exactly how he had come there. He had, like a boy sliding down a railing, flown like lightning down the steps, and was running down among the carriages, carts and people. The latter directed looks of wonder at him, and from several lips came laughing, half mocking exclamations. He was unaware that these referred to him; his glance was seeking the young lady and he thought that he distinguished her dress a few dozen steps ahead of him, but only the upper part; of the lower half, and of her feet, he could perceive nothing, for they were concealed by the crowd thronging on the sidewalk.

Now an old, comfortable, vegetable woman stretched her hand toward his sleeve, stopped him and said, half grinning, 'Say, my dear, you probably drank a little too much last night, and are you looking for your bed here in the street? You would do better to go home and look at yourself in the mirror.'

A burst of laughter from those nearby proved it true that he had shown himself in garb not suited to public appearance, and brought him now to realization that he had heedlessly run from his room. That surprised him because he insisted upon conventionality of attire and, forsaking his project, he quickly returned home, apparently, however, with his mind still somewhat confused by the dream and dazed by illusion, for he had perceived that, at the laughter and exclamation, the young lady had turned her head a moment, and he thought he had seen not the face of a stranger, but that of Gradiva looking down upon him.

Translated by H. M. Downey

GROUSSAC

Among Dreams

This is a passage from an essay by Paul Groussac, a Frenchman who lived in Argentina, which was published in 1904 in the volume *El viaje intelectual*.

I was living in Salta, twenty-three years ago, in the house of a tradesman from Tucumán. Being young and close friends, we used to sleep in the same room, so that we could carry on talking between our beds, although there were many unoccupied bedrooms in our colonial mansion, which could have lodged Noah's family with ease. We almost always retired together; for, when by some great chance the programme of evening activities was not shared, the first to return to the fold would wait for the other in the neighbouring 'Lavin's Billiard Saloon'. Since by that time I had the very bad habit of reading in bed, I would keep vigil for an hour or two over my friend's sleep. Now he, who never broke a plate when awake, once asleep became a *mauvais coucheur*. At his most peaceful, he would snore like a German top until waking up frightened by his own trumpeting. But this was not his worst excess. My companion would dream out loud, suffering cruel nightmares which had me with my . . . heart in my mouth, – if one may thus describe what the anxiety produced in me. When the drawbacks of sharing the same room made themselves felt, it was very late to do anything about them. First of all fondness deterred me; then curiosity, or rather, a growing interest in the cerebral drama which was being played out before my eyes, or if you like before my ears and with the curtain down, and in the playing of which I shifted unconsciously from being a silent witness to becoming an expert collaborator . . .

My friend in Salta was not strictly speaking a sleepwalker, though on two or three occasions I saw him sit up in his sleep and begin to dress; but his troubled dreams occurred almost daily. He suffered from a chronic stomach complaint; and, of course, when he had occasion to dine the nightmare never failed. It would arrive with the first phase of sleep, displaying almost always the same external shape, as if it corresponded to an almost invariable, internal drama, which I had asked him to tell me at least twenty times. Sparing the details, it was almost always a quarrel with men wearing *ponchos*, labourers or craftsmen (my friend owned a sugar mill), who insulted him; the sleeping figure would grow indignant, uttering threats which announced to me the inevitable catastrophe; there quickly followed a brief howl, accompanied by prolonged groans: he had received a stab wound in the epigastrium and felt he was dying . . .

My poor companion related the scene to me with moving lucidity and colouring. As I have said, this did not vary except for certain secondary features. After a short while, I began to know it off by heart as well as the story of *Bluebeard.* What surprised me at first, was the fantastic pace of the vicissitudes which, in the story, appeared to last hours, and in reality happened one after another and crowded together within a few seconds. By now acquainted with the incident, and almost always awake at that moment, I frequently managed to ward off the attack, by changing the position of the dreamer. On other occasions, I would intervene in the scene, pretending to lend assistance to the assaulted person, placing myself by his side, and pointing out to him his enemies in flight, or stretched out on the ground by our heroic offensive. This suggestion was generally effective, and since, in addition to being beneficent, it was entertaining for me, I began to use it lavishly, seeking new effects.

When the patient awoke immediately upon my intervention, he would tell of exploits that involved me that left me speechless: my four actual shouts were a brief and coarse canvas which the dream process transformed into a fantastic epic poem. However, if it happened that, once the crisis was over and the digestion assisted, my friend should enter without waking into normal sleep, the next morning he would not retain the slightest recollection of his aborted nightmare.

Translated by J. Lyons

HUCH

The Falling Child

For Friedrich Huch, see page 81.

I am together with a number of other people on a stone veranda. A woman with two small children stands quite near me against the balustrade. She has her back turned to it, so she can't see the children standing on the balustrade. One of them is trying to push the other off, but this child is standing quite motionless as before. I try to decide whether it's my business to rush up to them; but I stay quite quietly in my place, curious as to what will happen. The first child gives another push, and the second falls slowly downward, head first. I hear the sound of cracking on a stone floor. A fearful commotion follows; then everything is still. I don't dare to look down, and remain motionless and apart. Someone tells me there's a kind of pulpy substance below, with a monstrous child's head; it has goggle eyes and a broad froggy mouth. I hear the sound of brooms at work, and when I finally look down I see a grey stone floor and a carmine-red puddle of sweepings.

Translated by M. Hollington

MACHADO

Alvargonzález

This dream is taken from *La tierra de Alvargonzález*, a story which Antonio Machado first published in the Parisian periodical *Mundial* in January 1912.

By now Alvargonzález's brow was wrinkled, and the blue down of his face was turning silver about the chin. His shoulders were still robust and his head, that only sported white at the temples, was held high.

One autumn morning he left his house alone: he did not set out, as on other occasions, in the midst of his elegant greyhounds, his shotgun slung across his back. He carried none of the accessories of the hunter nor was he thinking of hunting. A long way he walked beneath the yellow poplars beside the river, he cut through the oak grove, and, next to a spring that was shaded by a huge elm, he halted exhausted. He wiped the sweat from his brow, took a few sips of water and lay down on the ground.

And, all alone, Alvargonzález spoke with God, saying: 'God, my lord, who filled with plenty the lands that my hands work, to whom I owe the bread on my table, the woman in my bed and through whom the sons that I engendered grew sturdy, through whom my sheepfolds are overflowing with white ewes and the trees in my orchard grow heavy with fruit and my beehives have honey, I want you to know, my God, that I am conscious of how much you have given me before you take it away.'

He gradually fell asleep as he was praying in this manner, for the shade of the branches and the water that gushed from the stone seemed to be telling him: 'Sleep and rest.'

And Alvargonzález slept: but his spirit was to have no rest because dreams cast storms over man's sleep.

And Alvargonzález dreamt that a voice was speaking to him, and he could see, like Jacob, a ladder of light that descended from the heavens to earth. Perhaps it was the band of light that filtered through the branches of the elm.

It is difficult to interpret dreams that untie the bundle of our designs so as to mix them with memories and fears. Many believe they can foretell what is to come by studying dreams. They are almost always mistaken, but occasionally they succeed. With bad dreams, that grieve the heart of the sleeper, it is not difficult to guess correctly. These dreams are memories of the past, disarranged and woven together by the clumsy and trembling hand of an invisible character: fear.

Alvargonzález was dreaming of his childhood. The merry fire in the hearth beneath the broad, black cowl of the kitchen, and around his parents and brothers. The knotty hands of the old man caressed the golden candle. The mother was running the beads of a black rosary through her fingers. On the smoke-stained wall hung the shining axe with which the old man made firewood from the oak branches.

Alvargonzález continued dreaming, and he was in the prime of his youth. A summer evening and a green meadow beyond the walls of an orchard. In the shade and on the grass, as the sun was dropping, tingeing the tops of the chestnut trees with orange light. Alvargonzález was raising the wineskin and the red wine was pouring into his mouth, refreshing his dry throat. Around him was the Peribáñez family: the parents and their three beautiful daughters. From the branches of the orchard and from the meadow grass a harmony arose of gold and crystal, as though the stars were singing on earth before appearing scattered in the silent sky. Evening was falling, and over the dark pine grove, golden and breathless, appeared the full moon, the beautiful moon of love, above the peaceful countryside.

As though the fairies that spin and weave our dreams had placed on their distaffs a bundle of black wool, Alvargonzález's dreaming suddenly darkened, and a golden door was flung open, wounding the sleeper's heart.

And a dimly-lit hollow appeared, and at the far end, illuminated by a faint radiance, the deserted hearth without logs. On the wall the burnished and shining axe hung from a hook.

The dream opened out into the brightness of day. Three children are playing at the door of the house. The wife watches over them, sews and smiles from time to time. Between the oldest hops a black, shiny, steely-eyed crow.

'Children, what are you doing?' she asks them.

The children look at each other and say nothing.

'Go up into the hills, my sons, and before nightfall, bring me an armful of chopped wood.'

The three children set off. The youngest, who is trailing behind, looks homeward and his mother calls him. The child returns towards the house and the brothers continue on their way towards the oak grove.

And now the hearth again, the extinguished and deserted hearth, and the shining axe was hanging from the wall.

Alvargonzález's older boys return from the hills in the evening, loaded with twigs. The mother lights the oil-lamp and the eldest son throws splinters and twigs over the oak log, and tries to make a fire in the hearth; the firewood crackles, and the big pieces barely catch light before they go out. The flame will not come alive in the home of Alvargonzález. By the light of the oil-lamp shines the axe on the wall, and this time it appears to be dripping blood.

'Father, the fire will not start: the wood is damp.'

The second son comes to help and also strives to get the fire going. But the fire does not wish to spring forth.

The youngest throws a handful of twigs on the hearth, and a red flame lights up the kitchen. The mother smiles, and Alvargonzález takes his son into his arms and sits him on his knee, to the right of the fire. 'Although you were born last, you are the first in my heart and the best of my lineage; because your hands make fire.'

His brothers, pale as death, move off into the corners of the dream. In the eldest's right hand shines the iron axe.

By the side of the spring slept Alvargonzález, when the evening star shone in the blue, and an emormous moon stained with purple rose above the lugubrious countryside. The water that gushed from the stone seemed to be telling an old and sad story: the story of the crime in the countryside.

The sons of Alvargonzález were walking stealthily, and they saw their father asleep next to the spring. The shadows that stretched the evening reached the sleeping figure before the murderers. Alvargonzález's brow had a dark groove between the eyebrows, like the mark of a blade on an oak trunk. Alvargonzález was dreaming that his sons were coming to kill him, and as he opened his eyes he saw that what he was dreaming was true.

A terrible death the wicked sons gave to the farmer by the spring. An axe-blow on the neck and four stab wounds to the chest put an end to the dream of Alvargonzález. The axe that had been handed down from their

grandparents and which had hewn so much wood for the hearth, sliced
through the sturdy neck that age had not yet bent, and the knife with which
the good father cut the dark bread which he distributed to his family seated
round the table, had cloven the most noble heart in those lands. Because
Alvargonzález was good to those in his house, but considerable too was his
charity in the home of the poor. He would be mourned as a father by all those
who at some time knocked at his door, or some time saw him on the threshold
of their own.

The sons of Alvargonzález do not know what they have done. They drag
their dead father towards a gully through which runs a river that feeds into the
Duero. It is a sombre valley full of ferns, beech and pine groves.

And they carry him to the Black Lagoon, that has no bottom, and there they
throw him in with a rock tied to his feet. The lagoon is surrounded by a mighty
wall of grey and greenish rocks, where eagles and vultures nest. The people of
the mountains in those times did not dare approach the lagoon not even on
bright days. Travellers, who visit those places, have led them to lose their fear.

The sons of Alvargonzález headed back through the valley amid the
towering pines and the decaying beeches. They could not hear the water that
rang out in the depths of the gully. Two wolves approached as they saw them
pass by. The wolves fled in terror. They went to cross the river, and the river
adopted another course, and they crossed it without getting wet. They were
making their way through the woods in order to reach their village in the depth
of the night, and the pines, the rocks and the ferns everywhere left a path for
them as though they were fleeing from the murderers. They passed close to
the spring again, and the spring, that was telling its old story, fell silent as they
went by, and waited until they were in the distance before resuming its tale.

In this manner the wicked sons inherited the property of the good farmer
who one autumn morning left his house and never did or could return. The
following day his cloak was found close to the spring and a trail of blood in the
direction of the gully. Nobody dared to accuse the sons of Alvargonzález of the
crime, since the peasant fears people with power, and no one ventured to
probe the lagoon, because it would have been pointless. The lagoon never
returns what it swallows. A pedlar who was wandering in those parts was
arrested and hanged in Soria, two months later, because the sons of Alvargonzález handed him over to the authorities, and with bought witnesses
managed to have him condemned.

The evil of those men is like the Black Lagoon, that has no bottom.

The mother died within a few months. Those who saw her dead one
morning, say that her face was hidden beneath her cold and stiff hands.

Translated by J. Lyons

The Spinners

This is the first poem of Machado's sequence 'Parabolas', published first in 1912, then included in the section 'Campos de Castilla' of his *Poesias completas* of 1917–18.

> Do you know the unseen
> Spinners of dreams?
> They are two: Hope, still green
> and grim Fear.
>
> They wage who shall spin
> more and more flax,
> she, with her golden hank,
> he, with his black.
>
> With the thread they give us
> we weave, when we weave at all.

Translated by I. Waters

God

This is an extract from a poem by Machado belonging to the sequence 'Proverbios y cantares' in the collection 'Campos de Castilla', published as a section of his *Poesias completas* in 1917–18.

> Last night I dreamed of God
> and in my dream I was speaking;
> and I dreamt he heard what I said.
> After that I dreamt I was dreaming.

Translated by I. Waters

DESNOS

Dreams

This dream by Robert Desnos was published in the Dadaist review, *Littérature*, in 1922. Although Breton's *Manifeste du Surréalisme* was only published in 1924, the first surrealist work, *Champs magnétiques*, by André Breton and Philippe Soupault, had already appeared in *Littérature* in 1919. 1922 is the year of the first sleeping séances organized by Breton during which he wrote down the words uttered by his friends who were sleeping under hypnosis. Desnos, though sceptical, took part in these séances, and was apparently the most sensitive of the group. He had been interested in dreams since his adolescence. His first recorded dream goes back to the time when he was sixteen.

August 1922

I am lying down and can see myself as I am in real life. André Breton walks into the room, a copy of the *Journal Officiel* in his hand. 'My dear friend,' he says, 'I have the pleasure of informing you of your promotion to the rank of senior quartermaster sergeant', then he turns around and leaves.

Translated by J. Romney

PIRANDELLO

The Reality of the Dream

This short story belongs to the collection *Novelle per un anno*, where Luigi Pirandello hoped to include 365 short stories, one for each day of the year, though he fell short of that aim. They were published in several volumes between 1922 and 1938.

Whenever he spoke, what he said seemed to be as much beyond question as his good looks. It was almost as though, just as there could be no doubt about the fact that he was very handsome, in the whole of his appearance, by the same token he could never be opposed in anything.

And he understood nothing, really nothing, of what went on inside her!

On hearing the self-confident way in which he justified some of his instinctive reactions, some of his possibly ill-founded dislikes and some of his feelings, she was seized by the temptation to round on him, scratching, slapping and biting.

All the more so because, for all his cool assurance and pride in being a handsome young man, at certain other times, when he turned to her because he needed her, his composure faltered. He then became timid, humble and pleading in a way far different from what she would have desired at such times. So she had yet another reason for growing irritated, to the extent that while she was naturally inclined to yield, she became harsh and reluctant. And the memory of each act of love, poisoned at its sweetest by that irritation, turned bitter within her.

He maintained that the awkwardness and embarrassment which she claimed to feel whenever there were men present were an obsession on her part.

'You feel like that, my dear, because you think you do', he said over and over again.

'I think I feel like that, my dear, because I really do!', she retorted. 'It's not an obsession! That's how I feel. That's how it is. And I have to thank my father for it, and the marvellous way he brought me up! Do you want to dispute that as well?'

She hoped that at least he wouldn't do that. He had had direct experience of it during their engagement. In the four months before they were married, right there in that dull little town of theirs, he had been forbidden not just to touch her hand but even to whisper a couple of endearments to her.

More jealous than a tiger, her father had instilled into her a real terror of men from the time she was a child. He had never allowed a real man worthy of the name into the house. All the windows were kept shut, and on the very rare occasions when he had taken her out he had forced her to walk with her head bowed like a nun, staring at the ground as if she were counting the pebbles on the path.

So why was it so surprising if now, in the presence of a man, she felt embarrassed and couldn't look anyone in the eye, incapable of speaking or moving?

It was true that for six years now she had been free from the nightmare of her father's ferocious jealousy. She saw people at home and in the street. And yet . . . It certainly wasn't that childish terror she had once felt, but she did feel embarrassed, that's all. However hard she tried, she simply couldn't meet anyone else's gaze. She became tongue-tied, and all of a sudden, without knowing why, she flushed bright red. So anyone might think that all kinds of dreadful things were passing through her mind, when she really wasn't thinking about anything at all. In fact, she found herself destined to make a bad impression and to seem foolish and inept, and she didn't want to. It was no good insisting. Thanks to her father, she had to live in seclusion, seeing no one, so that at least she wasn't vexed by that utterly stupid and ridiculous embarrassment which was beyond her control.

His best friends, those he was fondest of and would have liked to grace his home, making up the little social circle he had hoped to gather around him when he had married six years previously, had already drifted away one by one. Of course! They used to come to his house and ask:

'Is your wife at home?'

His wife had fled as soon as the bell rang. He would pretend to go and call her, and then really go. He would stand before her with a sad expression on his face and his hands outstretched, but he knew all the time that it was useless and that his wife would silence him with her eyes blazing with anger and shout 'idiot' at him through clenched teeth. He would turn round and go back to his friend, thinking God alone knows what but outwardly smiling, to announce:

'Please forgive her. She doesn't feel well. She's resting.'

This happened once, twice and a third time. In the end, understandably, they grew tired of it. How could he blame them?

There were still two or three left, more faithful or braver than the rest. There was one in particular, a man of real learning, whose hatred for pedantry might even have been a little ostentatious. He was a very clever journalist. In short, a dear friend.

On occasion, these few remaining friends had actually met his wife, either because she was caught by surprise or because, in a good moment, she had given in to his pleading. And for heaven's sake she certainly hadn't made a bad impression! Quite the contrary!

'Because when you aren't thinking, you see . . . when you let yourself go . . . you're lively . . .'

'Thank you!'

'You're intelligent . . .'

'Thank you!'

'And you're not at all awkward, I promise you! Look, why should I be pleased if you make a bad impression? You express yourself frankly sometimes . . . well of course, you're quite charming, really you are! Your whole being glows, and far from staring at the floor your eyes sparkle my dear . . . And . . . some of the things you say are quite daring . . . Are you surprised? I don't say unseemly . . . but daring for a woman. You speak fluently, naturally, with animation in fact, honestly you do!'

His praises redoubled as he noted that, while protesting that she didn't believe a word of it, deep down she was pleased, and she blushed, not knowing whether to smile or frown.

'That's how it is, really. Believe me, all you have is an obsession . . .'

He should at least have been warned by the fact that she didn't protest at his use for the hundredth time of that word 'obsession', and by the obvious pleasure with which she accepted his praise of her frank, natural and even daring way of speaking.

When and to whom had she spoken like that?

A few days ago, to that 'dear' friend, the man who, naturally, she disliked most of all. Certainly she admitted that she was unfair in some of her dislikes, and that she particularly disliked those men in whose presence she felt most embarrassed.

But now her pleasure at having been able to express herself to him with apparent effrontery came from the fact that he (no doubt in order secretly to provoke her), in the course of a long discussion on the eternal subject of the honesty of women, had dared to maintain that excessive modesty is a sure sign of a sensual nature. So you shouldn't trust a woman who blushes at nothing and who daren't raise her eyes as she thinks that everything represents an attack on her modesty, and every glance and word is a snare for her virtue. This means that such a woman is forever haunted by the presence of tempta- tion. She goes in constant fear of it. The mere thought of it troubles her. Isn't that true? While other women whose senses are not easily aroused have none of this reserve and can speak quite openly about some very intimate physical matters, not thinking that there can be anything wrong in . . . for example, a blouse with rather a low neck, or a lacy stocking of the kind you can see through, or a skirt which allows you to see just a little bit above the knee.

Of course, all this didn't mean that in order to avoid being taken for sensual a woman should act immodestly and shamelessly and show what shouldn't be shown. That would be contradictory. He was talking about modesty. And for him modesty was the vengeance exacted by insincerity. Not that it wasn't sincere in itself. It was, on the contrary, very sincere, but as an expression of sensuality. A woman who wants to deny that she is sensual by pointing to the modest blushes on her cheeks is insincere. And such a woman can be insincere even without wishing it, even without knowing it. Because nothing is more complex than sincerity. All of us pretend quite spontaneously, not so much for the benefit of others as for our own. We all believe of ourselves what we want to believe, and we see ourselves not as we really are but according to the idealized picture which we have of ourselves. So it can happen that a woman, who might well be very sensual without even knowing it, will sincerely base her belief in her own virtue and in her contempt and horror of sensuality on the mere fact that she blushes at nothing. So blushing at nothing, which is in fact the most genuine possible expression of her real sensuality, is inter- preted by her as proof of her imagined virtue. And being so interpreted, it naturally becomes insincere.

'Come now, dear lady,' that dear friend had concluded a few evenings previously, 'women by their nature (given a few exceptions, of course) live entirely by their senses. You simply have to know how to approach them, arouse them and dominate them. Those who are too modest don't even need arousing. As soon as you touch them, their passions immediately kindle and blaze of their own accord.'

Not for one moment had she doubted that the whole of this speech was about her. As soon as the friend had left, she turned fiercely on her husband, who had just smiled like a fool during the whole long discussion and agreed.

'He insulted me in every possible way, and as for you, instead of defending me you smiled and agreed, letting him believe that what he said was true, because you, as my husband, were in a position to know . . .'

'Know what?' he had exclaimed, astounded. 'You're out of your mind . . . Me? Agree that you're sensual? What on earth are you saying? He was talking about women in general, so what has it got to do with you? If he had suspected even for a moment that you might think he was talking about you, he would have kept his mouth shut! And then, look here, how could he think that when you didn't behave in the least like the prudish sort of woman he was talking about? You didn't blush at all, and you defended your point of view vigorously and warmly. And I smiled because I was pleased to see it, because I thought it proved what I have kept on and on saying to you, in other words, when you don't think about it you aren't in the least awkward and embarrassed, and all this supposed embarrassment of yours is nothing but an obsession. So how does the kind of modesty he was talking about come into it?'

She hadn't known how to reply to her husband's vindication of himself. She had retired darkly into herself to brood on why she had felt so deeply offended by that speech. No, no and no again, what she felt wasn't modesty, that disgusting modesty he was talking about. It was embarrassment, pure, sheer embarrassment. But no doubt someone as malicious as he might imagine that her embarrassment was really modesty, and so take her for . . . for the kind of woman he was describing!

However, if she hadn't seemed embarrassed, as her husband maintained, she still felt embarrassment. Sometimes she could conquer it, forcing herself not to show it, but she still felt it nevertheless. But if her husband refused to believe that she was embarrassed, that meant that he noticed nothing at all. So that he wouldn't have realized either if her embarrassment was really something else, in other words that modesty his friend had been talking about.

Was it possible? Oh, God, no! The mere thought of it filled her with horror and disgust.

And yet . . .

The revelation came in the dream.

That dream began as a challenge, as a trial to which that hateful man challenged her as a result of his discussion with her three evenings before.

She had to prove to him that nothing could make her blush, that he could do anything he liked to her and she would be neither upset nor in any way perturbed.

And now, coolly and audaciously, he began the trial. First he ran one hand lightly over her face. At the touch of that hand she made a violent effort to hide the shiver which ran throughout her body, doing her utmost not to lower her eyelids and to keep her eyes still and expressionless, with just a little smile on her lips. And now his fingers moved towards her mouth. Gently, he turned down her lower lip, and there, on the moist underside, he placed a long, warm, drowning kiss of infinite sweetness. She stiffened and then went limp in her effort to dominate the trembling, the quivering of her body. And then he began calmly to uncover her breast, and . . . Was anything wrong? No, no, nothing at all. But . . . oh, God, no . . . treacherously, his caress lingered . . . no, no . . . it was too much . . . and . . . Defeated, lost without at first conceding it she began to yield, and not because of him but because of the agonizing weakness of her own body. And in the end . . .

Ah! She woke with a convulsive start, routed, trembling, full of horror and loathing.

She peered at her husband sleeping next to her all unaware. And the shame within her was at once transformed into hatred for him, as though he were the cause of that disgrace and dishonour which had left her with such feelings of pleasure and abhorrence. He was to blame, for stupidly insisting on inviting those friends home.

Well then, she had betrayed him in a dream. And what she felt was not remorse but anger for herself, because she had given way, and bitter enmity for him, as in six years of marriage he had never ever been able to make her feel what she had felt just now in a dream, with another man.

Ah, women live entirely by their senses. Was it true, then?

No it was not! The fault was his, her husband's, for refusing to believe in her embarrassment and forcing her to control herself, to violate her own nature, exposing her to those trials and challenges which had given rise to the dream. How could she withstand such a trial? It was her husband who had wanted it. And this was his punishment. She would have revelled in it if she had been able to savour her malicious delight in his punishment without feeling shame on her own behalf.

And now?

Things came to a head on the afternoon of the following day, after she had remained obstinately deaf to her husband's repeated questions about why she was behaving like that and what had happened to her.

It came about when the usual visit of that dear friend was announced.

Hearing that voice in the hall, she started, jerked out of her silence. Her eyes blazed with a furious anger. She flew at her husband, shaking from head to foot, and ordered him not to receive that man.

'No! I won't have it! Send him away!'

At first he was appalled rather than surprised by her furious outburst. He could not understand why she felt such repugnance. On the contrary, because of what he himself had said after that discussion he already believed that she had begun to warm towards his friend, and he reacted with fierce resentment to her absurd and imperious command.

'You're mad, or you want to drive me mad! Must I really lose all my friends because of your idiotic behaviour?'

And shaking her off because she was clinging to him he ordered the maid to show the gentleman in.

She sprang for refuge in the bedroom next door, throwing him a look of hatred and contempt before she disappeared behind the door curtain.

She slumped down into the armchair, as though her legs had suddenly been cut from under her. But her blood tingled in her veins, and in that state of desperate abandon her whole being rebelled when through the closed door she heard her husband give a hearty welcome to the man she had betrayed him with, last night, in the dream. And, oh, God, that man's voice . . . the touch of his hands . . .

All of a sudden, as she huddled in the chair sinking her clawed fingers into her arms and breast, she gave a shriek and fell to the ground, seized by a terrifying fit of hysterics, by a real onset of madness.

The two men rushed into the room. For a moment, they stood paralysed at the sight of her writhing on the floor like a snake, whimpering and howling. Her husband tried to lift her, and his friend rushed to help him. If only he had stayed where he was! At the touch of those hands her whole body, unconsciously giving itself up to the yearning of her senses, began to throb with pleasure. And before her husband's very eyes she seized hold of that man, begging him frantically and with dreadful urgency for the frenzied caresses of the dream.

Horror-struck, her husband tore her away from his friend's breast. She cried out, struggled and then fell back almost lifeless and was put to bed.

The two men looked at each other in terror, not knowing what to think or to say.

His friend's grief-stricken bewilderment was such clear proof of his innocence that her husband could not suspect him for a moment. He invited him to leave the bedroom. He told him that since that morning his wife had been upset and in an unusually nervous state. He accompanied him to the door, asking his forgiveness for sending him away because of that painful and unexpected incident. Then he rushed back to her room.

He found her already conscious on the bed, curled up like a wild beast with her eyes glazed. All her limbs trembled and jerked violently, as though from cold, and from time to time she started.

As he came to stand over her, sternly, to ask her to explain what had happened, she pushed him back with both arms, and through clenched teeth, and full of the desire to wound, she flung in his face the confession of her betrayal. Smiling feverishly and malevolently and drawing back with her hands wide she said:

'In the dream! . . . In the dream! . . .'

And she didn't spare him a single detail. Not the kiss inside her lip nor the caress on her breast . . . in the treacherous conviction that while, like her, he would realize that the betrayal was real, and so irrevocable and beyond repair, because it really had happened and had been savoured to the full, he could not blame her for it. He might beat that body of hers, and torture and lacerate it, but it would still be there, and had given itself to another man in the unconsciousness of the dream. The fact of that betrayal did not exist for that other man. But it had happened. And for her, in her body which had enjoyed such pleasure, it remained as a living reality.

Whose fault was it? And what could he do to her?

Translated by J. Dashwood

GRAVES

The Shout

This is an extract from Robert Graves's short story *The Shout*, first published in 1929. Jerzy Skolimovsky freely adapted it for the screen.

Richard awoke one morning saying to Rachel: 'But what an unusual dream.'

'Tell me, my dear,' she said, 'and hurry, because I want to tell you mine.'

'I was having a conversation,' he said, 'with a person (or persons, because he changed his appearance so often) of great intelligence, and I can clearly remember the argument. Yet this is the first time I have ever been able to remember any argument that came to me in sleep. Usually my dreams are so different from waking that I can only describe them if I say: "It is as though I were living and thinking as a tree, or a bell, or middle C, or a five-pound note; as though I had never been human." Life there is sometimes rich for me and sometimes poor, but I repeat, in every case so different, that if I were to say: "I had a conversation," or "I was in love," or "I heard music," or "I was angry," it would be as far from the fact as if I tried to explain a problem of philosophy, as Rabelais's Panurge did to Thaumast, merely by grimacing with my eyes and lips.'

'It is much the same with me,' she said. 'I think that when I am asleep I become, perhaps, a stone with all the natural appetites and convictions of a stone. "Senseless as a stone" is a proverb, but there may be more sense in a stone, more sensibility, more sensitivity, more sentiment, more sensibleness, than in many men and women. And no less sensuality,' she added thoughtfully.

It was Sunday morning so that they could lie in bed, their arms about each other, without troubling about the time; and they were childless so breakfast could wait. He told her that in his dream he was walking in the sand-hills with this person or persons, who said to him: 'These sand-hills are a part neither of the sea before us nor of the grass links behind us, and are not related to the mountains beyond the links. They are of themselves. A man walking on the sand-hills soon knows this by the tang in the air, and if he were to refrain from eating and drinking, from sleeping and speaking, from thinking and desiring, he could continue among them for ever without change. There is no life and no death in the sand-hills. Anything might happen in the sand-hills.'

Rachel said that this was nonsense, and asked: 'But what was the argument? Hurry up!'

He said it was about the whereabouts of the soul, but that now she had put it out of his head by hurrying him. All that he remembered was that the man was first a Japanese, then an Italian and finally a kangaroo.

In return she eagerly told her dream, gabbling over the words. 'I was walking in the sand-hills; there were rabbits there, too; how does that tally with what he said of life and death? I saw the man and you walking arm-in-arm towards me, and I ran from you both and I noticed that he had a black silk handkerchief; he ran after me and my shoe-buckle came off and I could not wait to pick it up. I left it lying, and he stooped and put it into his pocket.'

'How do you know that it was the same man?' he asked.

'Because,' she said, laughing, 'he had a black face and wore a blue coat like that picture of Captain Cook. And because it was in the sand-hills.'

He said, kissing her neck: 'We not only live together and talk together and sleep together, but it seems we now even dream together.'

So they laughed.

Then he got up and brought her breakfast.

At about half-past-eleven, she said: 'Go out now for a walk, my dear, and bring home something for me to think about: and be back in time for dinner at one o'clock.'

It was a hot morning in the middle of May, and he went out through the wood and struck the coast-road, which after half a mile led into Lampton.

He went a hundred yards along the coast-road, but then turned off and went across the links: thinking of Rachel and watching the blue butterflies and looking at the heath-roses and thyme, and thinking of her again, and how strange it was that they could be so near to each other; and then taking a pinch of gorse-flower and smelling it, and considering the smell and thinking, 'if she should die what would become of me?' and taking a slate from the low wall and skimming it across the pond and thinking, 'I am a clumsy fellow to be her husband'; and walking towards the sand-hills, and then edging away again, perhaps half in fear of meeting the person of their dream, and at last making a half-circle towards the old church beyond Lampton, at the foot of the mountain.

The morning service was over and the people were out by the cromlechs behind the church, walking in twos and threes, as the custom was, on the smooth turf. The Squire was talking in a loud voice about King Charles, the Martyr: 'A great man, a very great man, but betrayed by those he loved best,' and the Doctor was arguing about organ-music with the Rector. There was a group of children playing ball. 'Throw it here, Elsie. No, to me, Elsie, Elsie, Elsie.' Then the Rector came up and pocketed the ball and said that it was Sunday; they should have remembered. When he was gone they made faces after him.

Presently a stranger came up and asked permission to sit down beside Richard: they began to talk. The stranger had been to the church service and wished to discuss the sermon. The text had been the immortality of the soul: the last of a series of sermons that had begun at Easter. He said that he could not grant the preacher's premiss that *the soul is continually resident in the body*. Why should this be so? What duty did the soul perform in the daily routine task of the body? The soul was neither the brain, nor the lungs, nor the stomach, nor the heart, nor the mind, nor the imagination. Surely it was a thing apart? Was it not indeed less likely to be resident in the body than outside the body? He had no proof one way or the other, but he would say: Birth and Death are so odd a mystery that the principle of life may well lie outside the body which is the visible evidence of living. 'We cannot,' he said, 'even tell to a nicety what are the moments of birth and death. Why, in Japan, where I have travelled, they reckon a man to be already one year old when he is born; and lately in Italy a dead man – but come and walk on the sand-hills and let me tell you my conclusions. I find it easier to talk when I am walking.'

Richard was frightened to hear this, and to see the man wipe his forehead with a black silk handkerchief. He stuttered out something. At this moment the children, who had crept up behind the cromlech, suddenly, at an agreed signal, shouted loud in the ears of the two men; and stood laughing. The stranger was startled into anger; he opened his mouth as if he were about to curse them, and bared his teeth to the gums. Three of the children screamed and ran off. But the one whom they called Elsie fell down in her fright and lay sobbing. The doctor, who was near, tried to comfort her. 'He has a face like a devil,' they heard the child say.

The stranger smiled good-naturedly: 'And a Devil I was not so very long ago. That was in Northern Australia, where I lived with the black fellows for twenty years. "Devil" is the nearest English word for the position that they gave me in their tribe; and they also gave me an eighteenth-century British naval uniform to wear as my ceremonial dress. Come and walk with me in the sand-hills and let me tell you the whole story. I have a passion for walking in the sand-hills: that is why I came to this town . . . My name is Charles.'

Richard said: 'Thank you, but I must hurry home to my dinner.'

'Nonsense,' said Charles, 'dinner can wait. Or if you wish, I can come to dinner with you. By the way, I have had nothing to eat since Friday. I am without money.'

Richard felt uneasy. He was afraid of Charles, and did not wish to bring him home to dinner because of the dream and the sand-hills and the handkerchief: yet on the other hand the man was intelligent and quiet and decently dressed and had eaten nothing since Friday; if Rachel knew that he had refused him a meal she would renew her taunts. When Rachel was out of sorts, her favourite complaint was that he was over-careful about money; though when she was at peace with him, she owned that he was the most generous man she knew, and that she did not mean what she said; when she was angry with him again, out came the taunt of stinginess: 'Tenpence-halfpenny,' she would say, 'tenpence-halfpenny and threepence of that in stamps'; his ears would burn and he would want to hit her. So he said now: 'By all means come along to dinner, but that little girl is still sobbing for fear of you. You ought to do something about it.'

Charles beckoned her to him and said a single soft word; it was an Australian magic word, he afterwards told Richard, meaning *Milk*: immediately Elsie was comforted and came to sit on Charles's knee and played with the buttons of his waistcoat for a while until Charles sent her away.

'You have strange powers, Mr Charles,' Richard said.

Charles answered: 'I am fond of children, but the shout startled me; I am pleased that I did not do what, for a moment, I was tempted to do.'

'What was that?' asked Richard.

'I might have shouted myself,' said Charles.

'Why,' said Richard, 'they would have liked that better. It would have been a great game for them. They probably expected it of you.'

'If I had shouted,' said Charles, 'my shout would have either killed them outright or sent them mad. Probably it would have killed them, for they were standing close.'

Richard smiled a little foolishly. He did not know whether or not he was expected to laugh, for Charles spoke so gravely and carefully. So he said: 'Indeed, what sort of shout would that be? Let me hear you shout.'

'It is not only children who would be hurt by my shout,' Charles said. 'Men can be sent raving mad by it; the strongest, even, would be flung to the ground. It is a magic shout that I learned from the chief devil of the Northern Territory. I took eighteen years to perfect it, and yet I have used it , in all, no more than five times.'

Richard was so confused in his mind with the dream and the handkerchief and the word spoken to Elsie that he did not know what to say, so he muttered: 'I'll give you fifty pounds now to clear the cromlechs with a shout.'

'I see that you do not believe me,' Charles said. 'Perhaps you have never before heard of the terror-shout?'

Richard considered and said: 'Well, I have read of the hero-shout which the ancient Irish warriors used, that would drive armies backwards; and did not Hector, the Trojan, have a terrible shout? And there were sudden shouts in the woods of Greece. They were ascribed to the god Pan and would infect men with a madness of fear; from this legend indeed the word "panic" has come into the English language. And I remember another shout in the *Mabinogion*, in the story of Lludd and Llevelys. It was a shriek that was heard on every May-Eve and went through all hearts and so scared them that the men lost their hue and their strength and the women their children, and the youths and maidens their senses, and the animals and trees, the earth and the waters were left barren. But it was caused by a dragon.'

'It must have been a British magician of the dragon clan,' said Charles. 'I belonged to the Kangaroos. Yes, that tallies. The effect is not exactly given, but near enough.'

They reached the house at one o'clock, and Rachel was at the door, the dinner ready. 'Rachel,' said Richard, 'here is Mr Charles to dinner; Mr Charles is a great traveller.'

Rachel passed her hand over her eyes as if to dispel a cloud, but it may have been the sudden sunlight. Charles took her hand and kissed it, which surprised her. Rachel was graceful, small, with eyes unusually blue for the blackness of her hair, delicate in her movements, and with a voice rather low-pitched; she had a freakish sense of humour.

Of Charles it would be difficult to say one thing or another: he was of middle age, and tall; his hair grey; his face never still for a moment; his eyes large and bright, sometimes yellow, sometimes brown, sometimes grey; his voice changed its tone and accent with the subject, his hands were brown and hairy at the back, his nails well cared for. Of Richard it is enough to say that he was a musician, not a strong man but a lucky one. Luck was his strength.

After dinner Charles and Richard washed the dishes together, and Richard suddenly asked Charles if he would let him hear the shout; for he thought that he could not have peace of mind until he had heard it. So horrible a thing was, surely, worse to think about than to hear: for now he believed in the shout.

Charles stopped washing up; mop in hand. 'As you wish,' said he, 'but I have warned you what a shout it is. And if I shout it must be in a lonely place where nobody else can hear; and I shall not shout in the first degree, the degree which kills certainly, but in the second, which terrifies only, and when you want me to stop put your hands to your ears.'

'Agreed,' said Richard.

'I have never yet shouted to satisfy an idle curiosity,' said Charles, 'but only when in danger of my life from enemies, black or white, and once when I was alone in the desert without food or drink. Then I was forced to shout, for food.'

Richard thought: 'Well, at least I am a lucky man, and my luck will be good enough even for this.'

'I am not afraid,' he told Charles.

'We will walk out on the sand-hills tomorrow early,' Charles said, 'when nobody is stirring; and I will shout. You say you are not afraid.'

But Richard was very much afraid, and what made his fear worse was that somehow he could not talk to Rachel and tell her of it: he knew that if he told her she would either forbid him to go, or she would come with him. If she forbade him to go, the fear of the shout and the sense of cowardice would hang over him ever afterwards; but if she came with him, either the shout would be nothing and she would have a new taunt for his credulity and Charles would laugh with her, or if it were something, she might well be driven mad. So he said nothing.

Charles was invited to sleep at the cottage for the night, and they stayed up late talking.

Rachel told Richard when they were in bed that she liked Charles and that he certainly was a man who had seen many things, though a fool and a big baby. Then Rachel talked a great deal of nonsense, for she had had two glasses of wine, which she seldom drank, and she said: 'Oh, my dearest, I forgot to tell you. When I put on my buckled shoes this morning while you were away I found a buckle missing. I must have noticed that it was lost before I went to sleep last night and yet not fixed the loss firmly in my mind, so that it came out as a discovery in my dream; but I have a feeling, in fact I am certain, that Mr Charles has that buckle in his pocket; and I am sure that he is the man whom we met in our dream. But I don't care, not I.'

KEROUAC

The Pink Sweater

This text comes from Jack Kerouac's *Book of Dreams*, first published in 1961. According to the author, these dreams were scribbled after he woke up. Unlike Dickens, Kerouac says that the characters of his novels reappear in his dreams, continuing the story of 'On the Road' and 'The Subterraneans'.

I wanted to steal a pink woollen sweater from the outside counter of a Jewish clothing store across the street from the park – right on the spot where I was when I watched the boy with the runaway horse and loose reins – New Haven, but also the Chicago of Parks and just as I woke up the realization that it was only the real Frisco and the park was just a Boston addition to it. But I grabbed the sweater, just like a can of Spam in the store, tried to fold it under my coat, or in my arms, walk casually across the Montreal traffic to the Park, but as I woke up it seemed he saw me and also that I only dream-daydreamed stealing it – pink, wool, I don't even need a sweater, Edna had a pink one, I had a red cashmere one for a while (where?) – (when?) – (Barbara Dale in Greenwich Village) – it is the middle-class security of pink wool sweaters I wanted.

LEIRIS

The Actor

For Michel Leiris's *Nights without Night*, see page 98.

28–29 August 1942
(morning dream, Saint-Leonard-de-Noblat)

I am the actor Jean Yonnel and I am declaiming a tragedy in the Racinian mould. Suddenly, I can no longer remember the lines of my part. So, speaking slowly, in short disjointed sentences, but still declaiming, and in a very emotional tone, I announce that as the present circumstances have made me aware of tragedy itself, I can no longer recite a particular tragedy, something of which I was capable only when I was not conscious of it.

Apart from the moral significance of this theme (the depreciation in value of aesthetic tragedy in relation to lived tragedy), this is how it is linked to the process of waking: as I gain consciousness (that is: as I leave the state of sleep), I find myself in no state to recite (or more exactly: I discover I was not really reciting at all, but only thought I was reciting). While I slept, I was reciting, or imagined I was (to be exact: without actually reciting, I was in the effective state of one reciting); just as I was about to wake (already half conscious), since I would now have to invent a genuine recitation, instead of acting as if I were reciting, I hit upon a compromise: to go on reciting, but that only to talk about recitation.

One of my great memories of the theatre is of Yonnel playing Orestes in *Andromaque*, and playing it in a style at once violent and yet conventional, using to the full all the modulations of his fine voice. I remember how painful I found it, on leaving the theatre still in that trance-like state into which every play ought to transport us, to fall back into the bustle of the Metro, and to suffer at the ticket office a sharp rebuke over some error I had made with the

small change. How it galled me, that I should have to return to my real self
and allow this myth in which I bathed to evaporate in the space of a second.

Translated by J. Romney

DYLAN

Bob Dylan's 115th Dream

This song by Bob Dylan belongs to the record *Bringin' it all back
home*, which came out in 1965.

　　　　I was riding on the mayflower
　　　　when I thought I spied some land
　　　　I yelled for captain ahab

　　　　I have you understand
　　　　who came running to the deck
　　　　said boys forget the whale
　　　　look on over yonder
　　　　cut the engines change the sail
　　　　haul on the bow line
　　　　we sang that melody
　　　　like all tough sailors do
　　　　when they're far away at sea

　　　　I think I'll call it america
　　　　I said as we hit land
　　　　I took a deep breath
　　　　I fell down I could not stand
　　　　captain ahab he started
　　　　writing up some deeds he said
　　　　let's set up a fort
　　　　and start buying the place with beads
　　　　just then this cop comes down the street
　　　　crazy as a loon
　　　　he throws us all in jail
　　　　for carrying harpoons

　　　　ah me I busted out
　　　　don't even ask me how
　　　　I went to get some help

I walked by a guernsey cow
who directed me down
to the bowery slums
where people carried signs around
saying ban the bums
I jumped right into line
saying I hope that I'm not late
when I realized that I hadn't eaten
for five days straight

I went into a restaurant
looking for the cook
I told him I was the editor
of a famous etiquette book
the waitress he was handsome
he wore a powder blue cap
I ordered some suzette
I said please could you make that crepe
just then the whole kitchen
exploded from boiling fat
food was flying everywhere
and I left without my hat

now I didn't mean to be nosey
but I went into a bank
to get some bail for ahab
and all the boys back in the tank
they asked me for some collateral
and I pulled down my pants
they threw me in the alley
when up comes this girl from france
who invited me to her house
I went but she had a friend
who knocked me out and robbed my boots
and I was on the street again

well I rapped upon a house
with the u s flag upon display
I said could you help me out
I got some friends down the way
the man says get out of here
I'll tear you limb from limb
I said you know they refused jesus too

he said you're not him
get out of here before I break your bones
I ain't your pop
I decided to have him arrested
and I went looking for a cop

I ran right outside
and hopped inside a cab
I want out the other door
this englishman said fab
as he saw me leap a hotdog stand
and a chariot that stood
parked across from a building
advertising brotherhood
I ran right through the front door
like a hobo sailor does
but it was just a funeral parlour
and the man asked me who I was

I repeated that my friends
were all in jail with a sigh
he gave me his card
he said call me if they die
I shook his hand and said goodbye
ran out to the street
when a bowling ball came down the road
and knocked me off my feet
a pay phone was ringing
it just about blew my mind
when I picked it up and said hello
this foot came through the line

well by this time I was fed up
at trying to make a stab
at bringing back any help
for my friends and captain ahab
I decided to flip a coin
like either heads or tails
would let me me know if I should go
back to the ship
or back to jail
so I hocked my sailor's suit and I got a coin to flip
it came up tails it rhymed with sails
so I made it back to the ship

well I got back and took
the parking ticket off the mast
I was ripping it to shreds
when this coastguard boat went past
they asked me my name
and I said captain kidd
they believed me but
they wanted to know
what exactly that I did
I said for the pope of eruke I was employed
they let me go right away
they were very paranoid

well the last I heard of ahab
he was stuck on a whale
that was married to the deputy
sheriff of the jail
but the funniest thing was
when I was leaving the bay
I saw three ships a sailing
they were all heading my way
I asked the captain what his name was
and how come he didn't got a truck
he said his name was columbus
I just said good luck

VONNEGUT

Poo-tee-weet

This is a passage from Kurt Vonnegut's *God Bless You, Mr Rose-water*, first published in 1965.

Eliot didn't look up again until the bus reached the outskirts of Indianapolis. He was astonished to see that the entire city was being consumed by a fire-storm. He had never seen a fire-storm, but he had certainly read and dreamed about many of them.

He had a book hidden in his office, and it was a mystery even to Eliot as to why he should hide it, why he should feel guilty every time he got it out, why he should be afraid of being caught reading it. His feelings about the book were those of a weak-willed puritan with respect to pornography, yet no book could be more innocent of eroticism than the book he hid. It was called *The Bombing of Germany*. It was written by Hans Rumpf.

And the passage Eliot would read over and over again, his features blank, his palms sweating, was this description of the fire-storms in Dresden:

> As the many fires broke through the roofs of the burning buildings a column of heated air rose more than two and a half miles high and one and a half miles in diameter ... This column was turbulent, and it was fed from its base by in-rushing cooler ground-surface air. One and one and a half miles from the fires this draught increased the wind velocity from eleven to thirty-three miles per hour. At the edge of the area the volocities must have been appreciably greater, as trees three feet in diameter were uprooted. In a short time the temperature reached ignition point for all combustibles, and the entire area was ablaze. In such fires complete burn-out occurred; that is, no trace of combustible material remained, and only after two days were the areas cool enough to approach.

Eliot, rising from his seat in the bus, beheld the fire-storm of Indianapolis. He was awed by the majesty of the column of fire, which was at least eight miles in diameter and fifty miles high. The boundaries of the column seemed absolutely sharp and unwavering, as though made of glass. Within the boundaries, helixes of dull red embers turned in stately harmony about an inner core of white. Then white seemed holy.

Everything went black for Eliot, as black as what lay beyond the ultimate rim of the universe. And then he awoke to find himself sitting on the flat rim of a dry fountain. He was dappled by sunlight filtering down through a sycamore tree. A bird was singing in the sycamore tree. '*Poo-tee-weet?*' it sang. '*Poo-tee-weet. Weet, weet, weet.*' Eliot was within a high garden wall, and the garden was familiar. He had spoken to Sylvia many times in just this place. It was the garden of Dr Brown's private mental hospital in Indianapolis, to which he had brought her so many years before. These words were cut into the fountain rim:

> 'Pretend to be good always, and even God will be fooled.'

Eliot found that someone had dressed him for tennis, all in snowy white, and that, as though he were a department store display, someone had even put a tennis racket in his lap. He closed his hand around the racket handle experimentally, to discover whether it was real and whether he was real. He watched the play of the intricate basketwork of his forearm's musculature, sensed that he was not only a tennis player, but a good one. And he did not wonder where it was that he played tennis, for one side of the garden was bounded by a tennis court, with morning-glories and sweet peas twining in the chicken wire.

'*Poo-tee-weet?*'

Eliot looked up at the bird and all the green leaves, understood that this garden in downtown Indianapolis could not have survived the fire he saw. So there had been no fire. He accepted this peacefully.

PEREC

The Dentist

For Georges Pérec's *La Boutique obscure*, from which these dreams are taken, see page 107.

December 1968

Deep inside a labyrinth of covered galleries, rather like a souk, I come to a dentist's surgery.

The dentist is not in, but I find his son, a young boy, who asks me to come back later, then changes his mind and tells me his mother will be back at any moment.

I start to leave. I bump into a very small woman, pretty and laughing. She is the dentist. She leads me into the waiting-room. I tell her I have no time to spare. She opens my mouth wide and, bursting into sobs, tells me that all my teeth are rotten but it is not worth doing anything for me.

My gaping mouth is immense. I have an almost concrete sensation of total decay.

My mouth is so big and the dentist so small that I have the impression she is about to put her head right into my mouth.

Translated by J. Romney

Fragment from a General History of Transport

April 1972

One can easily imagine a particularly exciting system for a car park: it is a gigantic spiral that goes right down underground, and the slope of which has been so well calculated that no more effort is needed to go up it than to go down, an even acceleration being required in both cases.

The only condition is that there should never be more than one vehicle on the spiral at one time: when there are two, one going up, the other coming down, they are bound to crash into each other, and then all hell is let loose. The employees whose job it is to check the comings and goings of the vehicles, one stationed above, the other below, therefore have a heavy responsibility, but if they are in cahoots, they can easily cause accidents: that is exactly how perfect crimes are hatched.

The spiral is made not out of concrete, but of very hard steel: its end is shaped like a screw: the energy generated by the vehicles passing over it causes it to turn, and so it sinks progressively (and extremely slowly, but at practically no cost) into the ground (a particularly hard rock which could not be drilled otherwise); in this way, the foundations of an enormous tower block are being dug, bearing in mind that there are several drills, that is, several car parks.

We can pass fairly easily from the above to a plan for a general history of transport, and more particularly, of cars. Alain Trutat is in charge of the project, and he was particularly enthusiastic when I offered to read a report on one of the lesser-known points of this history – but nevertheless, one of the most important: the hispanization (or more precisely, the castillation, or castillification, or castillianization) of Gascony following the rise to power of Catherine de Medici: the Gascon mentality, mores and customs are even today totally incomprehensible unless you bear in mind that for several decades Gascony was purely and simply a colony, an annexe dependent on Castille.

I start to read my report in a rather ordinary classroom, in front of a sparse audience. I very soon realize that I have obviously not prepared it sufficiently, and, what is much worse, I cannot make my audience see the connection, obvious though it is, between the history of the car and the history of Spain.

The whole thing is going up the spout. An absolute flop. I am blathering away. Alain Trutat leaves the room. To create a salutary diversion, someone suggests some music. A band is formed, with various instruments.

I go out for a walk. Maybe I'd like to find Trutat? I am walking in a big French-style park, covered with snow.

I return to the classroom. Another band has been set up under the direction of R.K., who seems to be the only competent musician in the assembly, and who has taken things in hand with great authority, and what is more, most effectively. I want to play a flute, but as I pick it up I notice I have broken the end: I was holding the flute in one hand, and in the other a sort of rosary made of three long olive-shaped beads, possibly made out of wood, white in colour, and it is this rosary which was meant to be the mouthpiece of the flute.

A little later, someone hands me what is possibly a clarinet.

Translated by J. Romney

BORGES

Prologue

This is J. L. Borges' Prologue to *El libro de sueños*, edited by himself and Miguel de Torre, which was published in 1976.

In an essay in *The Spectator* (September 1712) Joseph Addison observed that the human soul, when it dreams, unencumbered by the body, is at the same time the theatre, the actors and the beholder. We can add that it is also the author of the fable that it is watching. Analogous statements can be found in Petronius and in Don Luis de Góngora.

A literal reading of Addison's metaphor could lead us to the thesis, dangerously attractive, that dreams constitute the most ancient and not least complex of literary genres. That curious thesis, which we may endorse without further ado for the sake of the fine execution of this prologue and for the reading of the text, could justify the composition of a general history of dreams and of their influence on the arts. This miscellaneous volume, compiled for the recreation of the curious reader, would furnish some material. That hypothetical history would explore the evolution and ramifications of this so ancient genre, from the prophetic dreams of the Orient to the allegorical and satirical ones of the Middle Ages, and to the pure games of Carroll and Franz Kafka. It would distinguish of course between the dreams invented by sleep and the dreams invented by wakedness.

This book of dreams, which the readers will dream again, encompasses dreams of the night – the ones signed by me, for example; dreams of the day, which are a voluntary exercise of our mind; and others whose origins are lost such as, for instance, the Anglo-Saxon Dream of the Cross.

The sixth book of the *Aeneid* follows a tradition in the *Odyssey* and states that there are two divine gates through which dreams reach us: the gate of ivory, which is the one for the fallacious dreams, and the gate of horn, which is the one for the prophetic dreams. Given the two materials selected, it could be said that the dreams that anticipate the future are less precious than the fallacious ones, which are a spontaneous invention of man in his sleep.

There is a type of dream which merits our particular attention. I am referring to *la pesadilla*, which in English bears the name of nightmare, or mare of the night, a word which suggested to Victor Hugo the metaphor of the *cheval noir de la nuit* but which, according to the etymologists, is equivalent to night fiction or fable. *Alp*, its German name, refers to the elf or incubus that oppresses the dreamer and imposes upon him horrendous images. *Ephialtes*, which is the Greek term, originates from a similar superstition.

Coleridge recorded in writing that the images of waking hours inspire feelings, while in dreams feelings inspire images. (What mysterious and complex feeling can have dictated Kubla Khan to him, which was the gift of a dream?) If a tiger entered this room, we would experience fear; if we experienced fear in a dream, we engender a tiger. This must be the visionary reason for our alarm. I said a tiger, but since fear comes before the apparition improvised in order to understand it, we can project horror on to any figure, which when awake does not necessarily provoke horror. A marble bust, a cellar, the other side of a coin, a mirror. There is not a single shape in the universe that cannot be contaminated by horror. Therein lies, perhaps, the peculiar taste of the nightmare, which is very different from the fright and the frights that reality is capable of inflicting upon us. The Germanic nations seem to have been more sensitive to that vague lurking evil than those of Latin origin; let us recall those untranslatable words, *eerie, weird, uncanny, unheimlich.* Each language produces what it needs.

The art of the night has penetrated the art of the day. The invasion has lasted centuries; the suffering kingdom of Dante's *Commedia* is not a nightmare, except perhaps in the fourth canto, of repressed affliction; it is a place in which terrible events take place. The lesson of the night has not been easy. The dreams of the Scripture are not in the style of dreams; they are prophecies which manipulate in a too coherent manner a mechanism of metaphors. Quevedo's dreams seem to be the work of someone who has never dreamt, like the Cimmerian people mentioned by Pliny. Others will come later. The influence of the night and of the day will be reciprocal; Beckford and De Quincey, Henry James and Poe, have their roots in the nightmare and they are accustomed to disturbing our nights. It is not improbable that mythologies and religions have an analogous origin.

Translated by J. Lyons

The Episode of the Enemy

We found this short story by J. L. Borges in *El libro de sueños*.

Running and waiting for so many years, and now the enemy was in my house. From the window I saw him climb the rugged hillside path with difficulty. He used a stick, an ungainly stick which in old hands could not serve as a weapon but as a walking aid. It took me a while to realize what I was waiting for: the faint knock on the door. I glanced, not without nostalgia, at my manuscripts, the draft half-finished and Artemidorus's treatise on dreams, a somewhat anomalous book here, since I know no Greek. Another wasted day, I thought. I had to struggle with the key. I was afraid the man would fall over, but he took a few unsteady paces, let go of the stick, which I did not see again, and fell on to my bed, exhausted. My anxiety had pictured him many times, but only then did I note that he resembled, in an almost fraternal way, the last portrait of Lincoln. It must have been about four in the afternoon.

I leant over him so that he could hear me.

'One thinks that one's years go by,' I said to him, 'but they also go by for the others. Here we find ourselves at the end and what happened before has no meaning.'

While I was talking, he had unbuttoned his overcoat. His right hand was in his jacket pocket. He was pointing something at me and I sensed it was a revolver.

He then said to me in a firm voice:

'In order to enter your house, I have resorted to compassion. I have you now at my mercy and I am merciless.'

I tried a few words. I am not a strong man and only words could save me. I came up with:

'It is true that some time ago I mistreated a child, but you are not that child and I am no longer that fool. Besides, revenge is no less vain and ridiculous than forgiveness.'

'Precisely because I am no longer that child,' he replied, 'I must kill you. It is not a question of revenge but of an act of justice. Your arguments, Borges, are mere wiles devised by your terror so that I won't kill you. You are now powerless to do anything.'

'I can do one thing,' I answered.

'What is that?' he asked.

'Wake up.'

And so I did.

Translated by J. Lyons

DAMIAN

Church Football

For François Damian, see page 117.

18 December

A screen wall takes up the greatest dimension of the room breadthwise. We are facing it, sitting in several rows, actually on the floor, men and women, including some nuns. Projected on the screen is a televised match in which the Church team, coached by John Paul II, is playing against a formation whose particulars are ambiguous. A victory for the Church, it seems to me, would be a lesser evil, but an evil all the same, especially for Belgium, which is the stake in this match. I have the feeling that whoever loses will really turn out to be the winner. Despite that, the Pope appears in close-up on the screen to give the victory sign. In the room, only two nuns stand up to applaud him. I swallow my rage, but it still sticks in my throat.

Translated by J. Romney

Symbolic dreams

Classifying dreams as 'symbolic' creates an immediate problem: what are they symbolic of? Who imposes the polarity of the symbolic message and steers the symbolic vehicle? Who sets the unreliable relation between the symbol and what the symbol stands for? Who is the legislator, the judge and the law-enforcer of the symbolic code? If I use the sign '?' to indicate a question, I do not have to worry about its inventor because I am confident I live in a community of readers for whom '?' has a precise received meaning. But if I dream of an eagle who turns into a vulture (as in Alciphron), what is the meaning of 'eagle' beyond 'eagle', of 'vulture' beyond 'vulture'? What does the metamorphosis of one bird into another indicate? Goethe claims that the pheasants with peacock tails in his dream have 'a symbolic relation to our lives and destinies', but does not venture into interpretation. I remember a professor of literature, endowed with the magical simple-mindedness of the very cultured and very stupid, who used to teach his students how to recognize 'symbolic' birds in Romantic literature: as if every fowl had a label round its neck saying either 'birdly bird: do not worry about further meanings', or 'symbolic bird: interpret carefully'. Who can vouch that the eagle in my dream, or in Alciphron's dream, is something more than a mere eagle? That its eagleness has an exemplary value, associated perhaps with Jupiter's totem, connoting wildness, pride, courage, ambition, cruelty, etc.? And what is the use of these symbols?

In the passage from *The Song of Roland* reproduced here, why does Charlemagne need a bear, a leopard and a hound in the second dream if the theme of this symbolic fight, presumably Ganelon's treason, has already been explicitly illustrated in the Emperor's first dream? Who creates, forces upon us and guarantees these analogies? If it is I, the dreamer, what use have I of a symbol if I have already reached the symbolized meaning on my own? If the symbolic analogies are set by the oneirocritics, whether Artemidorus or Freud, who has given them the secret code for deciphering the message of the dream? If they rest in the age-old wisdom of the spoken language of everyday, who can swear to the equivalence between the sunlit language of waking and the moonlit language of dreaming? If it all depends on the collective unconscious, the universal grammar or *l'esprit humain*, well, we have no personal acquaintance with these folks and we would ask for their passport, birth certificate and banker's reference before we start trusting them. What-ever our approach, the 'symbolic' is a highly problematic issue, and we might be tempted to ignore it altogether, or to dismiss it among the fantasies of dreamers and dream-chroniclers who like to enrich the protocols of their dreams with a further dimension.

Yet it is enough to consider this possibility for one minute to realize that it is an absurdity. Man is a symbolic animal who cannot refrain from symbolizing his personal experience and to translate back the symbols he comes across in terms of his experience. If you see a rose, it is not just a rose: a rose is always something more. If a dreamer dreams of a rose, he cannot help wondering about the ulterior meaning of this flower. All things have perforce extra-linguistic connotations for everyone, though the degree of interpretative *hubris* varies from person to person. Artemidorus, the great oneiromancer of classi-cal times, wanted to explain every single occurence through a delirium of analogies, since he believed everything can be paraphrased according to the mysterious grammar of dreams ('The most skilful interpreter of dreams is he who has the faculty of observing resemblances,' wrote Aristotle). Through the rules of analogy, the experience of the dream is transposed into the experience of waking. In the pages of his *Interpretation of Dreams* the several forms of sexual intercourse the dreamer can have with various partners (mother, daughter, son, slave, master, brother, etc.) always have two meanings: the first and obvious one is the libidinous instinct which initiates every erotic practice; the second is the symbolic value of this sexual act, interpreted and translated according to rigid, though seemingly arbitrary, criteria.

Freud, the great oneirocritic of modern times, is not content with explaining everything: he has the presumption of ascertaining the causes of every relevant or irrelevant detail of the dream, with a raving mania for analogy and etiology parading as the fiercest deterministic system of our days. If his patient dreams of white wolves with fox tails and dog ears crouching on a tree outside the window, everything falls into a pattern in which each fragment of the dream can be reconnected with an event of the patient's experience: the animals, their colour, their number, their hybrid anatomy, their position – nothing escapes Freud's deterministic grid. This mad craving of explanation, which runs parallel to the history of dream studies, has elicited parodies of the oneirocritic, and ironic interpretations of the art of interpretation, as in the passages we have included from Ovid, Rabelais or Pérec.

The episode from Ovid's *Amores*, taken out of its larger context, might easily be misread as an example of rigid literalism in the interpretation of dreams: heat=heat of lust; heifer=dreamer's girl, bull=dreamer; crow=procuress; the departing heifer=the ditching of the lover; the bruise on her throat=the taint of adultery. But it is in fact a very subtle passage where the irony is never explicit, since it rests with the intuition of the reader who can also enjoy the mental laziness of another potential reader who would not get the joke. The interpreter, 'nocturnae imaginis augur', 'pondered ...' – and these ponderings can only bring forth the triteness of the symbol chasers, the professional oneiromancers of Ovid's time who have now been replaced by the relentless Freudian greyhounds. This derision of any sort of rigid explanation is more accented still in Jacopo Ferretti's libretto for Rossini's *Cinderella*, where the stupidity of Don Magnifico, father of the two evil stepsisters, is underlined by his cheap interpretative assurance: 'Ecco il simbolo spiegato' (literally: 'here is the symbol unfolded'). It is legitimate, of course, to ask oneself or others for the signification of our dreams – but we must not expect a ready answer. In Brecht, Joan Dark thinks she *understands* the meaning of her dream, although the cries of the strikers were shouted 'in a tongue [she] did not know'; Pérec's jigsaw begs for an interpretation, which is not available; Alciphron's dreamer is looking for a professional who would explain to him the latent signification of his nocturnal fancy. But one must beware of automatic solutions.

The only way to gain sure access to the secret of dreams is to trust in God, the unimpeachable witness who guarantees the truthfulness of the dream and its unambiguous meaning. Thus we have Thutmosis who is visited in his dream by his 'divine father' Armakhis-Khépri-Râ-Toum; Jacob's dream, where he converses with the Lord; Saint Augustine's mother, who sees the angel of the Lord 'in a halo of splendour'; the exaltation of the Palatine Princess when she recognizes the presence of Christ in the blind beggar of her dream; Swedenborg who is addressed by the Redemptor in a room strewn with wriggling snakes and evil toads – all these dreams have a supernaturally guaranteed interpretation which gives absolute strength to their prophecies.

The supernatural gives authority to the dream and vouches for its interpretation. But in the natural reign, everything becomes ambiguous and ambivalent, and the reading keys proliferate. Sometimes the doubt does not arise from the text, but from our perception of it, as in the passage of Ovid discussed above; but it can also be explicit in the context of the dream, as in the passage from Rabelais, where the horns on Panurge's head are successively explained as marks of cuckholding or horns of abundance, and the drum stands either for a beaten-up husband or for a jolly sexually satisfied partner; and so on. Or in Pérec's 'The Condemnation', where the dreamer is not sure whether the crowd licking his feet are paying homage to him or trying to throw him down from his pedestal with their tongues. (How Pérecian are these dreams by Pérec, who confesses that he had started to write down the dreams he was dreaming, and ended up dreaming so that he could write down his dreams.)

But perhaps nothing is true in the dream world. According to Homer, the nocturnal visitors come through two different gates: the gate of horn for the truthful dreams, the gate of ivory for the beguiling ones. The legend apparently expresses a religious faith in the prophetic capacity of dreams, though, as Borges points out: 'Given the two materials selected, it could be said that the poet has felt in some obscure manner that the dreams that anticipate the future are less precious than the fallacious ones, which are a spontaneous invention of the dreamer.' And the dreams meaning nothing, which gate do they come from? Besides, our perception of truthful dreams is marred by our knowledge of the existence of lying dreams: we have no way to know which gate they did come through. Both kinds are sent by a God, or perhaps by a God called *Dream*. The modern position tends to compromise between natural and supernatural elements (only the most bloody-minded positivists would deny the mystery lurking at the core of the dream and hence its partial – or even temporary – departure from the natural laws). The case of Gibbon seems to us emblematic. His whole cultural formation should lead him to deny the truth of Constantine's dream: Eusebius, the chronicler of this episode, does not bring any testimony of living witnesses to prove his story, but invokes a visitation by the deceased emperor, many years after the event, who would have sworn to the truth of the dream by a solemn oath. Yet Gibbon's intelligence, his 'knowledge of human nature, of Constantine and Christianity', prevents him from rejecting the story of the dream: vanity and ambition would have elicited Constantine's 'true' dream about the cross and the prophecy of victory. Similarly, in Gide's *Vatican Cellars*, the atheist and rabidly anti-clerical Anthime is as stupid and crass in his faith after his conversion by the Virgin's apparition as he was before in his blasphemies: nothing has changed in him. The dream is 'true' because of the dreamer's narrow-mindedness (Gide's attitude to Anthime's miracle is similar to Gibbon's judgement on Constantine's vision).

We have so far considered clear and explicit symbols which would almost make the interpreters redundant. In Browning, Eça de Queiroz, Dante, Eckermann, Melville, Seferis or Sophocles, the symbols are wide open. Their interpretation is so obvious that we wonder what was the point of transforming the obviousness of experience into the obviousness of crystal-clear symbols (apart from the literary strength of imagery, of course: from Dante's siren to Melville's iceberg; from Browning's perfect city at war with brute nature to the overwhelming image of fertility and renewal in Sophocles). Jean Paul is one of the most disturbing dream-writers, and in the episode selected here he frightens the reader with a dead man who is happily dreaming away until someone living comes and wakes him up, forcing him to open an eye he hasn't got – being a corpse. Yet even in this frightening, surrealistic evocation, the symbolic figures are too obvious: the dial-plate of Eternity, the eye of God, the rising vapours of the future, and so on. The most outrageous symbols become familiar in the grid of dream experience (or in the language used to reproduce dream experience).

As Caillois asks in the book quoted before, how can we call these dreams symbolic if they show us, almost overtly, what the exegetes think they should hide? What is the use of this complex symbolic machinery? In contradiction with the psychologists who want to make everything clear in the depths of our souls, we think that the most useful experience is the confrontation with dark, or only partially accessible, symbols. Descartes' dream, in our opinion one of the gems of this anthology, forces us to think because we cannot explain away the melon, brought from some foreign land, that some people try to offer the philosopher in his incongruous fancy. Dreams are perhaps a huge practical joke played on mankind by God knows what supernatural force; in this case the scandal of the Cartesian melon seems more interesting and fascinating than the well marked paths of the symbols, and of their easy explanation, that dreams normally force us to take. At another point in his dream Descartes is looking up a quotation in an anthology, but he realizes that the book he is holding is not the edition he is used to, which makes his search for the passage in question difficult. This is for us a splendid *symbol* of the mystery of dreaming. Dreaming and waking are the same book but in two different editions, and every attempt at interpretation is impeded by the radical divergence of editorial criteria. It is an idea that would appeal to Borges, perhaps the only contemporary writer who could make adequate use of it.

But the most mysterious example in this section is probably the dream reconstructed and interpreted by Daniel in the Bible. In the whole Western literature on dreams, the most recent statement which seems to us 'true', unimpeachable and frightening in its rigorous definition, is some 2500 years old. In the sixth century BC, Heraclitus ('the first depth psychologist' according to James Hillman) said: 'For the waking there is one common world only; but when asleep, each man turns to his own private world.' Dreaming would therefore be the reign of absolute privacy, hence of incommunicability (not only with the external world, but even within the dreaming system, between the dreamer and his dream). We can speak of our day life because it belongs to the public experience, to the territory of sociality and community; we cannot speak of our dreaming experience because it only concerns the actual dreamer.

The story of Daniel who digs out and explains the dream forgotten by Nebuchadnezzar is a challenge to this privacy. Daniel inverts the forgetting process of the despot in an operation of terrifying psychological violence. The private world of the dreamer, who is allured and repelled by his dream and tries to remember and forget it at the same time, is invaded and violated by the prophet. We can protect ourselves from psychoanalytic prevarication by refusing to collaborate; but the American laboratory which shall invent a machine, named *Daniel*, to read other people's dreams, shall break down this last line of defence. Today the naive patient who runs to his analyst (or his guru, or his confessor) to tell him his dreams of the night before is protected by the other part of himself which hastens to forget these dreams as soon as they are over; but nothing can rescue the integrity of ignorance, the safety of our misunderstanding and misinforming ourselves, the mystery of our own latent will, from this monstrous invention: *Daniel*. This raises a crucial question: will man still be entitled to the name of man if he loses the right to forget, change, distort, invert his own dreams? This is for us a sacred issue: we must defend our right to lie to others (I dream of a horse and I say I have dreamt of a donkey), and our right to lie to ourselves (I dream of a horse, and I cannot remember whether it was a donkey or a zebra). The mystery of the dream saves us from the horror of clarity and knowledge.

EGYPT

Thutmosis and the God

This text, written on a stone slab near the Sphinx of Gizeh, sounds like a justification of the conquests of Thutmosis IV, the pharaoh of the eighteenth dynasty who reigned between 1412 and 1402 BC and was the protagonist of the unification of the two kingdoms of Aegypt, completed under his son Amenothep III. Although Thutmosis was a true zealot of the god Amon Rê, his celestial father as it appears in this text, the heresy of Aton probably started during his reign: his grandson Amenothep III actually adopted the new creed and changed his name to Akhenaten.

Thutmosis was still very young, like the child Horus in the Buto swamp; he was as beautiful as Horus, his father's protector, and one could behold in him the god himself. The soldiers were happy to love him. . .

He liked above all to disport himself on the southern and northern edge of the desert plateau of Memphis, aiming at a copper target with his bow, hunting lions and gazelles, racing on his chariot with his horses swifter than the wind, in the company of one or two of his servants, but unbeknown to the rest of the world.

When the time came to give rest to his companions, he was on the terrace of Harmakhis, near Sokharis. . . In this place, there is a colossal statue of the almighty and sublime god Khepri which is touched by the shadow of Râ. The citizens of Memphis and of all the neighbouring villages come here, with rich offerings for the god, their arms raised in adoration. One day, the royal prince Thutmosis had come here; at noon, he sat in the shadow of this great god, the Sphinx, and sleep and dreams overpowered him when the sun was at its highest point. He noted that the majesty of this holy god was speaking from his own mouth, as a father to his son, saying: 'Look at me, raise thy eyes on me, O Thutmosis, my son; I am thy father, Armakhis-Khépri-Râ-Toum. I grant thee my royal power on earth, as king of the living: thou shalt therefore wear the white crown and the red crown on the throne of Geb, the inheriting god; thine will be the country, in its length and in its breadth, as well as everything that is lightened by the eye of the universal lord. Thou shalt receive food from both lands, as well as a conspicuous tribute from all foreign countries, and a life-span of many years . . .

'My face is turned towards thee, and my heart is flying to thee: see my pitiful state, my aching body, though I am master of the Gizeh plateau! The sand of the desert on which I reign is moving towards me; hence I must haste to entrust thee with the realization of my wishes, for I know thou art my son and shalt protect me: come nearer, see, I am with thee, and I am thy guide!'

As soon as the god had finished, the royal prince woke up, because he had just heard this speech ... He understood that they were the words of this god, and kept silent in his heart.

Translated from the French by C. Béguin

THE BIBLE

Jacob's Ladder

This dream by Jacob is told in *Genesis*, which was probably written in the thirteenth century BC.

And Jacob went out from Beer-sheba, and went toward Haran.

And he lighted upon a certain place, and tarried there all night, because the sun was set; and he took of the stones of that place, and put *them for* his pillows, and lay down in that place to sleep.

And he dreamed, and behold a ladder set up on the earth, and the top of it reached to heaven: and behold the angels of God ascending and descending on it.

And, behold, the LORD stood above it, and said, I *am* the LORD God of Abraham thy father, and the God of Isaac: the land whereon thou liest, to thee will I give it, and to thy seed;

And thy seed shall be as the dust of the earth, and thou shalt spread abroad to the west, and to the east, and to the north, and to the south: and in thee and in thy seed shall all the families of the earth be blessed.

And, behold, I *am* with thee, and will keep thee in all *places* whither thou goest, and will bring thee again into this land; for I will not leave thee, until I have done *that* which I have spoken to thee of.

And Jacob awaked out of his sleep, and he said, Surely the LORD is in this place; and I knew *it* not.

And he was afraid, and said, How dreadful *is* this place! this *is* none other but the house of God, and this *is* the gate of heaven.

King James's Version

The Forgotten Dream

This most peculiar feat of interpretation of a forgotten dream is
recounted in the Book of Daniel, written in the sixth century BC.

And in the second year of the reign of Nebuchadnezzar Nebuchadnezzar
dreamed dreams, wherewith his spirit was troubled, and his sleep brake from
him.

Then the king commanded to call the magicians, and the astrologers, and
the sorcerers, and the Chaldeans for to shew the king his dreams. So they
came and stood before the king.

And the king said unto them, I have dreamed a dream, and my spirit was
troubled to know the dream.

Then spake the Chaldeans to the king in Syriack, O king, live for ever: tell
thy servants the dream, and we will shew the interpretation.

The king answered and said to the Chaldeans, The thing is gone from me:
if ye will not make known unto me the dream, with the interpretation thereof,
ye shall be cut in pieces, and your houses shall be made a dunghill.

But if ye shew the dream, and the interpretation thereof, ye shall receive of
me gifts and rewards and great honour: therefore shew me the dream, and the
interpretation thereof.

They answered again and said, Let the king tell his servants the dream, and
we will shew the interpretation of it.

The king answered and said, I know of certainty that ye would gain the
time, because ye see the thing is gone from me.

But if ye will not make known unto me the dream, *there is but* one decree for
you: for ye have prepared lying and corrupt words to speak before me, till the
time be changed: therefore tell me the dream, and I shall know that ye can
shew me the interpretation thereof.

The Chaldeans answered before the king, and said, There is not a man
upon the earth that can shew the king's matter: therefore *there is* no king, lord,
nor ruler, *that* asked such things at any magician, or astrologer, or Chaldean.

And *it is* a rare thing that the king requireth, and there is none other that
can shew it before the king, except the gods, whose dwelling is not with flesh.

For this cause the king was angry and very furious, and commanded to
destroy all the wise *men* of Babylon.

And the decree went forth that the wise *men* should be slain; and they
sought Daniel and his fellows to be slain.

Then Daniel answered with counsel and wisdom to Arioch the captain of
the king's guard, which was gone forth to slay the wise *men* of Babylon:

He answered and said to Arioch the king's captain, Why *is* the decree *so*
hasty from the king? Then Arioch made the thing known to Daniel.

Then Daniel went in, and desired of the king that he would give him time, and that he would shew the king the interpretation.

Then Daniel went to his house and made the thing known to Hananiah, Mishael, and Azariah, his companions:

That they would desire mercies of the God of heaven concerning this secret; that Daniel and his fellows should not perish with the rest of the wise *men* of Babylon.

Then was the secret revealed unto Daniel in a night vision. Then Daniel blessed the God of heaven.

Daniel answered and said, Blessed be the name of God for ever and ever: for wisdom and might are his:

And he changeth the times and the seasons: he removeth kings, and setteth up kings: he giveth wisdom unto the wise, and knowledge to them that know understanding:

He revealeth the deep and secret things: he knoweth what *is* in the darkness, and the light dwelleth with him.

I thank thee, and praise thee, O thou God of my fathers, who hast given me wisdom and might, and hast made known unto me now what we desired of thee: for thou has *now* made known unto us the king's matter.

Therefore Daniel went in unto Arioch, whom the king had ordained to destroy the wise *men* of Babylon: he went and said thus unto him; Destroy not the wise *men* of Babylon: bring me in before the king, and I will shew unto the king the interpretation.

Then Arioch brought in Daniel before the king in haste, and said thus unto him, I have found a man of the captives of Judah, that will make known unto the king the interpretation.

The king answered and said to Daniel, whose name *was* Belteshazzar, Art thou able to make known unto me the dream which I have seen, and the interpretation thereof?

Daniel answered in the presence of the king, and said, The secret which the king hath demanded cannot the wise *men*, the astrologers, the magicians, the soothsayers, shew unto the king;

But there is a God in heaven that revealeth secrets, and maketh known to the king Nebuchadnezzar what shall be in the latter days. Thy dream, and the visions of thy head upon thy bed, are these;

As for thee, O king, thy thoughts came *into thy mind* upon thy bed, what should come to pass hereafter: and he that revealeth secrets maketh known to thee what shall come to pass.

But as for me, this secret is not revealed to me for *any* wisdom that I have more than any living, but for *their* sakes that shall make known the interpretation to the king, and that thou mightest know the thoughts of thy heart.

Thou, O king, sawest, and behold a great image. This great image, whose brightness *was* excellent, stood before thee; and the form thereof *was* terrible.

This image's head *was* of fine gold, his breast and his arms of silver, his belly and his thighs of brass.

His legs of iron, his feet part of iron and part of clay.

Thou sawest till that a stone was cut out without hands, which smote the image upon his feet *that were* of iron and clay, and brake them to pieces.

Then was the iron, the clay, the brass, the silver, and the gold, broken to pieces together, and became like the chaff of the summer threshingfloors; and the wind carried them away, that no place was found for them: and the stone that smote the image became a great mountain, and filled the whole earth.

This *is* the dream; and we will tell the interpretation thereof before the king.

Thou, O king, *art* a king of kings: for the God of heaven hath given thee a kingdom, power, and strength, and glory.

And wheresoever the children of men dwell, the beasts of the field and the fowls of the heaven hath he given into thine hand, and hath made thee ruler over them all. Thou *art* this head of gold.

And after thee shall arise another kingdom inferior to thee, and another third kingdom of brass, which shall bear rule over all the earth.

And the fourth kingdom shall be strong as iron: forasmuch as iron breaketh in pieces and subdueth all *things*: and as iron that breaketh all these, shall it break in pieces and bruise.

And whereas thou sawest the feet and toes, part of potters' clay and part of iron, the kingdom shall be divided; but there shall be in it of the strength of the iron, forasmuch as thou sawest the iron mixed with miry clay.

And *as* the toes of the feet *were* part of iron, and part of clay, *so* the kingdom shall be partly strong, and partly broken.

And whereas thou sawest iron mixed with miry clay, they shall mingle themselves with the seed of men: but they shall not cleave one to another, even as iron is not mixed with clay.

And in the days of these kings shall the God of heaven set up a kingdom, which shall never be destroyed: and the kingdom shall not be left to other people, *but* it shall break in pieces and consume all these kingdoms, and it shall stand for ever.

Forasmuch as thou sawest that the stone was cut out of the mountain without hands, and that it brake in pieces the iron, the brass, the clay, the silver, and the gold; the great God hath made known to the king what shall come to pass hereafter: and the dream *is* certain, and the interpretation thereof sure.

Then the king Nebuchadnezzar fell upon his face, and worshipped Daniel, and commanded that they should offer an oblation and sweet odours unto him.

The king answered unto Daniel, and said, Of a truth *it is*, that your God *is* a God of gods, and a Lord of kings, and a revealer of secrets, seeing thou couldest reveal this secret.

Then the king made Daniel a great man, and gave him many great gifts, and made him ruler over the whole province of Babylon, and chief of the governors over all the wise *men* of Babylon.

Then Daniel requested of the king, and he set Shadrach, Meshach, and Abed-nego, over the affairs of the province of Babylon but Daniel *sat* in the gate of the king.

King James's Version

EURIPIDES

The Fawn and the Wolf

At the beginning of Euripides' *Hecuba*, probably written in 424 BC, the Queen recounts her dreams. She still hopes to avert the prophecy contained in these visions, but the spectator has already had confirmation of its veracity: in the prologue the ghost of Polydorus has told the audience about his own treacherous assassination at the hands of Polymnestor, and announced the execution of his sister Polyxena.

Hecuba
Lead forth, O my children, the stricken in years from the tent.
O lead her, upbearing the steps of your fellow-thrall
Now, O ye daughters of Troy, but of old your queen.
Clasp me, uphold, help onward the eld-forspent,
Laying hold of my wrinkled hand, lest for weakness I fall;
And, sustained by a carving arm, there on as I lean,
    I will hasten onward with tottering pace,
    Speeding my feet in a laggard's race.
O lightning-splendour of Zeus, O mirk of the night,
   Why quake I for visions in slumber that haunt me
With terrors, with phantoms? O Earth's majestic might,
Mother of dreams that hover in dusk-winged flight,
   I cry to the vision of darkness 'Avaunt thee!'—
The dream of my son who was sent into Thrace to be saved from the slaughter,
The dream that I saw of Polyxena's doom, my dear-loved daughter,
    Which I saw, which I knew, which abideth to daunt me.
    Gods of the Underworld, save ye my son,
Mine house's anchor, its only one,

By the friend of his father warded well
Where the snows of Thrace veil forest and fell!
    But a strange new stroke draweth near,
And a strain of wailing for them that wail.
Ah, never as now did the heart in me quail
    With the thrilling of ceaseless fear.
O that Cassandra I might but descry
To arrede me my dreams, O daughters of Troy,
    Or Helenus, god-taught seer!
For a dappled fawn I beheld which a wolf's red fangs were tearing,
Which he dragged from my knees whereto she had clung in her piteous
despairing.
    This terror withal on my spirit is come.
That the ghost of the mighty Achilles hath risen, and stood
   High on the crest of his earth-heaped tomb:
And he claimeth a guerdon of honour, the spilling of blood,
    And a woe-stricken Trojan maiden's doom.
O Gods, I am suppliant before you! – in any wise turn, I implore you,
    This fate from the child of my womb!

Translated by A. S. Way

The Central Pillar

In *Iphigenia Taurica* by Euripides, probably written in 414 BC, the
daughter of Agamemnon and Clytemnestra has been saved from
the sacrifice requested by the gods to release the Greek boats;
Diana has carried her to her temple in Tauris, where all Greeks
disembarking are systematically sacrificed to the goddess;
Iphigenia's function is to prepare the human victims.

> *Iphigenia:*
> I came to Aulis: o'er the pyre, – ah me! –
> High raised was I, the sword in act to slay, –
> When Artemis stole me, for the Achaeans set
> There in my place a hind, and through clear air
> Wafted me, in this Taurian land to dwell,
> Where a barbarian rules barbarians,
> Thoas, who, since his feet be swift as wings
> Of birds, hath of his fleetness won his name.
> And in this fane her priestess made she me:
> Therefore in rites of that dark cult wherein

Artemis joys, – fair is its name alone;
But, for its deeds, her fear strikes dumb my lips, –
I sacrifice – 'twas this land's ancient wont –
What Greek soever cometh to this shore.
I consecrate the victim; in the shrine
The unspeakable slaughter is for others' hands.
Now the strange visions that the night hath brought
To heaven I tell – if aught of help be there.
In sleep methought I had escaped this land,
And dwelt in Argos. In my maiden-bower
I slept: then with an earthquake shook the ground.
I fled, I stood without, the cornice saw
Of the roof falling, – then, all crashing down,
Turret and basement, hurled was the house to earth.
The central pillar alone, meseemed, was left
Of my sires' halls; this from its capital
Streamed golden hair, and spake with human voice.
Then I, my wonted stranger-slaughtering rite
Observing, sprinkled it, as doomed to death,
Weeping. Now thus I read this dream of mine:
Dead is Orestes – him I sacrificed; –
Seeing the pillars of a house be sons,
And they die upon whom my sprinklings fall.

Translated by A. S. Way

SOPHOCLES

Clytemnestra's Dream

This dream occurs in *Electra*, a play by Sophocles of which we do not know the exact date, although it is deemed to be roughly contemporary to Euripides's play of the same title, which is dated 413 BC. The first dramatic treatment of the myth was Aeschylus' *Choephori* (458 BC). At the beginning of Sophocles' play Orestes, who has been smuggled away as a child after the murder of Agamemnon, comes back to Argos. His prayers on the tomb of his dead father are interrupted by the arrival of his sister Electra who recounts the calamities of the house of Atreus in a dialogue with the chorus. Enter the other sister, Chrysothemis, who tries to

convince Electra to submit to the power of their mother Clytemnestra, and of her new husband Aegisthus: frightened by her
rebellion, Aegisthus has decided to bury her alive. As Electra states
that she would prefer this horrible fate to living with her criminal
family, Chrysothemis gives up her attempt to persuade her sister and
decides to carry on with her errand. This is where our passage begins.

> *Electra:* Whither art bound? For whom to burn those gifts?
> *Chrysothemis:* Sent by my mother to my father's tomb
> To pour libations to him.
> *El.* How? To him?
> Most hostile to her of all souls that are?
> *Chr.* Who perished by her hand – so thou wouldst say.
> *El.* What friend hath moved her? Who hath cared for this?
> *Chr.* Methinks 'twas some dread vision, seen by night.
> *El.* Gods of my father, O be with me now!
> *Chr.* What? art thou hopeful from the fear I spake of?
> *El.* Tell me the dream, and I will answer thee.
> *Chr.* I know but little of it.
> *El.* Speak but that.
> A little word hath ofttimes been the cause
> Of ruin or salvation unto men.
> *Chr.* 'Tis said she saw our father's spirit come
> Once more to visit the abodes of light;
> Then take and firmly plant upon the hearth
> The sceptre which he bore of old, and now
> Ægisthus bears: and out of this upsprang
> A burgeoned shoot, that shadowed all the ground
> Of loved Mycenæ. So I heard the tale
> Told by a maid who listened when the Queen
> Made known her vision to the god of Day.
> But more than this I know not, save that I
> Am sent by her through terror of the dream.
> And I beseech thee by the gods we serve
> To take my counsel and not rashly fall.
> If thou repel me now, the time may come
> When suffering shall have brought thee to my side.
> *El.* Now dear Chrysothemis, of what thou bearest
> Let nothing touch his tomb.   'Tis impious
> And criminal to offer to thy sire
> Rites and libations from a hateful wife.
> Then cast them to the winds, or deep in dust
> Conceal them, where no particle may reach

His resting-place: but lie in store for her
When she goes underground. Sure, were she not
Most hardened of all women that have been,
She ne'er had sent this loveless drink-offering
To grace the sepulchre of him she slew.
For think how likely is the buried king
To take such present kindly from her hand,
Who slew him like an alien enemy,
Dishonoured even in death, and mangled him,
And wiped the death-stain with his flowing locks –
Sinful purgation! Think you that you bear
In those cold gifts atonement for her guilt?
It is not possible. Wherefore let be.
But take a ringlet from thy comely head,
And this from mine – a scanty gift, I know,
Unmeet for offering. Ah! but give it to him,
All I can give, and this my maiden-zone,
Not glistening with the smoothness of delight.
Then, falling prostrate, pray that from the ground
He would arise to help us 'gainst his foes,
And grant his son Orestes with high hand
Strongly to trample on his enemies;
That in our time to come from ampler stores
We may endow him, than are ours today.
I cannot but imagine that his will
Hath part in visiting her sleep with fears.
But howsoe'er, I pray thee, sister mine,
Do me this service, and thyself, and him,
Dearest of all the world to me and thee,
The Father of us both, who rests below.

Translated by L. Campbel

CICERO

The Augural Arts

For Cicero's *De Divinatione*, see page 135.

May I not recall to your memory some stories to be found in the works of Roman and of Greek poets? For example, the following dream of the Vestal Virgin is from Ennius:

The vestal from her sleep in fright awoke
And to the startled maid, whose trembling hands
A lamp did bear, thus spoke in tearful tones;
'O daughter of Eurydice, thou whom
Our father loved, from my whole frame departs
The vital force. For in my dreams I saw
A man of beauteous form, who bore me off
Through willows sweet, along the fountain's brink,
To places strange. And then, my sister dear,
Alone, with halting step and longing heart,
I seemed to wander, seeking thee in vain;
There was no path to make my footing sure.
And then I thought my father spoke these words:
"Great sorrows, daughter, thou must first endure
Until thy fortune from the Tiber rise."
When this was said he suddenly withdrew;
Nor did his cherished vision come again,
Though oft I raised my hand to heaven's dome
And called aloud in tearful, pleading voice.
Then sleep departing left me sick at heart.'

This dream, I admit, is the fiction of a poet's brain, yet it is not contrary to our experience with real dreams. It may well be that the following story of the dream which greatly disturbed Priam's peace of mind is fiction too:

When mother Hecuba was great with child,
She dreamed that she brought forth a flaming torch.
Alarmed at this, with sighing cares possessed,
The king and father, Priam, to the gods
Did make a sacrifice of bleating lambs.
He, seeking peace and answer to the dream,
Implored Apollo's aid to understand
What great events the vision did foretell.
Apollo's oracle, with voice divine,
Then gave this explanation of the dream:
'Thy next-born son forbear to rear, for he
Will be the death of Pergamos and Troy.'

Grant, I repeat, that these dreams are myths and in the same category put Aeneas's dream, related in the Greek annals of our countryman, Fabius Pictor. According to Pictor everything that Aeneas did or suffered turned out just as it had been predicted to him in a dream.

Translated by W. A. Falconer

OVID

A Cuckold

This passage comes from the third book of Ovid's *Amores*, a collection of lyrics, written around 20 BC, which describes different kinds of love affairs, ranging from a relation based on reciprocal affection or passion to the wily manoeuvres of the seducer.

Darkness, sleep drowning my weary eyes – and then a nightmare
    That scared me silly. This was the way of it:
Picture a sunlit hillside, with thick-clustering ilex
    On its lower slopes, and birds
Everywhere in the treetops, a grassy meadow beyond, and
    One lush green overgrown spot
With a *drip-drip-drip* of water. It was hot. I sought shelter under
    Those leafy branches – yet even there the heat
Oppressed me still. Then, suddenly, a white heifer
    Came into sight, cropping the flowery grass,
Whiter than fresh-fallen snowdrifts, before they've melted
    To wet slush, whiter than sheep's
Milk as it hisses and froths in the bucket at milking-time
    Straight from the udder. A bull,
Her privileged mate, was with her, and settled down on
    The meadow-grass by her side:
Lay there, ruminant, slowly chewing the grassy
    Cud as it rose in his throat, till I saw
Him begin to nod, and sleepily lower that great horned
    Head to the ground.
Then a carrion-crow swooped down on widespread pinions
    And sat cawing there in the grass:
Three times, with mischievous beak, it pecked at the heifer's
    Breast, and tore out a snow –
White tuft. The heifer at last abandoned bull and meadow,
    A livid bruise on her throat.
And seeing other bulls at pasture in the distance,
    Bulls in the distance, and fine
Pasturage to be had, moved over and joined them,
    In quest of more fertile fields,
A richer diet. So tell me, my unseen expounder
    Of dreams (if such dreams do have significance), what
Does mine portend?'

> The interpreter pondered on all
> I'd told him,
> Then answered: 'That heat you tried
> To escape from by sheltering under the breeze-stirred branches,
> Yet in vain, was the heat of desire.
> The heifer stood for your girl – white, a most appropriate colour –
> The bull, her companion, was you.
> The sharp-beaked crow that pecked at her breast was some elderly
> Bawd fast-talking her into another affair.
> Just as the heifer, at last, after long hesitation,
> Left her bull, so you too will be left
> Alone in your own cold bed. The bruise on her breast bears witness
> To the stain of adultery.'
> There
> His interpretation ended. At those words the blood ran freezing
> From my face, and the world went black before my eyes.

Translated by P. Green

PLUTARCH

Caesar's Death

This is Plutarch's version of Calpurnia's dream about Caesar's death. It appears in his *Life of Caesar*. The exact chronology of the *Lives* is not known, but they must have been written at the turn of the second century AD.

After this, while he was sleeping as usual by the side of his wife, all the windows and doors of the chamber flew open at once, and Caesar, confounded by the noise and the light of the moon shining down upon him, noticed that Calpurnia was in a deep slumber, but was uttering indistinct words and inarticulate groans in her sleep; for she dreamed, as it proved, that she was holding her murdered husband in her arms and bewailing him.

Some, however, say that this was not the vision which the woman had; but that there was attached to Caesar's house to give it adornment and distinction, by vote of the senate, a gable-ornament, as Livy says, and it was this which Calpurnia in her dreams saw torn down, and therefore, as she thought, wailed and wept. At all events, when day came, she begged Caesar, if it was possible, not to go out, but to postpone the meeting of the senate; if, however, he had no concern at all for her dreams, she besought him to enquire by other modes of divination and by sacrifices concerning the future. And Caesar also, as it would appear, was in some suspicion and fear. For never before had he perceived in Calpurnia any womanish superstition, but now he saw that she was in great distress. And when the seers also, after many sacrifices, told him that the omens were unfavourable, he resolved to send Antony and dismiss the senate.

Translated by B. Perrin

ARTEMIDORUS

Varieties of Incest

Artemidorus lived in the second half of the second century AD. His *Interpretation of Dreams* was translated into Arabic in the ninth century, and then into European languages during the Renaissance. The book became quite popular in the sixteenth century, as we can note from the reference to Artemidorus in the passage from Rabelais included in this section. What is striking in *The Interpretation of Dreams* is the mixture of would-be scientific method and fantastic conclusions. The author claims to have read all former literature on dreams, and to take accurate consideration of the background of his dreamer (age, health, financial status, profession), but his interpretations seem at times totally arbitrary.

If a man dreams that he is masturbating privately, he will possess either a male or female slave, because the hands that are embracing his penis are like attendants. But if he has no servants, he will suffer a loss, because of the useless elimination of seed. I know of a slave who dreamt that he stroked his master's penis, and he became the companion and attendant of his children, for in his hands he held his master's penis, which is the symbol of his children. Then, again, I know of a slave who dreamt that his penis was stroked and aroused by his master's hands. He was bound to a pillar and received many strokes and was, in this way, extended by his master.

We must interpret dreams involving illegal sexual intercourse in the following manner. To possess a son who is not yet five years old signifies, I have observed, the child's death. That the dream should have this meaning is quite understandable, since the small child will be corrupted and we call corruption 'death'. But if the child is more than five years old but less than ten, he will be sick and the dreamer will be involved in some disgrace as the result of some thoughtless undertaking. The child, because he has been possessed while he is still too young, will suffer pain and, in this way, will be sick. The dreamer will be disgraced because of his foolishness. For no man with any self-control at all would possess either his own son or any other child of so tender an age.

But if the son is more than a child, it has the following meaning. If the father is poor, he will send his son to school and pay his expenses, and will strain off his resources into him in this way. If a rich man has this dream, he will give and transfer to his son considerable property, and in this way spend part of his resources on him.

To have sexual intercourse with one's son, if he is already a grown man and is living abroad, is auspicious. For the dream signifies that they will be reunited and live with one another because of the word 'intercourse' (συνουσία). But if the son is not far away and is living with his father, it is inauspicious. For they must separate because intercourse generally takes place between men when they are not face to face. But to be forcibly possessed by one's son signifies that the dreamer will be injured by his son but also that his son will regret the injury.

If, on the other hand, a son dreams that he possesses his father, he will be banished from his homeland or will enter into a hostile relationship with his father. For either his father will turn away from him, or the public, which corresponds to his father.

A little daughter who is very small, not yet five years old – but still less than ten years old, has the same meaning as a son. But if the girl is ready for marriage, she will enter her husband's house and the dreamer will furnish a dowry and will spend his substance upon his daughter in this way. I know of a man who lost his wife after this dream. This was both normal and logical, since his daughter was then in charge of the household and filled the roles of both wife and daughter.

But if a man dreams that he has sexual intercourse with a married daughter, she will leave her husband and come to him so that she is with him and lives with him. It is good for a poor man to have sexual intercourse with a rich daughter. For he will receive great assistance from his daughter and, in this way, take pleasure in her. But frequently rich fathers have, even against their original resolution, given something to their daughters after this dream, and sick fathers have died and left behind an inheritance for their daughters.

But it is not necessary to discuss the case of a sister, since it has the same meaning as that of a daughter.

Possessing a brother, whether he is older or younger, is auspicious for dreamer. For he will be on top of his brother and disdainful of him. And whoever possesses his friend will become his enemy, since he will have injured his friend without provocation.

The case of one's mother is both complex and manifold and admits of many different interpretations – a thing not all dream interpreters have realized. The fact is that the mere act of intercourse by itself is not enough to show what is portended. Rather, the manner of the embraces and the various positions of the bodies indicate different outcomes.

First, then, we will discuss face-to-face intercourse between a dreamer and his living mother, since a mother who is alive does not have the same meaning as a mother who is dead. Therefore, if anyone possesses his mother through face-to-face intercourse, which some also call the 'natural' method, if she is still alive and his father is in good health, it means that he and his father will become enemies because of the jealousy that generally arises between rivals (which would be greater in their case). But if his father is sick, he will die, since the dreamer will take care of his mother both as a son and as a husband . . .

The meaning will not be the same in the case of a sick man, if his mother is dead. For then the dreamer will himself die very soon afterwards, since the anatomical structure of a corpse is broken down into the material from which it has been formed and composed. And, since bodies are generally made from earth, they are changed into their proper substance. Furthermore, we speak of 'Mother Earth,' and what else would intercourse with a dead mother signify to a sick man if not that he will have intercourse with the earth?

But for a man who is involved in a lawsuit over land rights, for a man who wants to purchase land, and for a man who would like to farm land, it is good to have intercourse with one's dead mother. Some people say that it indicates bad luck only for farmers. For they will cast their seeds down into, as it were, dead land. That is, it will bear no fruit. In my opinion, this does not seem to be the case at all unless, of course, the person dreams that he repents or is distressed by the intercourse. It signifies, moreover, that a person abroad will return to his homeland and that a man who is involved in a dispute over his mother's property will win, and thus take delight not in the body of his mother but rather in her property.

But if a man has the dream in his native land, he will leave it. For it is impossible to remain near one's maternal hearth after such a crime. If he feels grief or remorse because of the intercourse, he will be banished from his native land. If not, he will travel abroad of his own free will.

It is not good to possess a mother who is looking away from one. For then either the mother herself will look away from the dreamer, or his native land, his trade, or any present undertaking. It is also unlucky to have intercourse with one's mother while she is standing. For men use this position only when they have neither bed nor mattress. Therefore it signifies constraint and oppression. It is also bad to have intercourse with one's mother while she is kneeling (and still more unseemly, while she is prostrate). For it signifies great poverty because of the mother's immobility. (For we interpret the mother as a symbol of birth, chance, some fate of the dreamer managing his affairs or as a universal first principle.)

Possessing one's mother from underneath while she is in the 'rider' position is interpreted by some as signifying death to the dreamer. For a mother is like the earth, since the earth is the nurse and mother of all things. But the earth lies above the dead only and not above the living. I myself have observed, however, that sick men regularly die after this dream whereas those who are in good health spend the rest of their lives in great comfort and doing whatever they want. This is both natural and reasonable. For, in the other positions, exhaustion and heavy breathing are generally associated with the male partner. The female partner exerts herself less. But in this position, just the opposite is true, since the male derives his pleasure without exerting himself. But it also signifies that a man will escape the notice of others and remain undetected, since heavy breathing is for the most part eliminated.

But it is not auspicious to use many different positions on one's mother. For it is not right to insult one's mother. But that men invented all the other positions as a result of wantonness, licentiousness, and intoxication, and that only the face-to-face position was taught them by nature is clear from the behaviour of other living creatures. For all types of animals employ a certain habitual position which they do not vary, since they follow their natural instinct. For example, some animals mount from behind, such as the horse, ass, goat, bull, stag, and the other four-footed animals. Others join their mouths first, such as the adder, the dove, and the weasel. Some have intercourse gradually, such as the ostrich. Others, such as birds, rise above their female partners and, by their weight, force them to sink down. Others have no contact at all, but the females gather up the seeds that have been squeezed out by the males, as, for example, fish. And so it is reasonable that men too have their own customary position in the face-to-face method, and that they have discovered the others by yielding to wantonness and licentiousness.

In my experience, however, the worst dream by far is one in which the dreamer practises *fellatio* with his mother. For this signifies to the dreamer the death of children, the loss of property, and grave illness. I know of a man who, after this dream, lost his penis. For it was understandable that he was punished in the part of the body with which he had sinned.

But if a man dreams that he has practised *fellatio* with his wife or mistress, it means hatred or the dissolution of the marriage or affair. For it is impossible for such a woman to share either a meal or a kiss unless, of course, she is pregnant; for she will have a miscarriage, since she has received the seeds in an unnatural fashion. Furthermore, if the woman is richer than her husband, she will pay off many debts on behalf of her husband. If she lives with a slave, she will bring money along with her in order to free the man. And in this way 'the necessary part' of the man (for this is what the penis is called), that is, his financial obligations, will be clean.

A man who has practised *fellatio* with a friend, a relative, or a child who is no longer a baby, will grow to hate the *fellator*. But if he has practised *fellatio* with a baby, he will bury the child. For it is no longer possible for him to kiss the child. *Fellatio* with an unknown person indicates a fine of some sort (for it is impossible to say with accuracy) because of the useless elimination of the seed.

But if a man dreams that he himself is the *fellator* and that he practises the act with a man or woman of his acquaintance, he will grow to hate that person since a union of mouths is no longer possible. If he does not know the person, the dream portends harm for all but those who earn their living through their mouths as, for example, flute-players, trumpeters, public speakers, sophists, and any other similar occupations.

About unnatural sexual intercourse, the following can be said. If a rich man dreams that he is having sexual intercourse with himself, it signifies the loss of his property, great poverty and hunger, since there is no other 'body' present. To a poor man, the dream means grave illness or extraordinary tribulations. For sexual intercourse with one's self would involve great agony.

If a childless man dreams that he is kissing his own penis, he will have children. If he who does so has children who are in a foreign country, he will live to see their return and will kiss them. Furthermore, many who were single have married after this dream. If a man dreams that he has practised *fellatio* with himself, it is auspicious, provided he is a poor man, a slave, or a debtor. For they will be released from their necessity. But it is bad for a father or for a man who wishes to be a father. For, in the case of the former, his children will die; in the case of the latter, they will not be born. For the penis corresponds to children; the mouth to a grave, since the mouth destroys and does not preserve what it receives. This dream predicts, moreover, the death of a wife or mistress. For a man who can furnish himself with sexual pleasure has no need for a woman. For other men, it prophesies either grave financial difficulties or illness. For they will have to resort to the 'bare necessities' in order to stay alive, that is, they will sell whatever they do not want, or their bodies will be consumed by illness so that they will be able to bring their mouths to their genitals because of their emaciated state.

If a woman dreams that she possesses another woman, she will share her secrets with the woman she has possessed. But if she is not familiar with the woman whom she possesses, she will attempt futile projects. But if a woman dreams that she is being possessed by another woman, she will be divorced from her husband or become a widow. She will learn besides the secrets of the woman with whom she has had sexual intercourse.

To have sexual intercourse with a god or goddess or to be possessed by a god signifies death for a sick man. For the soul predicts meetings and intercourse with the gods when it is about to abandon the body in which it dwells. But for other men, provided that they have derived pleasure from the intercourse, it signifies assistance from one's superiors. If they did not derive any pleasure from the act, it means fears and confusion.

Intercourse with Artemis, Athena, Hestia, Rhea, Hera, and Hecate and with these alone, is not auspicious, even if one derives pleasure from it. For the dream prophesies death in the near future for the dreamer. For these goddesses inspire awe and it is my opinion that those who lay a hand upon them will receive no agreeable reward.

Intercourse with the moon is entirely auspicious for ship-masters, pilots, merchants, astronomers, people fond of travelling, and vagabonds. But for other men, it signifies dropsy. For it is a good sign for travellers because of the motion and for astronomers, since no valid theory of celestial observation can be formulated without it. But it is unlucky for sufferers from dropsy because it is moist.

To possess a corpse, whether male or female, with the exception of one's mother, sister, wife, or mistress, or to be possessed by a corpse is thoroughly inauspicious. For the dead are changed into earth. To possess them, therefore, signifies being thrust into the ground, and to be possessed by them means receiving earth into one's body. Indeed, both of these dreams signify death, except for those who live in a foreign country, if it is one where the corpses are not buried. For, to them, it prophesies a return to their homeland. It also means that those who wish to leave their homeland will be detained.

If a person dreams that he is having sexual intercourse with any animal whatsoever and that he himself is doing the mounting, he will derive benefits from a person or thing that corresponds to the animal. We shall give an account of each of these in the section on hunting and animals. But if a man dreams that he has been mounted by the animal, he will endure terrible acts of violence. Many men, moreover, have died after this dream. So much, then, for sexual intercourse.

Translated by R. J. White

ALCIPHRON

The Eagle

Alciphron lived at the end of the second century AD. He wrote
four books of satirical letters: *Letters from Fishermen*, *Letters from
Peasants*, *Letters from Prostitutes* and *Letters from Parasites*. This
extract comes from the latter book, which we present in a modern
colloquial version.

S. Tarvegut to U. N. Chewed

I should like to go to one of those fellows who put out their boards by the
temple of Iacchus and profess to interpret dreams. I would pay him these two
shillings – here they are, you see, in my hand – if he could explain the sight I
saw in my sleep. Indeed I may as well confide to you, my friend, this strange
and incredible vision. I dreamed that I was a comely youth, not such a one as
you meet every day but Ganymede himself, the son of Tros, the paragon of
Ilium, the well-beloved. I had a shepherd's staff and a shepherd's flute, my
head was covered with a Phrygian cap, and I was tending my flock on Mount
Ida. Suddenly there swooped down upon me a great eagle with curved talons,
glaring eyes, and hooked beak. He lifted me up by his claws from the rock
where I was sitting, and carried me high into the air until in hasty flight he
brought me to the heavenly realm. But just as I was going to touch the Gate of
the Seasons a thunderbolt struck me and hurled me down. The bird too was
no longer the great eagle who flies in the sky but a stinking vulture, and I was
once again the S. Tarvegut you know, as naked as when I was born, stripped
as though for a bath or wrestling-match. The shock of my fall naturally awoke
me, and I am still worried about this uncanny dream. I should like expert
advice as to its meaning if I can only find someone who really knows and
moreover will tell me the truth.

Translated by F. A. Wright

AUGUSTINE

The Angel

Saint Augustine wrote *The Confessions* around 400 AD. The dream
of his mother, Saint Monica, appears in the third book.

But *you sent down your help from above* and rescued my soul from the depths of this darkness because my mother, your faithful servant, wept to you for me, shedding more tears for my spiritual death than other mothers shed for the bodily death of a son. For in her faith and in the spirit which she had from you she looked on me as dead. You heard her and did not despise the tears which streamed down and watered the earth in every place where she bowed her head in prayer. You heard her, for how else can I explain the dream with which you consoled her, so that she agreed to live with me and eat at the same table in our home? Lately she had refused to do this, because she loathed and shunned the blasphemy of my false beliefs.

She dreamed that she was standing on a wooden rule, and coming towards her in a halo of splendour she saw a young man who smiled at her in joy, although she herself was sad and quite consumed with grief. He asked her the reason for her sorrow and her daily tears, not because he did not know, but because he had something to tell her, for this is what happens in visions. When she replied that her tears were for the soul I had lost, he told her to take heart for, if she looked carefully, she would see that where she was, there also was I. And when she looked, she saw me standing beside her on the same rule.

Where could this dream have come from, unless it was that you listened to the prayer of her heart? For your goodness is almighty; you take good care of each of us as if you had no others in your care, and you look after all as you look after each. And surely it was for the same reason that, when she told me of the dream and I tried to interpret it as a message that she need not despair of being one day such as I was then, she said at once and without hesitation 'No! He did not say "Where he is, you are", but "Where you are, he is".'

I have often said before and, to the best of my memory, I now declare to you, Lord, that I was much moved by this answer, which you gave me through my mother. She was not disturbed by my interpretation of her dream, plausible though it was, but quickly saw the true meaning, which I had not seen until she spoke. I was more deeply moved by this than by the dream itself, in which the joy for which this devout woman had still so long to wait was foretold so long before to comfort her in the time of her distress. For nearly nine years were yet to come during which I wallowed deep in the mire and the darkness of delusion. Often I tried to lift myself, only to plunge the deeper. Yet all the time this chaste, devout, and prudent woman, a widow such as is close to your heart, never ceased to pray at all hours and to offer you the tears she shed for me. The dream had given new spirit to her hope, but she gave no rest to her sighs and her tears. *Her prayers reached your presence* and yet you still left me to twist and turn in the dark.

Translated by R. S. Pine-Coffin

SONG OF ROLAND

Charlemagne's Dream

This medieval poem, probably composed in the early twelfth century in an Anglo-Norman dialect, is known through a manuscript written down towards 1170. When the following passage begins Charlemagne, after a long war with the Moorish King of Spain, Marsilius, has been offered peace by his enemy. Ganelon, Charlemagne's brother-in-law and Roland's stepfather, though unwilling, has been sent as ambassador to Marsilius, under Roland's taunts. In order to take revenge against his stepson Ganelon betrays the plans of retreat of the Frankish army to Marsilius, who plans to attack the rearguard, led by Roland. Charles' dream takes place the night before the retreat begins.

> Karl the Great hath wasted Spain
> Her cities sacked, her castles ta'en
> But now 'My wars are done,' he cried
> 'And home to gentle France we ride.'
> Count Roland plants his standard high
> Upon a peak against the sky;
> The Franks around encamping lie –
> Alas! the heathen host the while
> Through valley deep and dark defile,
> Are riding on the Christians' track
> All armed in steel from breast to back;
> Their lances poised, their helmets laced,
> Their falchions glittering from the waist,
> Their bucklers from the shoulder swung,
> And so they ride the steeps among,
> Till, in a forest on the height,
> They rest to wait the morning light.
> Four hundred thousand crouching there.
> O God! The Franks are unaware.
>
> The day declined, night darkling crept,
> And Karl, the mighty Emperor, slept.
> He dreamt a dream: he seemed to stand
> In Cizra's pass, with lance in hand.
> Count Ganelon came athwart, and lo,
> He wrenched the ashen spear him fro,

Brandished and shook it along with might,
Till it brake in pieces before his sight;
High towards heaven the splinters flew;
Karl awoke not, he dreamt anew.

In his second dream he seemed to dwell
In his palace of Aix, at his own Chapelle.
A bear seized grimly his right arm on
And bit the flesh to the very bone.
Anon a leopard from Arden wood,
Fiercely flew at him where he stood.
When lo! from his hall, with leap and bound,
Sprang to the rescue a gallant hound.
First from the bear the ear he tore,
Then on the leopard the ear he bore.
The Franks exclaim, 'Tis a striving fray,
But who the victor none may say.
Karl awoke not – he slept away.

Translated by J. O'Hagan

ESCHENBACH

Snake Birth

Wolfram von Eschenbach wrote *Parzival* at the beginning of the thirteenth century. When this dream takes place, Herzeloide is pregnant with Parzival. Just after the dream, she is told that her husband has died in the war with the Infidels.

One noonday the lady lay in troubled sleep, when a dreadful vision came to her. It seemed to her as though a shooting-star swept her to the upper air where a host of fiery thunderbolts assailed her, flying at her all together so that her long tresses hissed and crackled with sparks. The thunder pealed with loud claps and showered down tears of fire. As she came to herself again a griffin snatched at her right hand – whereat all was changed for her! For now she marvelled at how she was mothering a serpent which then rent her womb and how a dragon sucked at her breasts and flew swiftly away and vanished from her sight! It had torn her heart from her body! Such terrors had she to behold! Never since has such anguish befallen a woman in her sleep. Till then she had been all that a knight could desire. Ah, the pity of it! This is all to change. Henceforth she will wear grief's pallor. Her losses grow apace. Sorrows to come are on their way to her.

The lady fell to kicking and writhing, moaning and wailing in her sleep, things unknown in her before. Some young ladies were sitting there: they leapt to the bedside and woke her.

At this point Tampanis, her husband's prudent squire-in-chief, rode in accompanied by numerous little pages. Then happiness was no more. With weeping and wailing they told of their lord's death. This so afflicted her that she fell in a swoon.

Translated by A. T. Hacco

DANTE

The Siren

This dream of Dante, the pilgrim in the nether world, is in canto XIX of *Purgatory*, the second section of *The Divine Comedy*, an epic poem written towards the beginning of the fourteenth century.

What hour the heat of day can warm no longer
　　The chill moon's influence, because the cold
Of earth, or sometimes Saturn's power, is stronger;

When geomancers, looking east, behold
　　Their Greater Fortune rising through a reach
Of sky that darkness cannot long enfold;

In dream a woman sought me, halt of speech,
　　Squint-eyed, on maimed feet lurching as she stept,
With crippled hands, and skin of sallowy bleach.

I gazed; and as to cold limbs that have crept
　　Heavy with night, the sun gives life anew,
Even so my look unloosed the string that kept

Her utterance captive, and right quickly drew
　　Upright her form that all misshappen hung,
And stained her withered cheek to love's own hue.

Then she began to sing, when thus her tongue
　　Was freed – and such a spell she held me by
As had been hard to break; and so she sung:

'Lo, the sweet Siren! yea, 'tis I, 'tis I
　　Who lead the mariners in mid-sea astray,
Such pleasures in my melting measures lie.

I turned Ulysses from his wandering way
  With music; few, I trow, to me who grow
  Know how to go, longing I so allay.'

Her lips yet moved to that melodious flow
  When hard at hand a lady I espied,
  Holy, alert, her guiles to overthrow.

'O Virgil, Virgil, who is this?' she cried
  Indignant; and he came, with heedful eyes
  On that discreet one, and on naught beside.

The first he seized, and rending her disguise
  In front, showed me her belly, which released
  So foul a stench, I woke with that surprise.

I looked about for my good lord: 'At least
  Three times,' said he, 'I've called thee; rise and come;
  Let's find the breach whereby thou enterest.'

Translated by D. Sayers

CHESTER MYSTERY PLAYS

Joseph and the Angel

This is from *The Nativity*, the fifth text from *The Chester Mystery Plays*, dating from the early fourteenth century. The text we reproduce here is from a modern English version by Maurice Hussey. *The Nativity* starts with the episode of the Annonciation between Mary and Gabriel. After this scene Joseph begins his lamentation.

Joseph:
Alas, alas, and woe is me!
Who hath made her with child?

Well, I feared an old man and a may
Could find accord in no way,
These many years I have had no play
Or worked any works so wild.

Three months she has been from me
And now she has gotten, as I see,
A great belly for her free
Since she went away.

And mine it is not, I make so bold
For I am both old and cold;
This thirty winter though I would
I have played no such play

Therefore I will sleep a while
Now my wife will me beguile
I will go from her; to defile
Myself, I am loth, I may say.

This case makes me so heavy
That sleep now craves this eye
Lord, thou on her have mercy
For her misdeed today.

                                        (he falls asleep)

Angel:
Joseph, leave that feeble thought
Take Mary, thy wife, and fear thee nought
For wickedly she has not wrought.
This is God's will.

That child that she shall bear, I wis,
Of the Holy Ghost begotten is
To save mankind that did amiss
A prophecy to fulfil.

Joseph:
Ah, now I know, Lord, it is so.
No man will dare to be her foe.
While I on earth way go
With her I shall be

Now Christ is come into our fold
As ancient prophets all foretold.
To thy light, Lord, I hold,
And ever worship thee.

Angel:

Joseph, I warn thee as I may
To Bethlem thou must make thy way
Lest in danger thou fallest today
If thou beest long.

Joseph:

Now since it must no other be,
Mary, dear wife, now hurry we.
An ox will I take off with me
Which there can be sold.

The money from him, it seems to me
Shall help us in this city
And pay for both the tribute fee
In silver and gold.

Modern Version by M. Hussey

RABELAIS

The Horns of Panurge

The double explanation of Panurge's dream, which occurs at
chapter XIV of the *Third Book* of Rabelais, shows one of the many
divinatory methods tried by Panurge to find out whether he should
marry or not. *The Third Book* was first published in 1546.

At seven o'clock of the next following morning, Panurge did not fail to present
himself before Pantagruel, in whose chamber were at that time Epistemon, friar
John of the Funnels, Ponocrates, Eudemon, Carpalim, and others: to whom, at
the entry of Panurge, Pantagruel said, 'Lo here cometh our dreamer.' 'That
word,' quoth Epistemon, 'in ancient times cost very much, and was dearly sold
to the children of Jacob.' Then said Panurge, 'I have been plunged into my
dumps so deeply, as if I had been lodged with gaffer Noddy-cap: dreamed
indeed I have, and that right lustily; but I could take along with me no more
thereof, that I did truly understand, save only that I in my vision had a pretty,
fair, young, gallant, handsome woman, who no less lovingly and kindly treated
and entertained me, hugged, cherished, cockered, dandled, and made much of
me, as if I had been another neat dillidarling minion, like Adonis. Never was
man more glad than I was then: my joy at that time was incomparable: she

flattered me, tickled me, stroked me, groped me, frizzled me, curled me, kissed me, embraced me, laid her hands about my neck, and now and then made, jestingly, pretty little horns above my forehead. I told her, in the like disport, as I did play the fool with her, that she should rather place and fix them in a little below mine eyes, that I might see the better what I should stick at with them: for being so situated, Momus then would find no fault therewith, as he did once with the position of the horns of bulls. The wanton, toying girl, notwithstanding any remonstrance of mine to the contrary, did always drive and thrust them further in: yet thereby (which to me seemed wonderful) she did not do me any hurt at all. A little after, though I know not how, I thought I was transformed into a tabor or drum, and she into a chough, or madge-howlet.

'My sleeping there being interrupted, I awaked in a start, angry, displeased, perplexed, chafing, and very wroth. There have you a large platter full of dreams; make thereupon good cheer, and, if you please, spare not to interpret them according to the understanding which you may have in them. Come Carpalim, let us to breakfast.'

'To my sense and meaning,' quoth Pantagruel, 'if I have skill or knowledge in the art of divination by dreams, your wife will not really, and to the outward appearance of the world, plant, or set horns, and stick them fast in your forehead, after a visible manner, as satyrs use to wear and carry them; but she will be so far from preserving herself loyal in the discharge and observance of a conjugal duty, that on the contrary she will violate her plighted faith, break her marriage-oath, infringe all matrimonial ties, prostitute her body to the dalliance of other men, and so make you a cuckold. This point is clearly and manifestly explained and expounded by Artemidorus, just as I have related it. Nor will there be any metamorphosis, or transmutation made of you into a drum or tabor; but you will surely be as soundly beaten, as e'er was tabor at a merry wedding: nor yet will she be changed into a chough, or madge-howlet; but will steal from you, chiefly in the night, as is the nature of that thievish bird. Hereby may you perceive your dreams to be in every jot conform and agreeable to the Virgilian lots: a cuckold you will be, beaten and robbed.' Then cried out friar John, with a loud voice: 'He tells the truth upon my conscience: thou wilt be a cuckold, an honest one, I warrant thee. O the brave horns that will be borne by thee! ha, ha ha, our good master de Cornibus, God save thee, and shield thee; wilt thou be pleased to preach but two words of a sermon to us, and I will go through the parish church to gather up alms for the poor.'

'You are,' quoth Panurge, 'very far mistaken in your interpretation; for the matter is quite contrary to your sense thereof. My dream presageth, that I shall, by marriage, be stored with plenty of all manner of goods; the hornifying of me shewing, that I shall possess a cornucopia, that amalthæan horn, which is called the horn of abundance, whereof the fruition did still portend the wealth of the enjoyer. You possibly will say, that they are rather like to be satyrs' horns; for you of these did make some mention: Amen, amen. Fiat, fiatur, ad differentiam papæ. Thus shall I have my touch-her-home still ready; my staff of love, sempiternally in a good case, will, satyr-like, be never toiled out; a thing which all men wish for, and send up their prayers to that purpose; but such a thing as nevertheless is granted but to few. Hence doth it follow, by a consequence as clear as the sun-beams, that I shall never be in the danger of being made a cuckold: for the defect hereof is, *causa sine qua non*; yea, the sole cause (as many think) of making husbands cuckolds. What makes poor scoundrel rogues to beg, I pray you? Is it not because they have not enough at home, wherewith to fill their bellies, and their poaks? What is it makes the wolves to leave the woods? Is it not the want of fresh meat? What maketh, women whores? you understand me well enough. And herein I submit my opinion to the judgment of learned lawyers, presidents, counsellors, advocates, procurers, attorneys, and other glossers and commentators on the venerable rubric, *de frigidis & maleficiatis.* You are in truth, sir, as it seems to (excuse my boldness if I have erred or transgressed) in a most palpable and absurd error, to attribute my horns to cuckoldry: Diana wears them on her head, after the manner of a crescent: is she a cucquean for that? how the devil can she be cuckolded, who never yet was married? Speak somewhat more correctly, I beseech you, lest she, being offended, furnish you with a pair of horns, shapen by the pattern of those which she made for Actæon. The goodly Bacchus also carries horns; Pan, Jupiter Hammon, with a great many others: are they all cuckolds? If Jove be a cuckold, Juno is a whore: this follows by the figure metalepsis: as to call a child, in the presence of his father and mother, a bastard, or whore's son, is, tacitly and underboard, no less than if one had said openly, the father is a cuckold, and his wife a punk. Let our discourse come nearer to the purpose: the horns that my wife did make me are horns of abundance, planted and grafted in my head for the increase and shooting up of all good things: this will I affirm for truth, upon my word, and pawn my faith and credit both upon it. As for the rest, I will be no less joyful, frolic, glad, cheerful, merry, jolly, and gamesome than a well-bended tabor in the hands of a good drummer, at a nuptial feast, still making a noise, still rolling, still buzzing and cracking. Believe me, Sir, in that consisteth none of my least good fortunes. And my wife will be jocund, feat, compt, neat, quaint, dainty, trim, tricked up, brisk, smirk and smug, even as a pretty little Cornish chough: who will not believe this, let hell or the gallows be the burden of his christmas carol.'

Translated by T. Urquhardt

COBO

The Inca

This dream is taken from Bernabé Cobo's *Historia del nuevo mundo*, written in the seventeenth century and first published in four volumes in Seville between 1890 and 1895.

Huayna Cápac was terrified of the plague. He shut himself away, and during his confinement he had a dream in which three dwarfs came to him and said: 'Inca, we have come to fetch you.' The plague reached Huayna Cápac and he ordered the oracle of Pachacámac to interpret what should be done so as to recover his health. The oracle declared that he should be brought out into the sun, that in this way he would recover. The Inca went out into the sun, and dropped dead on the spot.

Translated by J. Lyons

BOSSUET

The Parable of the Blind Man

Jacques Bénigne Bossuet was, together with Bourdaloue, the greatest Jesuit preacher of the reign of Louis XIV. The Funeral Oration, from which this passage is taken, was pronounced on the occasion of the death of Anne de Gonzague, Princesse Palatine. Anne was one of the most picturesque characters in the French court, refusing to conform to etiquette. She has left extremely vivid memoirs.

Such was the deep abyss of perdition into which the Palatine princess was heading. It is true that she ardently desired to know truth. But how can there be truth without faith, a faith she felt she would never know, unless God instilled it in her by some miracle. What did it avail her to have retained her knowledge of the Divinity? Even the most dissolute souls do not reject the idea of it, so as not to have to reproach themselves with a blindness too visible. A God which we form to our own requirements, as patient, as indifferent as our passions demand, will not inconvenience us. We allow ourselves the liberty to think whatever we will, and feel as if we are breathing afresh. We imagine we have full sway over ourselves and our desires; and believing we have acquired the right to allow ourselves anything, imagine we have all the world's delights in our grasp, and taste them in advance.

And so, Christians, now that she was in this state, her faith itself lost, that is, the very foundation of our existence upturned, what remained for our princess? What remained for a soul which, by the just judgement of God, was bereft of all graces and which no longer retained any link with Jesus Christ? What remained her, Christians, if not that which Saint Augustine has described? What remained was sovereign misery and sovereign mercy: *Restabat magna miseria et magna misericordia.* There remained the hidden eye of a merciful Providence, which intended to recall her from the extremities of earthly life; and I will now tell you of its first stroke. Listen well, gentlemen, for there is something truly miraculous about it. It was a splendid dream, of the sort which God Himself sends from Heaven by the good ministry of the angels, one of those dreams whose images are so clear and perfectly distinguished, and in which we see a touch of the celestial. She dreamt – and this is as she herself told it to the reverend father. Listen well, and above all, as you listen, take care not to scorn the order of divine warnings and the ways of grace – she dreamt, as I was saying, that while walking alone in a forest she had met a blind man in a little cabin. She went up and asked him whether he had been blind from birth or lost his sight as the result of some accident. He replied he had been blind from birth. Then you do not know, she said, what it is to see the light, so lovely and sweet, and the sun, all shining in its beauty? I have never known the pleasure of that lovely object, he said, and I cannot imagine how it must look. But, he continued, I have never ceased to believe that it is ravishingly beautiful. Then the blind man's voice and face seemed to change; and taking on a tone of authority, he spoke thus: 'My example should teach you that there are certain things most excellent and most glorious which are not accessible to our sight and which for all that are no less desirable, although we can neither understand them nor conceive of them.' For indeed, unbelievers lack a sense, just like the blind man; and this sense is given us by God, as Saint John says: 'He has given us a sense that we might know the true God, and that we might be one in his true Son: *Dedit nobis sensum, ut cognoscamus verum Deum et simus in vero Filio ejus.*'

Our princess understood. There and then, in the middle of this most mysterious dream, she applied the blind man's wonderful comparison to the verities of religion and of the other life: and it is her own words that I am telling you now. God, who needs neither time, nor long circuitous reasoning to make Himself understood, instantly opened her eyes. At that moment, in a sudden burst of illumination, she felt herself so enlightened, as she herself goes on, and moved to such profound joy at having found what she had been seeking for so long, that she could not help embracing the blind man, whose words had revealed to her a light much more beautiful than the one he was denied. And, she says, my heart was filled with a joy so sweet and a faith so strong that words cannot express it. You are wondering, Christians, how she will awake from such a gentle and marvellous sleep. Listen, and you will see that this dream is truly divine. Thereupon, she says, she woke, and found herself just as she had been in the dream, that is, so utterly changed that she could hardly believe it. The miracle she was waiting for had come to pass; she believed, who had once thought faith impossible; God had changed her by a sudden illumination and by a dream akin to ecstasy.

All follows in her with the same force. 'I rose up quickly,' she continues; 'my actions were mixed with joy and extraordinary vitality.' As you can see, this new vivacity which informed her actions can still be felt in her words. 'Everything I read on religion moved me till my tears flowed. At mass I found myself in a state quite unlike that to which I was accustomed.' For this, of all mysteries, was the one she found most incredible. 'But now,' she says, 'I seemed to feel the real presence of Our Lord, almost as one senses things which are visible and not to be doubted.' Thus she passed immediately from a deep obscurity to a manifest enlightenment. The clouds around her soul are dispersed: a miracle as astounding as that by which Jesus Christ caused instantly to drop from Saul's converted eyes those scales which covered them. Who then would not cry out at such a suddden change: *The hand of God is here*! What follows lets no doubt remain, and the operation of grace reveals itself in its fruits. From that happy moment forth, our princess's faith was unshakeable; and even that tangible joy she found in believing remained with her for some time.

But, amidst these celestial comforts, divine justice too came in its turn. The humble princess did not believe she would yet be permitted to approach the holy sacraments. Three whole months she passed in tearfully reviewing the years that had fled by amidst so many illusions, and in preparing her confession. As the awaited day approached on which she hoped to confess, she fell into a faint which left her with neither colour, nor pulse, nor respiration. On awaking from such a long, strange fainting fit, she found herself plunged anew into a greater pain; and, after the pangs of death, she now felt all the horrors of Hell. A fitting effect of the sacraments of the Church, which, granted or deferred, let the soul feel God's forgiveness or all the weight of his vengeance! She calls for her confessor, who, arriving, finds her without strength, unable to apply herself and barely able to utter a few broken phrases; and so he was obliged to postpone the confession until the next day. But she herself must tell you of the night she passed in waiting.

Who knows whether Providence might not have brought some strayed soul here that he might be touched by this story? 'It is impossible,' she says, 'to imagine the strange pains of my soul, unless one has felt them. I feared that my fainting might return at any moment, and with it my death and my damnation. I knew well I was not worthy of a mercy I had so long neglected, and in my heart I said to God I had no right to complain of his justice, but that at last, oh how unbearable, I would be eternally among his enemies, go eternally without loving him, eternally hated by him. I felt this displeasure most tenderly, and I even felt it, so I believe (and these are her own words) entirely separate from the other pains of Hell.' And here, dear Sisters, is that pure love you know so well, the love which God himself sows in our hearts, with all its delicacy and in all its truth. Here is that fear which transforms hearts; not the fear of the slave who dreads the coming of a harsh master, but that of a chaste wife who fears to lose that which she loves. These tender sentiments, mixed with tears and dread, sharpened her pain unto the utmost extremity; no one could tell the cause, and her convulsions were attributed to the fever that racked her.

As she was in this piteous state, feeling herself to be as one outcast almost without hope of salvation, God, who makes his truths understood in such manner and by such figures as he pleases, continued to instruct her as he did Joseph and Solomon; and while she was prostrate with torpor, he placed in her soul this parable, so similar to those of the Gospel. There appeared before her the very image that Jesus Christ did not disdain to give us as the emblem of tenderness, a mother hen leading her chicks, which clustered round her. One of them having strayed, our ailing friend sees it seized in the jaws of a greedy dog. She runs up and tears the innocent creature away from it. At that moment, a voice cries out from another side, telling her to return it to its ravisher, whose ardour she would extinguish if she removed its prey. 'No,' she says, 'I will never return it.' At that moment, she awoke, and instantly understood the meaning of the image she had been shown, as if someone had said to her: 'If you, who are wicked, cannot bring yourself to return this little creature that you have saved, how can you believe that God, who is infinitely good, will return you to the Devil, after saving you from his power? Hope, and take courage.' Upon these words, she remained in a state of calm and of inexpressible joy, 'as if an angel had taught her (these are still her words) that God would not abandon her.' So too did the fury of the winds and the waters suddenly abate before the admonishing voice of Jesus Christ; and he performed no less a miracle in the soul of our holy penitent when, among the terrors of an alarmed conscience and the pains of Hell, he let her instantly feel, by a vital faith, with the remission of her sins, that *peace which surpasseth all understanding.* For now a heavenly joy overcame all her senses and the humiliated bones trembled. Remember then, O holy Pontiff, when you hold in your hands the holy victim who carries away the sins of this world, remember this miracle of his grace. And you, holy priests, come; and you, holy Daughters, and you, Christians, and come too, O sinners; and let us all sing out with one voice the hymn of his deliverance, and let us never cease to repeat, in David's words, that *God is good and his mercy everlasting.*

Translated by J. Romney

BAILLET

Descartes' Dreams

These dreams were first reported by A. Baillet in his *Vie de Monsieur Des Cartes*, published in 1691. According to the author they had a decisive influence on Descartes' *Discours de la Méthode* (1637). The philosopher did not make use of them in his works, but they were included in the edition of his complete works (Descartes, *Oeuvres*, ed. by Charles Adam and Paul Tannery, Paris, J. Vrin, 1964–74, vol. X, pp. 179–88).

... He tells us that on the tenth of November sixteen hundred and nineteen, having gone to bed full of his inspiration and engrossed in the thought that he had that day discovered the foundations of his remarkable science, he had three consecutive dreams in one night, which could only, he surmised, have come from above. When he had fallen asleep he found his mind's eye confronted with the image of several phantoms appearing before him, and which terrified him so greatly that, as he walked through the streets in his dream, he was obliged to lean over on to his left side in order to go where he wanted, for his right side felt so weak that he could not hold himself up. Ashamed to be walking in this manner, he made an effort to straighten himself; but just then a great gust of wind carried him up in a sort of whirlwind and spun him round three or four times on his left foot. But that was not the most frightening part. He had such difficulty dragging himself along that he seemed to fall at every step, until finally, noticing a college open along his way, he went inside in search of shelter and a remedy for his pain.

His first thought was to find the college chapel and to go and pray there; but realizing that he had just passed a man he knew without greeting him, he was about to turn back to pay his compliments, only to be knocked violently backwards by the wind blowing on to the chapel. Just then, he noticed another person standing in the middle of the courtyard, who called him by name most politely and amiably, and suggested he go and see Monsieur N., who had something to give him. M. Descartes assumed it must be a melon, brought from some foreign land. But he was more surprised to see that the crowd who had gathered around him with the other person to join in conversation were all standing upright and steady on their feet; while he himself was still hunched and wobbling about, although standing on the same ground, and although the wind, which had contrived to knock him over several times, had greatly diminished.

With this image in his mind, he awoke, and at that very moment, felt a real pain in his side, which made him fear some spirit of evil might be at work to lead him astray. He turned immediately on to his right side; for it was on his left side that he had fallen asleep, and that he had had the dream. He prayed to God to preserve him from the evil effects of his dream, and from all the woes that might befall him as a punishment for his sins, which he thought might be sufficiently grave to bring the bolts of heaven's vengeance crashing on his head; although he had till then lived a life quite irreproachable in the eyes of men.

So it was that he went back to sleep, after nearly two hours sunk in various thoughts of the good and evil that attend us in this world. A new dream came to him right away, in which he thought he heard a loud, explosive noise, which he took to be a thunderclap. He instantly woke up in fright; and opening his eyes, saw that the room was filled with fiery sparks scattered all around. This had already happened to him on other occasions; and it was not unusual for him to wake in the middle of the night with his eyes so sparkling that he could see the objects closest to him. But on this occasion, he decided to look to Philosophy for an explanation; and from it he arrived at a conclusion that satisfied his intelligence, after observing, by opening then closing his eyes in succession, the nature of the phenomena before him. In this way his fear evaporated and he went back to sleep in a reasonably calm state.

A moment later, he had a third dream, which was nothing like as fearsome as the first two. In this one, he found a book on the table, although he did not know who had put it there. He opened it and was delighted to see that it was a *Dictionary*, for he hoped he might find it rather useful. At the very instant, he found he had his hand on another book; this one, too, he had never seen before, and had no idea where it had come from. It turned out to be a collection of poems by different authors, entitled *Corpus Poetarum* etc. He was curious to read some of it; and opening the book, he came upon the line, *Quod vitae sectabor iter?* etc.

At that moment, he saw a man he did not know, who handed him a piece of verse beginning with the words *Est & Non*, and recommended it as excellent. M. Descartes told him he knew what it was, that the piece was one of the Idylls of Ausonius, which was included in the large collection of poets that he had on his table. He decided to show it to the man, and began to leaf through the book, whose order and arrangement he prided himself on knowing perfectly. As he was searching for the place, the man asked him where he had had the book, and M. Descartes replied that he had no idea; and that he had just a moment earlier held another in his hand, but it had just vanished, without his knowing who had brought it nor who had taken it away again. No sooner had he said this than he saw the book reappear at the other end of the table. But the dictionary was no longer complete as it had been when he had first seen it. However, he finally came to the poems of Ausonius, in the collection of poets he was leafing through; and as he was unable to find the piece which began *Est & Non*, he told the man he knew an even finer one by the same poet, and which began *Quod vitae sectabor iter?*

The man asked him to show it to him, and M. Descartes was setting about to find it when he came upon several small portraits in copper-plate engraving; the book was indeed very fine, he had to admit, but it was certainly not the same edition as the one he knew. Before he could say any more, books and man both vanished from his mental vision, although he still did not wake up. What is most remarkable is that, not knowing whether what he had seen was a dream or a vision, he not only decided, while still asleep, that it was a dream, but even managed to interpret it before sleep had left him. The dictionary, he decided, signified nothing else but all the sciences gathered together; and the collection of poetry, entitled *Corpus Poetarum*, signified in particular, and in a more distinct manner, Philosophy and Wisdom conjoined. For he did not find it particularly surprising that poets, even the mere witless rhymers among them, should be full of maxims more weighty, more sensible and better expressed than those found in the writings of philosophers. He attributed this marvel to the divinity of Inspiration, and to the power of the Imagination, which brings out the seeds of wisdom (which exist in the minds of all men, as sparks of fire in pebbles) with much greater facility and even greater brilliance than Reason can in philosophers. M. Descartes, continuing to interpret his dream in his sleep, concluded that the poem on the uncertainty of the type of life one should choose, the one beginning *Quod vitae sectabor iter*, showed the good counsel of a wise person, or even Moral Theology itself.

Translated by J. Romney

GIBBON

By This Sign

The six volumes of Edward Gibbon's *Decline and Fall of the Roman Empire*, from which this version of Constantine's dream is taken, were published between 1776 and 1788.

In all occasions of danger or distress it was the practice of the primitive Christians to fortify their minds and bodies by the sign of the cross, which they used in all their ecclesiastical rites, in all the daily occurrences of life, as an infallible preservative against every species of spiritual or temporal evil. The authority of the church might alone have had sufficient weight to justify the devotion of Constantine, who, in the same prudent and gradual progress, acknowledged the truth and assumed the symbol of Christianity. But the testimony of a contemporary writer, who in a formal treatise has avenged the cause of religion, bestows on the piety of the emperor a more awful and sublime character. He affirms, with the most perfect confidence, that, in the night which preceded the last battle against Maxentius, Constantine was admonished in a dream to inscribe the shields of his soldiers with the *celestial sign of God*, the sacred monogram of the name of Christ; that he executed the commands of Heaven, and that his valour and obedience were rewarded by the decisive victory of the Milvian Bridge. Some considerations might perhaps incline a sceptical mind to suspect the judgement or the veracity of the rhetorician, whose pen, either from zeal or interest, was devoted to the cause of the prevailing faction. . .

If the dream of Constantine is separately considered, it may be naturally explained either by the policy or the enthusiasm of the emperor. Whilst his anxiety for the approaching day, which must decide the fate of the empire, was suspended by a short and interrupted slumber, the venerable form of Christ, and the well-known symbol of his religion, might forcibly offer themselves to the active fancy of a prince who reverenced the name, and had perhaps secretly implored the power, of the God of the Christians. As readily might a consummate statesman indulge himself in the use of one of those military stratagems, one of those pious frauds, which Philip and Sertorius had employed with such art and effect. The præternatural origin of dreams was universally admitted by the nations of antiquity, and a considerable part of the Gallic army was already prepared to place their confidence in the salutary sign of the Christian religion. The secret vision of Constantine could be disproved only by the event; and the intrepid hero who had passed the Alps and the Apennine might view with careless despair the consequences of a defeat under the walls of Rome. The senate and people, exulting in their own deliverance from an odious tyrant, acknowledged that the victory of Constantine surpassed the powers of man, without daring to insinuate that it had been obtained by the protection of the *gods*. The triumphal arch, which was erected about three years after the event, proclaims, in ambiguous language, that, by the greatness of his own mind, and by an *instinct* or impulse of the Divinity, he had saved and avenged the Roman republic. The Pagan orator, who had seized an earlier opportunity of celebrating the virtues of the conqueror, supposes that he alone enjoyed a secret and intimate commerce with the Supreme Being, who delegated the care of mortals to his subordinate deities; and thus assigns a very plausible reason why the subjects of Constantine should not presume to embrace the new religion of their sovereign.

The philosopher, who with calm suspicion examines the dreams and omens, the miracles and prodigies, of profane or even of ecclesiastical history, will probably conclude that, if the eyes of the spectators have sometimes been deceived by fraud, the understanding of the readers has much more frequently been insulted by fiction. Every event, or appearance, or accident, which seems to deviate from the ordinary course of nature, has been rashly ascribed to the immediate action of the Deity; and the astonished fancy of the multitude has sometimes given shape and colour, language and motion, to the fleeting but uncommon meteors of the air. Nazarius and Eusebius are the two most celebrated orators who, in studied panegyrics, have laboured to exalt the glory of Constantine . . .

The Christian fable of Eusebius, which, in the space of twenty-six years, might arise from the original dream, is cast in a much more correct and elegant mould. In one of the marches of Constantine he is reported to have seen with his own eyes the luminous trophy of the cross, placed above the meridian sun, and inscribed with the following words: BY THIS CONQUER. This amazing object in the sky astonished the whole army, as well as the emperor himself, who was yet undetermined in the choice of a religion: but his astonishment was converted into faith by the vision of the ensuing night. Christ appeared before his eyes; and displaying the same celestial sign of the cross, he directed Constantine to frame a similar standard, and to march, with an assurance of victory, against Maxentius and all his enemies. The learned bishop of Cæsarea appears to be sensible that the recent discovery of this marvellous anecdote would excite some surprise and distrust among the most pious of his readers. Yet, instead of ascertaining the precise circumstances of time and place, which always serve to detect falsehood or establish truth; instead of collecting and recording the evidence of so many living witnesses, who must have been spectators of this stupendous miracle, Eusebius contents himself with alleging a very singular testimony, that of the deceased Constantine, who, many years after the event, in the freedom of conversation, had related to him this extraordinary incident of his own life, and had attested the truth of it by a solemn oath. The prudence and gratitude of the learned prelate forbade him to suspect the veracity of his victorious master; but he plainly intimates that, in a fact of such a nature, he should have refused his assent to any meaner authority. This motive of credibility could not survive the power of the Flavian family; and the celestial sign, which the Infidels might afterwards deride, was disregarded by the Christians of the age which immediately followed the conversion of Constantine. But the Catholic church, both of the East and of the West, has adopted a prodigy which favours, or seems to favour, the popular worship of the cross. The vision of Constantine maintained an honourable place in the legend of superstition till the bold and sagacious spirit of criticism presumed to depreciate the triumph, and to arraign the truth, of the first Christian emperor.

The Protestant and philosophic readers of the present age will incline to believe that, in the account of his own conversion, Constantine attested a wilful falsehood by a solemn and deliberate perjury. They may not hesitate to pronounce that, in the choice of a religion, his mind was determined only by a sense of interest; and that (according to the expression of a profane poet) he used the altars of the church as a convenient footstool to the throne of the empire. A conclusion so harsh and so absolute is not, however, warranted by our knowledge of human nature, of Constantine, or of Christianity. In an age of religious fervour the most artful statesmen are observed to feel some part of the enthusiasm which they inspire; and the most orthodox saints assume the dangerous privilege of defending the cause of truth by the arms of deceit and falsehood. Personal interest is often the standard of our belief, as well as of our practice; and the same motives of temporal advantage which might influence the public conduct and professions of Constantine would insensibly dispose his mind to embrace a religion so propitious to his fame and fortunes. His vanity was gratified by the flattering assurance that *he* had been chosen by Heaven to reign over the earth: success had justified his divine title to the throne, and that title was founded on the truth of the Christian revelation. As real virtue is sometimes excited by undeserved applause, the specious piety of Constantine, if at first it was only specious, might gradually, by the influence of praise, of habit, and of example, be matured into serious faith and fervent devotion.

JEAN PAUL

The Orphaned Christ

This passage is taken from Jean Paul's *Flowers, Fruit And Thorn Pieces, Or The Married Life, Death And Wedding Of The Advocate Of The Poor Firmian Stanislaus Siebenkäs*, first published in 1796 and revised in 1818. The title of the novel indicates both its general narrative line and its rambling manner. It is the story of a life, but broken up by thoughts and dreams. Madame de Stael quoted the section reproduced here in *De l'Allemagne*.

When we are told in childhood, that at midnight, when our sleep reaches near unto the soul, and even darkens our dreams, the dead rise out of *their* sleep and mimic the religious service of the living in the churches, we shudder at death on account of the dead; and in the loneliness of night we turn away our gaze from the long narrow windows of the silent church, fearing to examine whether their glitter proceeds from the moonbeams, or not.

Childhood, and especially its terrors and raptures, once more assume wings and brightness in our dreams, and play like glow-worms in the little night of the soul. Crush not these little fluttering sparks! Leave us even our dark painful drams, as relieving middle tints of reality! And what could compensate us for our dreams, which bear us away from beneath the roar of the waterfall into the mountain-heights of childhood, where the stream of life, yet silent in its little plain, and a mirror of heaven, flowed towards its precipices?

Once on a summer evening I lay upon a mountain in the sunshine, and fell asleep; and I dreamt that I awoke in the churchyard, having been roused by the rattling wheels of the tower-clock, which struck eleven. I looked for the sun in the void night-heaven; for I thought that it was eclipsed by the moon. All the graves were unclosed, and the iron doors of the charnel-house were opened and shut by invisible hands. Shadows cast by no one flitted along the walls, and other shadows stalked erect in the free air. No one slept any longer in the open coffins but the children. A grey, sultry fog hung suspended in heavy folds in the heavens, and a gigantic shadow drew it in like a net, ever nearer, and closer, and hotter. Above me I heard the distant fall of avalanches; beneath me, the first step of an immeasurable earthquake. The church was heaved up and down by two incessant discords, which struggled with one another, and in vain sought to unite in harmony. Sometimes a grey glimmer flared up on the windows, and, molten by the glimmer, the iron and lead ran down in streams. The net of fog and the reeling earth drove me into the temple, at the door of which brooded two basilisks with twinkling eyes in two poisonous nests. I passed through unknown shadows, on whom were impressed all the centuries of years. The shadows stood congregated round the altar; and in all the breast throbbed and trembled in the place of a heart. One corpse alone, which had just been buried in the church, lay still upon its pillow, and its breast heaved not, while upon its smiling countenance lay a happy dream; but on the entrance of one of the living he awoke, and smiled no more. He opened his closed eyelids with a painful effort, but within there was no eye; and in the sleeping bosom, instead of a heart, there was a wound. He lifted up his hands, and folded them in prayer; but the arms lengthened out and detached themselves from the body, and the folded hands fell down apart. Aloft, on the church-dome, stood the dialplate of Eternity; but there was no figure visible upon it, and it was its own index; only a black finger pointed to it, and the dead wished to read the time upon it.

A lofty, noble form, having the expression of a never-ending sorrow, now sank down from above upon the altar, and all the dead exclaimed 'Christ! is there no God?' And he answered, 'There is none!' The whole shadow of each dead one, and not the breast alone, now trembled, and one after another was severed by the trembling.

Christ continued: 'I traversed the worlds. I ascended into the suns, and flew with the milky ways through the wildernesses of the heavens; but there is no God! I descended as far as Being throws its shadow, and gazed down into the abyss, and cried aloud 'Father, where art thou?' but I heard nothing but the eternal storm which no one rules; and the beaming rainbow in the west hung, without a creating sun, above the abyss, and fell down in drops; and when I looked up to the immeasurable world for the Divine Eye, it glared upon me from an empty, bottomless socket, and Eternity lay brooding upon chaos, and gnawed it, and ruminated it. Cry on, ye discords! cleave the shadows with your cries; for he is not!'

The shadows grew pale and melted, as the white vapour formed by the frost melts and becomes a warm breath, and all was void. Then there arose and came into the temple – a terrible sight for the heart – the dead children who had awakened in the churchyard, and they cast themselves before the lofty form upon the altar, and said, 'Jesus! have we no Father?' and he answered with streaming eyes, 'We are all orphans, I and you; we are without a Father.'

Thereupon the discords shrieked more harshly; the trembling walls of the temple split asunder, and the temple and the children sank down, and the earth and the sun followed, and the whole immeasurable universe fell rushing past us; and aloft upon the summit of infinite Nature stood Christ, and gazed down into the universe, chequered with thousands of suns, as into a mine dug out of the Eternal Night, wherein the suns are the miners' lamps, and the milky ways the veins of silver.

And when Christ beheld the grinding concourse of worlds, the torch-dances of the heavenly *ignes fatui*, and the coral-banks of beating hearts; and when he beheld how one sphere after another poured out its gleaming souls into the sea of death, as a drop of water strews gleaming lights upon the waves, sublime, as the loftiest finite being, he lifted up his eyes to the Nothingness, and to the empty Immensity, and said: 'Frozen, dumb Nothingness! cold, eternal Necessity! insane Chance! know ye what is beneath you? When will ye destroy the building and me? Chance! knowest thou thyself when with hurricanes thou wilt march through the snowstorm of stars and extinguish one sun after the other, and when the sparkling dew of the constellations shall cease to glisten as thou passest by? How lonely is every one in the wide charnel of the universe! I alone am in company with myself. O Father! O Father! where is thine infinite bosom, that I may be at rest? Alas! if every being is its own father and creator, why cannot it also be its own destroying angel? . . . Is that a man near me? Thou poor one! Thy little life is the sigh of Nature, or only its echo. A concave mirror throws its beams upon the dust-clouds composed of the ashes of the dead upon your earth, and thus ye exist, cloudy, tottering images! Look down into the abyss over which clouds of ashes are floating by. Fogs full of worlds arise out of the sea of death. The future is a rising vapour, the present a falling one. Knowest thou thy earth?' Here Christ looked down, and his eyes filled with tears, and he said, 'Alas! I too was once like you – then I was happy, for I had still my infinite Father, and still gazed joyfully from the mountains into the infinite expanse of heaven; and I pressed my wounded heart on his soothing image, and said, even in the bitterness of death: "Father, take thy Son out of his bleeding shell, and lift him up to thy heart." Ah, ye too, too happy dwellers of earth, ye still believe in him. Perhaps at this moment your sun is setting, and ye fall amid blossoms, radiance, and tears, upon your knees, and lift up your blessed hands, and call out to the open heaven, amid a thousand tears of joy, "Thou knowest me too, thou infinite One, and all my wounds, and thou wilt welcome me after death, and wilt close them all." Ye wretched ones! after death they will not be closed.

When the man of sorrows stretches his sore wounded back upon the earth to slumber towards a lovelier morning, full of truth, full of virtue and of joy, behold, he awakes in the tempestuous chaos, in the everlasting midnight, and no morning cometh, and no healing hand, and no infinite Father! Mortal who art near me, if thou still livest, worship him, or thou hast lost him for ever!'

And as I fell down and gazed into the gleaming fabric of worlds, I beheld the raised rings of the giant serpent of eternity, which had couched itself round the universe of worlds, and the rings fell, and she enfolded the universe doubly. Then she wound herself in a thousand folds round Nature, and crushed the worlds together, and, grinding them, she squeezed the infinite temple into one churchyard church – and all became narrow, dark, and fearful, and a bell-hammer stretched out to infinity was about to strike the last hour of Time, and split the universe asunder – when I awoke.

My soul wept for joy, that it could again worship God; and the joy, and the tears, and the belief in him, were the prayer. And when I arose, the sun gleamed deeply behind the full purple ears of corn, and peacefully threw the reflection of its evening blushes on the little moon, which was rising in the east without an aurora. And between the heaven and the earth a glad fleeting world stretched out its short wings and lived like myself in the presence of the infinite Father, and from all nature around me flowed sweet peaceful tones, as from evening bells.

Translated by E. H. Noel

LA MOTTE-FOUQUE

The Crystal Vault

This dream is taken from *Undine*, a romantic novel by Friedrich de La Motte-Fouqué first published in 1811. Undine, the sea-fairy, is adopted by two fisherfolk, whose daughter Bertholda has been kidnapped by the fairy's Uncle Kühleborn (literally, 'cool fount'). Knight Huldibrand falls in love with Undine, takes her to his castle and marries her. But Kühleborn and the water fairies watch over her, and when Huldibrand falls in love with Bertholda, who has been sent back to earth on purpose, they take Undine back to the bottom of the sea. During the preparations for his marriage with Bertholda, Huldibrand has the following dream:

It was between the darkness and the dawn of day that the knight lay half awake, half asleep, on his bed. When he tried to fall wholly asleep again, it seemed to him as though a horror stood and thrust him back, because there were ghosts in the land of sleep. But if he thought completely to rouse himself, there seemed to blow about him a noise of the wings of swans and caressing sounds of pleasure, which sent his brain reeling back into its doubtful state. At last he must have fallen asleep in good earnest, for it seemed to him as if the rustling of swans seized him on soft pinions and bore him far away over land and sea, singing all the while in a most delightful melody, 'Sound of the swan! song of the swan!' More and more definitely he kept saying to himself, 'Perhaps this is death?' But probably it had another significance. Suddenly it seemed to him that he was being borne over the Mediterranean Sea. A swan was chanting harmoniously in his ear, 'This is the Mediterranean Sea.' And while he looked down on the waters they became transparent crystal, so that he could see through them down to the bed of the sea. He was glad of that, for he could see Undine, where she was sitting under the clear vault of crystal. She was weeping sorely, and looked much more sad than she did in happier hours, when he and she had lived together in Ringstetten Castle, especially at first, and towards the last, too, a little while before that luckless voyage down the Danube began.

The knight could reflect on all this very thoroughly and deeply, but it did not seem that Undine was aware of his presence. Meanwhile Kühleborn had stepped up to her, and proposed to reprove her for weeping. Then she drew herself together, and gazed at him with a mien so majestic in entreaty that it almost frightened him. 'If I do live here under the waters,' she said, 'I have yet brought my soul with me. And therefore must I weep, even if you cannot divine what such tears can be. And they are blessed, as everything is blessed to one in whom a faithful soul resides.' He shook his head incredulously, and said after some reflection, 'And yet, my niece, you are subjected to the laws of our elements, and his life must be forfeited to you if he should wed again and be to you unfaithful.' 'Until this hour he remains a widower,' said Undine, 'and bears me in love upon his aching heart.' 'Yet is he a bridegroom also,' laughed Kühleborn scornfully, 'and in a day or two the priestly benediction will be uttered, and then must you slay the husband of two wives.' 'But I can't,' Undine smiled back. 'I have sealed up the fountain, and closed it against my like and me.' 'But if he quits his castle,' said Kühleborn, 'or if one of these days he should have the fountain reopened? For you may be sure he takes very little heed of all these things.' 'For that very reason,' said Undine, and smiled once more through her tears, 'for that very reason he is now poised in spirit over the Middle Sea, and in a warning dream listens to our speech. I have deliberately so arranged it.' Then Kühleborn looked up spitefully at the knight, menaced him, stamped with his foot, and as swiftly as an arrow darted under the waves. It seemed as though rage had bloated him into a whale. The swans began to chant, to flutter, to fly, it seemed to the knight that he soared along over alps and over rivers, swooped at last into Ringstetten Castle, and awoke upon his bed.

It was true that he awoke upon his bed, and with that his squire came and told him that Father Heilmann was still lingering in the neighbourhood: he had met him in the forest the night before under the shelter of a hut which he had constructed of the stems of trees, and had fitted up with moss and brushwood. When he asked him what he was doing there, since he would not give the benediction, he answered, 'There are other benedictions than that which is given at the marriage-altar, and, if I am not come to the wedding, it may be I shall be needed for some other ceremony. We must be ready for all chances. Besides, there is no great difference between wedding and weeping, and he who does not wilfully blind himself, has to recognize that.'

The knight fell into all manner of strange speculation with regard to these words and to his dream. But he held it to be a very strong measure for a man to break off an engagement that he had thoroughly made up his mind to, and so the end of it was that no change was made in his plans.

Translated by E. Gosse

FERRETTI

The Winged Ass

This dream is taken from Jacopo Ferretti's libretto for Rossini's opera *Cinderella*, first performed in Rome in 1817. This is a down-to-earth version of the traditional tale: no more good fairies, but Alidoro, the wise preceptor of prince Ramiro, who selects Cinderella for her 'innocence and goodness'; no more evil step-mother but a stepfather, Don Magnifico, a stupid and ridiculous baron, obsessed with the idea of arranging a royal match for his other two daughters. At the beginning of the opera Cinderella's stepsisters are rejoicing at the announcement of the ball given by the Prince. Don Magnifico is awakened by the noise.

Don Magnifico:
Sprouts of my house, I blush and must disown you!
You come to spoil a glorious dream of mine.
(How mortified they are!) Oh worthy daughters!
Come, silence and attention; mind my dream.
This morn I dreamt I was a handsome ass,
Yes, a most handsome ass, when, oh prodigious!
A thousand feathers sprung and fledged my shoulders.
Pop! I flew up, and perched upon a steeple:
With gravity I sat, when straight below me
The bells struck up ding-dong! When in you came,
And with your chi! chu! waked me. But I've found
The meaning of the dream. Bells sound a feast;
This bodes joy to our house. Then, those feathers,
Are you. And that grand flight? Baron's adieu!
But then the ass remains – that ass am I.
Who sees you, knows that your sire must be an ass.
You shall be teeming queens – I, grand-papa,
Shall dandle nephews by dozens; here, a little king,
And there a little king! oh glorious day for me.

Anonymous translation

SCHUBERT

The Outsider

Franz Schubert recounts this dream in a text written on 3 July 1822.

My Dream

I was the brother of many brothers and sisters. Our father and mother were good people. I was deeply and lovingly devoted to them all. Once my father took us to a feast. There my brothers became very merry. I, however, was sad. Then my father approached me and bade me enjoy the delicious dishes. But I could not, whereupon my father, becoming angry, banished me from his sight. I turned my footsteps and, my heart full of infinite love for those who disdained it, I wandered into far-off regions. For long years I felt torn between the greatest grief and the greatest love. And so the news of my mother's death reached me. I hastened to see her, and my father, mellowed by sorrow, did not hinder my entrance. Then I saw her corpse. Tears flowed from my eyes. I saw her lie there like the old happy past, in which according to the deceased's desire we were to live as she had done herself.

And we followed her body in sorrow, and the coffin sank to earth. From that time on I again remained at home. Then my father once more took me to his favourite garden. He asked whether I liked it. But the garden wholly repelled me, and I dared not say so. Then, reddening, he asked me a second time; did the garden please me? I denied it, trembling. At that my father struck me, and I fled. And I turned away a second time, and with a heart filled with endless love for those who scorned me, I again wandered far away. For many and many a year I sang songs. Whenever I attempted to sing of love, it turned to pain. And again, when I tried to sing of pain, it turned to love.

Thus were love and pain divided in me.

And one day I had news of a gentle maiden who had just died. And a circle formed around her grave in which many youths and old men walked as though in everlasting bliss. They spoke softly, so as not to wake the maiden.

Heavenly thoughts seemed for ever to be showered on the youths from the maiden's gravestone, like fine sparks producing a gentle rustling. I too longed sorely to walk there. Only a miracle, however, can lead you to that circle, they said. But I went to the gravestone with slow steps and lowered gaze, filled with devotion and firm belief, and before I was aware of it, I found myself in the circle, which uttered a wondrously lovely sound; and I felt as though eternal bliss were gathered together into a single moment. My father too I saw, reconciled and loving. He took me in his arms and wept. But not as much as I.

Translated by E. Blom

GOETHE

The Pheasants

Goethe's travels in Italy lasted from September 1786 to June 1788, but his observations were first published only in 1829. More than a diary, it is a collection of open letters, in the manner of so many travellers of that time.

Since this rush of so many good and desirable things rather alarms me, I must tell my friends of a dream I had about a year ago which I felt to be significant. I dreamed that I landed from a fairly large boat on the shore of a fertile island with a luxuriant vegetation, where I had been told one could get the most beautiful pheasants. I immediately started bargaining for these birds with the natives, who killed them and brought them to me in great numbers. I knew they were pheasants, although, since dreams usually transform things, they had long tails covered with iridescent eyelike spots similar to those of peacocks or rare birds of paradise. The natives brought them on board and neatly arranged them so that the heads were inside the boat and their long gaily-coloured feather tails hung outside. In the brilliant sunshine, they made the most splendid pile imaginable, and there were so many of them that there was hardly room for the steersman and the rowers. Then we glided over calm waters and I was already making a mental list of the names of friends with whom I meant to share these treasures. At last we reached a great port. I lost my way among huge masted ships, and climbed from one deck to another, looking for some place where I could safely moor my little boat.

Such fantastic images give us great delight, and, since they are created by us, they undoubtedly have a symbolic relation to our lives and destinies.

Translated by W. H. Auden and E. Mayer

ECKERMANN

The Swim

This dream comes from J. P. Eckermann's *Conversations with Goethe*, the first two parts of which were published in 1836, whereas the third appeared in 1848. The passage we have selected is rather peculiar in its personal tone. Most of the time Eckermann is just a faithful transcriber of the master's utterances, but here he appears in the first person and takes the stage.

Wednesday, 12 March 1828.
After I had quitted Goethe yesterday evening, the important conversation I had carried on with him remained constantly in my mind. The discourse had also been upon the sea and sea air; and Goethe had expressed the opinion, that he considered all islanders and inhabitants of the sea-shore in temperate climates far more productive, and possessed of more active force, than the people in the interior of large continents.

Whether or not it was that I had fallen asleep with these thoughts, and with a certain longing for the inspiring powers of the sea; suffice it to say, I had in the night the following pleasant, and to me very remarkable dream.

I saw myself in an unknown region, amongst strange men, thoroughly cheerful and happy. The most beautiful summer day surrounded me in a charming scene, such as might be witnessed somewhere on the shores of the Mediterranean, in the south of Spain or France, or in the neighbourhood of Genoa. We had been drinking at noon round a merry table, and I went with some others, rather young people, to make another party for the afternoon.

We had loitered along through bushy and pleasant low lands, when we suddenly found ourselves in the sea, upon the smallest of islands, on a jutting rock, where there was scarcely room for five or six men, and where one could not stir for fear of slipping into the water. Behind us, whence we had come, there was nothing to be seen but sea; but before us lay the shore at about a quarter of an hour's distance, spread out most invitingly. The shore was in some places flat, in others rocky and somewhat elevated; and one might observe, between green leaves and white tents, a crowd of joyous men in light-coloured clothes, recreating themselves with music, which sounded from the tents. 'There is nothing else to be done,' said one of us to the other, 'we must undress and swim over.' 'It is all very well to say so,' said I, 'you are young, handsome fellows, and good swimmers; but I swim badly, and I do not possess a shape fine enough to appear, with pleasure and comfort, before the strange people on shore.' 'You are a fool,' said one of the handsomest, 'undress yourself, give me your form and you shall have mine.' At these words I undressed myself quickly, and was soon in the water, and immediately found myself in the body of the other as a powerful swimmer. I soon reached the shore, and, naked and dripping, stepped with the most easy confidence amongst the men. I was happy in the sensation of these fine limbs; my deportment was unconstrained, and I at once became intimate with the strangers, at a table before an arbour, where there was a great deal of mirth. My comrades had now reached land one by one, and had joined us, and the only one missing was the youth with my form, in whose limbs I found myself so comfortable. At last he also approached the shore, and I was asked if I was not glad to see my former self?

At these words I experienced a certain discomfort, partly because I did not expect any great joy from myself, and partly because I feared that my young friend would ask for his own body back again. However, I turned to the water, and saw my second self swimming close up to me, and laughing at me with his head turned a little on one side. 'There is no swimming with those limbs of yours,' exclaimed he, 'I have had a fine struggle against waves and breakers, and it is not to be wondered at that I have come so late, and am last of all.' I at once recognized the countenance; it was my own, but grown young, and rather fuller and broader, with the freshest complexion. He now came to land, and whilst he raised himself, and first stepped along the sand, I had a view of his back and legs, and was delighted with the perfection of the form. He came up the rocky shore to us, and as he came up to me he had completely my new stature. 'How is it,' thought I to myself, 'that your little body has grown so handsome. Have the primeval powers of the sea operated so wonderfully upon it, or is it because the youthful spirit of my friend has penetrated the limbs?' Whilst we enjoyed ourselves together for some time, I silently wondered that my friend did not show any inclination to resume his own body. 'Truly,' thought I, 'he looks bravely, and it may be a matter of indifference to him in which body he is placed, but it is not the same thing to me; for I am not sure whether in that body I may not shrink and become as diminutive as before.' In order to satisfy myself on this point, I took my friend aside, and asked him how he felt in my limbs? 'Perfectly well,' said he; 'I have the same sensation of my own natural power as before; I do not know what you have to complain of in your limbs. They are quite right with me; and you see one only has to make the best of oneself. Remain in my body as long as you please; for I am perfectly contented to remain in yours through all futurity.' I was much pleased by this explanation and, as in all my sensations, thoughts, and recollections, I felt quite as usual, my dream gave me the impression of a perfect independence of the soul, and the possibility of a future existence in another body.

'That is very pretty dream,' said Goethe, when, after dinner today, I imparted to him the principal features. 'We see,' continued he, 'that the muses visit you even in sleep, and, indeed, with particular favour; for you must confess that it would be difficult for you to invent anything so peculiar and pretty in your waking moments.'

'I can scarcely conceive how it happened to me,' returned I; 'for I had felt so dejected all day that the contemplation of so fresh a life was far from my mind.'

'Human nature possesses wonderful powers,' returned Goethe, 'and has something good in readiness for us when we least hope for it. There have been times in my life when I have fallen asleep in tears; but in my dreams the most charming forms have come to console and to cheer me, and I have risen the next morning fresh and joyful.'

Translated by J. Oxenford

NERVAL

The Woman

This passage is taken from Gérard de Nerval's *Aurélia*. This was his last novel, inspired partly by his own fight against madness. The first part of the book appeared in January 1855, but Nerval's suicide at the end of the month interrupted the completion of the second part, which was published posthumously in its unfinished state in February of the same year.

Another dream of mine confirmed me in this belief. I suddenly found myself in a room which formed part of my grandfather's house, only it seemed to have grown larger. The old furniture glowed with a miraculous polish, the carpets and curtains were as if new again, daylight three times more brilliant than natural day came in through the windows and the door, and in the air there was a freshness and perfume like the first warm morning of spring. Three women were working in the room and, without exactly resembling them, they stood for relatives and friends of my youth. Each seemed to have the features of several of them. Their facial contours changed like the flames of a lamp, and all the time something of one was passing to the other. Their smiles, the colour of their eyes and hair, their figures and familiar gestures, all these were exchanged as if they had lived the same life, and each was made up of all three, like those figures painters take from a number of models in order to achieve a perfect beauty.

The eldest spoke to me in a vibrant, melodious voice which I recognized as having heard in my childhood, and whatever it was she said struck me as being profoundly true. But she drew my attention to myself and I saw I was wearing a little old-fashioned brown suit, entirely made of needlework threads as fine as a spider's web. It was elegant, graceful, and gently perfumed. I felt quite rejuvenated and most spruce in this garment which their fairy fingers had made, and I blushingly thanked them as if I had been a small boy in the presence of beautiful grown-up ladies. At that moment one of them got up and went towards the garden.

It is a well-known fact that no one ever sees the sun in a dream, although one is often aware of some far brighter light. Material objects and human bodies are illumined through their own agencies. Now I was in a little park through which ran long vine arbours, loaded with heavy clusters of black and white grapes; and as the lady, guiding me, passed beneath these arbours, the shadows of the intertwined trellis-work changed her figure and her clothes. At last we came out from these bowers of grapes to an open space. Traces of the old paths which had once divided it cross-wise were just visible. For some years the plants had been neglected and the sparse patches of clematis, hops and honeysuckle, of jasmine, ivy, and creepers, had stretched their long clinging tendrils between the sturdy growths of the trees. Branches of fruit were bowed to the ground and a few garden flowers, in a state of wildness now, bloomed among the weeds.

At distant intervals were clumps of poplars, acacias and pinetrees, and in the midst of these were glimpses of statues blackened by time. I saw before me a heap of rocks covered with ivy, from which gushed a spring of fresh water whose splashes echoed melodiously over a pool of still water, half-hidden by huge water-lilies.

The lady I was following stretched her slender figure in a movement that made the folds of her dress of shot taffeta shimmer, and gracefully she slid her bare arm about the long stem of a hollyhock. Then, in a clear shaft of light, she began to grow in such a way that gradually the whole garden blended with her own form, and the flowerbeds and trees became the patterns and flounces of her clothes, while her face and arms imprinted their contours on the rosy clouds in the sky. I lost her thus as she became transfigured, for she seemed to vanish in her own immensity.

'Don't leave me!' I cried. 'For with you Nature itself dies.'

With these words I struggled painfully through the brambles trying to grasp the vast shadow that eluded me. I threw myself on a fragment of ruined wall, at the foot of which lay the marble bust of a woman. I lifted it up and felt convinced it was of *her* ... I recognized the beloved features and as I stared around me I saw that the garden had become a graveyard, and I heard voices crying: 'The universe is in darkness.'

Translated by G. Wagner

SWEDENBORG

'Eat not so much'

This dream of Swedenborg is told by his biographer William White in a book published in 1868.

Swedenborg usually dated his seership from 1745, probably regarding the experiences we have been perusing as the painful preliminaries to the great change whereby Heaven and Hell became familiar to his eyes.

From him we have no description of the momentous event of 1745, but from his friend, Robsahm, we draw the following –

'I inquired of Swedenborg where and in what manner his revelations began. He said –

' "I was in London and dined late at my usual quarters, where I had engaged a room in which to prosecute my studies in Natural Philosophy. I was hungry and ate with great appetite. Towards the end of the meal, I remarked a kind of mist spread before my eyes, and I saw the floor of my room covered with hideous reptiles, such as serpents, toads, and the like. I was astonished, having all my wits about me, being perfectly conscious. The darkness attained its height and then passed away. I now saw a Man sitting in the corner of the chamber. As I had thought myself.alone, I was greatly frightened, when he said to me, 'Eat not so much.' My sight again became dim, but when I recovered it I found myself alone in my room. The unexpected alarm hastened my return home. I did not suffer my landlord to perceive that anything had happened, but thought over the matter attentively, and was not able to attribute it to chance or any physical cause.

' "The following night the same Man appeared to me again. I was this time not at all alarmed. The Man said – 'I am God, the Lord, the Creator, and Redeemer of the World. I have chosen thee to unfold to men the Spiritual Sense of the Holy Scripture. I will myself dictate to thee what thou shalt write.'

' "The same night the World of Spirits, Hell and Heaven, were convincingly opened to me, where I found many persons of my acquaintance of all conditions. From that day forth I gave up all worldly learning, and laboured only in spiritual things, according to what the Lord commanded me to write. Thereafter the Lord daily opened the eyes of my Spirit to see in perfect wakefulness what was going on in the other World, and to converse, broad awake, with Angels and Spirits." '

MELVILLE

The Berg

This poem by Hermann Melville comes from *John Marr and Other Sailors*, a collection of poems first published in 1888 in a private edition of twenty-five copies to be distributed to a few friends. The poem was apparently written almost forty years before, sometime in the late 1840s or early 1850s.

> I saw a ship of martial build
> (Her standards set, her brave apparel on)
> Directed as by madness mere
> Against a stolid iceberg steer,

Nor budge it, though the infatuate ship went down.
The impact made huge ice-cubes fall
Sullen, in tons that crashed the deck;
But that one avalanche was all –
No other movement save the foundering wreck.

Along the spurs of ridges pale,
Not any slenderest shaft and frail,
A prism over glass-green gorges lone,
Toppled; or lace of traceries fine,
Nor pendant drops in grot or mine
Were jarred, when the stunned ship went down.
Nor sole the gulls in cloud that wheeled
Circling one snow-flanked peak afar,
But nearer fowl the floes that skimmed
And crystal beaches, felt no jar.
No thrill transmitted stirred the lock
Of jack-straw needle-ice at base;
Towers undermined by waves – the block
Atilt impending – kept their place.
Seals, dozing sleek on sliddery ledges
Slipt never, when by loftier edges
Through very inertia overthrown,
The impetuous ship in bafflement went down.

Hard Berg (methought), so cold, so vast,
With mortal damps self-overcast;
Exhaling still thy dankish breath –
Adrift dissolving, bound for death;
Though lumpish thou, a lumbering one –
A lumbering lubbard loitering slow,
Impingers rue thee and go down,
Sounding thy precipice below,
Nor stir the slimy slug that sprawls
Along thy dead indifference of walls.

BROWNING

Bad Dreams III

See note on Robert Browning's 'Bad Dreams I', page 176.

This was my dream: I saw a Forest
   Old as the earth, no track nor trace
Of unmade man. Thou, Soul, explorest –
   Though in a trembling rapture – space
Immeasurable! Shrubs, turned trees,
Trees that touch heaven, support its frieze
Studded with sun and moon and star:
While – oh, the enormous growths that bar
Mine eye from penetrating past
   Their tangled twine where lurks – nay, lives
Royally lone, some brute-type cast
   I' the rough, time cancels, man forgives.

On, Soul! I saw a lucid City
   Of architectural device
Every way perfect. Pause for pity,
   Lightning! nor leave a cicatrice
On those bright marbles, dome and spire,
Structures palatial, – streets which mire
Dares not defile, paved all too fine
For human footstep's smirch, not thine –
Proud solitary traverser,
   My Soul, of silent lengths of way –
With what ecstatic dread, aver,
   Lest life start sanctioned by thy stay!

Ah, but the last sight was the hideous!
   A City, yes, – a Forest, true –
But each devouring each. Perfidious
   Snake-plants had strangled what I knew
Was a pavilion once: each oak
Held on his horns some spoil he broke
By surreptitiously beneath
Upthrusting: pavements, as with teeth,
Griped huge weed widening crack and split
   In squares and circles stone-work erst.
Oh, Nature – good! Oh, Art – no whit
   Less worthy! Both in one – accurst!

IBSEN

All is Vanity

This dream of Henrik Ibsen is recounted by R. Lothaer in his
biography of the playwright (*Henrik Ibsen*, 1899).

While wandering on a high mountain range, myself and some friends, we
became tired and then despondent, and were suddenly surprised by night. Like
Jacob, we lay down to sleep and rested our heads on stones. My companions
soon went off to sleep but I was not so successful in this. Finally I succumbed to
weariness and in a dream an angel appeared before me, saying, 'Arise, and
follow me.'

'Whither will you lead me in this darkness?' I asked, and received the reply:
'Come, I will reveal to you human existence in its true reality.'

Full of foreboding, I followed my guide and we descended a number of steep
steps; and rocks towered above us like gigantic arches, while spread before us
lay a vast city of death with horrible remnants and tokens of mortality and
transient existence – a perished grandeur, an immense, sunken world of
corpses, death's silent subjects. Over all hovered a withered, ghastly twilight
that enveloped churchyards, graves and sepulchres. In a stronger light row upon
row of white skeletons reflected a prosphorescent glow. A fear seized me as I
stood by the angel's side.

'Here, you see, all is vanity,' he said.

Then came a roar like that which heralds a storm, which grew to a raging
hurricane so that the dead moved and stretched their arms towards me, and
with a cry I awoke wet from the cold night-dew.

Translated by R. Lothar

ECA DE QUEIROZ

In Search of the Butcher

This dream comes from *The Illustrious House of Ramirez*, by Eça de
Queiroz, the popular Portuguese novelist. This novel was published in 1900.

Along the road to the Tower, Gonçalo's thoughts immediately flew, with
irresistible temptation, to Dona Ana – to her *décolletages* and her lazy baths in
which she lay and read the newspaper. Really, he thought, what the deuce! This

Dona Ana was so honest, so perfumed, so magnificently beautiful, that she had only one drawback – even contemplated as a wife – her papa the butcher! And her voice, too – the voice that had repelled him so much at the Holy Fountain ... But Mendonça had assured him that she lost that thick, grating tone among intimates, and her voice became smooth, almost sweet ... And anyway, after months of living together, one got accustomed to the most unpleasant of voices – he himself, now did not even notice Manuel Duarte spoke nasally! No, the only really irreparable defect was the butcher father. But with mankind descended as it was from one man, who didn't have a butcher grandfather among the thousands of his ancestors stretching back to Adam? Even he, a well-bred nobleman, offshoot of a house of Kings from which dynasties had been founded, would surely come across a butcher Ramires if he enquired diligently enough into the past. Whether the butcher appeared prominently in the last generation, in a butcher's shop which still had clients, or was only vaguely discerned through the veil of centuries, among his ancestors thirty generations ago – he was there, all the same, with his knife and his chopping-block, and the bloodstains on his sweaty arm ...

This thought did not leave him until he reached the Tower – or even afterwards, as he stood at the window of his room, finishing his cigar and listening to the chirping of the crickets. Even after he had lain down and his eyes were closing, he felt his impatient steps probing the past, the dim past of his House, amid the tangled webs of History – in search of the butcher ... He was already far beyond the Visigoth Empire, when his bearded ancestor Recesvinto, golden orb in hand, had reigned. Exhausted, panting for breath, he had traversed civilized cities peopled with men of culture, and had penetrated the forests where the mastodon still plodded. Amid the thick, humid foliage he had already come across vague Ramires, grunting as they carried bundles of wood or a dead beast. Others emerged from smoky holes, baring their sharp, greenish teeth to smile at their great-grandson who was passing by. Then, across gloomy wastes, in gloomy silence, until he arrived at a misty lagoon. At the edge of the muddy water, among the clumps of reeds, a monstrous man, hairy as a beast, was crouching in the mud and, with hefty strokes of his stone axe chopping off slabs of human flesh. It was a Ramires. In the grey sky above hovered the black goshawk. Then, across the mist of the lagoon, he waved towards Santa Maria de Craquede, towards the beautiful, perfumed Dona Ana, shouting above Empires and Centuries: 'I have found my butcher ancestor!'

Translated by A. Stevens

HUCH

The Parcel

For Friedrich Huch's *Träume*, from which this episode is taken, see page 81.

I have an oblong-shaped parcel in my arm. I know there's the dead body of a little child inside, and I'm supposed to get rid of it somewhere. I go up and down the stairs, but every time I'm about to lay it down, or want to pretend to lose it carelessly, a door opens somewhere, or I can see a face looking in my direction through a staircase window. So then I slip the loop of the string of the parcel over my finger and dangle it down as careless as can be so that it bangs against the stairposts and banisters. Then I meet a young girl whom I go out with for a walk, thinking again and again: how unsuspecting she is, jostling her elbow against my parcel!

Then I notice that the outer wrapping has come undone, and I keep her at arm's length. Now I can very clearly feel the child's head and at the same time the sopping wet of the cardboard inside. Panic-stricken, I try to wrap the parcel up tighter and tighter, but the more I do this, the more it comes open. I want to go down to the river, but now I'm standing in a low circular stone court chamber, surrounded by my judges. And I learn now to my greatest astonishment something that I have in fact known for a long time but appear to have forgotten: that all of this is a Christmas mystery, that the child is the Christ child, I myself Judas Iscariot, with the judges the apostles.

Translated by M. Hollington

MACHADO

Awake

This is a poem by the Spanish poet Antonio Machado, which belongs to the section 'Proverbios y cantares' of the volume *Campos de Castilla*, written between 1907 and 1917.

> Last night I dreamt I heard
> God crying: Rouse up, for my sake.
> After that it was God who was sleeping
> And I shouting out: Awake!

Translated by I. Waters

FREUD

Seven White Wolves

This dream was first published by Sigmund Freud in *The Occurrence in Dreams of Material from Fairy Tales* in 1913. It appears again in *The Case History of the Wolf Man* (1914).

A young man told me the following dream. He had a chronological basis for his early memories in the circumstance that his parents moved from one country estate to another just before he was five years old; the dream, which he said was his earliest one, occurred while he was still upon the first estate.

'*I dreamt that it was night and that I was lying in my bed. (My bed stood with its foot towards the window: in front of the window there was a row of old walnut trees. I know it was winter when I had the dream, and night-time.) Suddenly the window opened of its own accord, and I was terrified to see that some white wolves were sitting on the big walnut tree in front of the window. There were six or seven of them. The wolves were quite white, and looked more like foxes or sheep-dogs, for they had big tails like foxes and they had their ears pricked like dogs when they pay attention to something. In great terror, evidently of being eaten up by the wolves, I screamed* and woke up. My nurse hurried to my bed, to see what had happened to me. It took quite a long while before I was convinced that it had only been a dream; I had had such a clear and life-like picture of the window opening and the wolves sitting on the tree. At last I grew quieter, felt as though I had escaped from some danger, and went to sleep again.

'The only piece of action in the dream was the opening of the window; for the wolves sat quite still and without making any movement on the branches of the tree, to the right and left of the trunk, and looked at me. It seemed as though they had riveted their whole attention upon me. – I think this was my first anxiety-dream. I was three, four, or at most five years old at the time. From then until my eleventh or twelfth year I was always afraid of seeing something terrible in my dreams.'

He added a drawing of the tree with the wolves, which confirmed his description. The analysis of the dream brought the following material to light.

He had always connected this dream with the recollection that during these years of his childhood he was most tremendously afraid of the picture of a wolf in a book of fairy tales. His elder sister, who was very much his superior, used to tease him by holding up this particular picture in front of him on some excuse or other, so that he was terrified and began to scream. In this picture the wolf was standing upright, striding out with one foot, with its claws stretched out and its ears pricked. He thought this picture must have been an illustration to the story of 'Little Red Riding-Hood'.

Why were the wolves white? This made him think of the sheep, large flocks of which were kept in the neighbourhood of the estate. His father occasionally took him with him to visit these flocks, and every time this happened he felt very proud and blissful. Later on – according to enquiries that were made it may easily have been shortly before the time of the dream – an epidemic broke out among the sheep. His father sent for a follower of Pasteur's, who inoculated the animals, but after the inoculation even more of them died than before.

How did the wolves come to be on the tree? This reminded him of a story that he had heard his grandfather tell. He could not remember whether it was before or after the dream, but its subject is a decisive argument in favour of the former view. The story ran as follows. A tailor was sitting at work in his room, when the window opened and a wolf leapt in. The tailor hit after him with his yard—no (he corrected himself), caught him by his tail and pulled it off, so that the wolf ran away in terror. Some time later the tailor went into the forest, and suddenly saw a pack of wolves coming towards him; so he climbed up a tree to escape from them. At first the wolves were in perplexity; but the maimed one, which was among them and wanted to revenge himself on the tailor, proposed that they should climb one upon another till the last one could reach him. He himself – he was a vigorous old fellow – would be the base of the pyramid. The wolves did as he suggested, but the tailor had recognized the visitor whom he had punished, and suddenly called out as he had before: 'Catch the grey one by his tail!' The tailless wolf, terrified by the recollection, ran away, and all the others tumbled down.

In this story the tree appears, upon which the wolves were sitting in the dream. But it also contains an unmistakable allusion to the castration complex. The *old* wolf was docked of his tail by the tailor. The fox-tails of the wolves in the dream were probably compensations for this taillessness.

Why were there six or seven wolves? There seemed to be no answer to this question, until I raised a doubt whether the picture that had frightened him could be connected with the story of 'Little Red Riding-Hood'. This fairy tale only offers an opportunity for two illustrations – Little Red Riding-Hood's meeting with the wolf in the wood, and the scene in which the wolf lies in bed in the grandmother's night-cap. There must therefore be some other fairy tale behind his recollection of the picture. He soon discovered that it could only be the story of 'The Wolf and the Seven Little Goats'. Here the number seven occurs, and also the number six, for the wolf only ate up six of the little goats, while the seventh hid itself in the clock-case. The white, too, comes into this story, for the wolf had his paw made white at the baker's after the little goats had recognized him on his first visit by his grey paw. Moreover, the two fairy tales have much in common. In both there is the eating up, the cutting open of the belly, the taking out of the people who have been eaten and their replacement by heavy stones, and finally in both of them the wicked wolf perishes. Besides all this, in the story of the little goats the tree appears. The wolf lay down under a tree after his meal and snored.

I shall have, for a special reason, to deal with this dream again elsewhere, and interpret it and consider its significance in greater detail. For it is the earliest anxiety-dream that the dreamer remembered from his childhood, and its content, taken in connection with other dreams that followed it soon afterwards and with certain events in his earliest years, is of quite peculiar interest. We must confine ourselves here to the relation of the dream to the two fairy tales which have so much in common with each other, 'Little Red Riding-Hood' and 'The Wolf and the Seven Little Goats'. The effect produced by these stories was shown in the little dreamer by a regular animal phobia. This phobia was only distinguished from other similar cases by the fact that the anxiety-animal was not an object easily accessible to observation (such as a horse or a dog), but was known to him only from stories and picture-books.

I shall discuss on another occasion the explanation of these animal phobias and the significance attaching to them. I will only remark in anticipation that this explanation is in complete harmony with the principal characteristic shown by the neurosis from which the present dreamer suffered later in his life. His fear of his father was the strongest motive for his falling ill, and his ambivalent attitude towards every father-surrogate was the dominating feature of his life as well as of his behaviour during the treatment.

If in my patient's case the wolf was merely a first father-surrogate, the question arises whether the hidden content in the fairy tales of the wolf that ate up the little goats and of 'Little Red Riding-Hood' may not simply be infantile fear of the father. Moreover, my patient's father had the characteristic, shown by so many people in relation to their children, of indulging in 'affectionate abuse'; and it is possible that during the patient's earlier years his father (though he grew severe later on) may more than once, as he caressed the little boy or played with him, have threatened in fun to 'gobble him up'. One of my patients told me that her two children could never get to be fond of their grandfather, because in the course of his affectionate romping with them he used to frighten them by saying he would cut open their tummies.

Standard Edition under the supervision of J. Strachey

GIDE

The Madonna Appears to the Atheist

The Vatican Cellars by André Gide was published in 1914. The various characters of this novel all converge on Rome; among them Anthime, a crippled scientist and a hard-boiled atheist. In the afternoon that precedes the dream he has mutilated a statue of the Virgin in the street.

That night Anthime had a dream. There was a knock at his bedroom door – not the door into the passage, nor the door into the next room; the knock was at another door, which he had not noticed in his waking hours and which led straight into the street. That was why he was frightened, and at first, instead of answering, lay low. There was a faint light which made the smallest objects in the room visible – a sort of dim effulgence, such as a night-light gives – but there was no night-light. As he was trying to make out where this light could come from, there was a second knock.

'What do you want?' he cried in a trembling voice.

At the third knock, he fell into a kind of daze; an extraordinary feeling of yielding – in which every trace of fear was swallowed up – paralysed him. He called it afterwards a tender resignation. He suddenly felt both that he was incapable of resistance and that the door was going to open. It opened noiselessly and for a moment he saw nothing but a dark alcove, which at first was empty, but in which, as he gazed, there appeared, as in a Shrine, the figure of the Holy Virgin. At first he took the small white form for his little niece Julie, dressed as he had just seen her, with her bare feet showing below her nightgown; but a second later he recognized her whom he had insulted; I mean that her appearance was the same as the wayside statue's; he could even make out the injury to her right arm; and yet the pale face was still more beautiful, still more smiling than before. Without seeming to walk exactly, she came gliding towards him, and when she was close up against his bedside:

'Dost thou think, thou who hast hurt me,' she asked, 'that I have need of my hand to cure thee?' And with this she raised her empty sleeve and struck him.

It seemed to him that it was from her that this strange effulgence emanated. But when the iron rod suddenly pierced his side he felt a stab of frightful pain and woke up in the dark.

Anthime was perhaps a quarter of an hour before coming to his senses. He felt in his whole body a strange kind of torpor – of stupefied numbness – and then a tingling which was almost pleasant, so that he doubted now whether he had really felt any pain in his side; he could not make out where his dream had begun or ended, and whether he was awake now or whether he had dreamt then. He pinched himself, felt himself all over, put his arm out and finally struck a match. Veronica was asleep beside him with her face to the wall.

Then, untucking the sheets and flinging aside the blankets, he let the tips of his bare feet slide down, till they rested on his slippers. His crutch was there, leaning beside the bedside table; without taking it, he raised himself by pushing with his hands against the bed; then he thrust his feet well into the leather slippers; then, stood bolt upright on his legs; then, still doubtful, with one arm stretched in front of him and one behind, he took a step – two steps alongside the bed – three steps; then across the room . . . Holy Virgin! Was he . . . ?

Noiselessly and rapidly he slipped into his trousers, put on his waistcoat, his coat . . . Stop, my pen! What rashness is yours? What matters the cure of a paralysed body, what matter all its clumsy agitations, in comparison with the flutterings of a newly liberated soul, when first she tries her wings?

When, a quarter of an hour later, Veronica, disturbed by some kind of presentiment, awoke, she became uneasy at feeling that Anthime was not beside her; she became still more uneasy when, having struck a match, she saw his crutch (which of necessity never left him) still standing by the bedside. The match went out between her fingers, for Anthime had taken the candle with him when he left the room; Veronica hastily slipped on a few things as best she could in the dark, and then in her turn leaving the room, she followed the thread of light which shone from beneath the laboratory door.

'Anthime, are you there, my dear?'

No answer. Veronica, listening with all her might and main, heard a singular noise. Then, sick with anxiety, she pushed open the door. What she saw transfixed her with amazement.

Her Anthime was there, straight in front of her. He was not sitting; he was not standing; the top of his head was on a level with the table and in the full light of the candle, which he had placed upon it; Anthime, the learned man of science, Anthime the atheist, who for many a long year had bowed neither his stiff knee nor his stubborn will (for it was remarkable how in his case body and soul kept pace with each other) – Anthime was kneeling!

He was on his knees, was Anthime; he was holding in his two hands a little fragment of plaster, which he was bathing with his tears, and covering with frantic kisses. At first he took no notice of her, and Veronica, astounded at this mystery, was afraid either to withdraw or to go forward and was already on the point herself of falling on her knees in the doorway opposite her husband, when, oh, miracle! he rose without an effort, walked towards her with a steady step, and, catching her in his arms:

'Henceforth,' he said, as he pressed her to his heart and bent his face towards hers, 'henceforth, my dearest, we will pray together.'

Translated by D. Bussy

BRECHT

Joan's Vision

Saint Joan of the Stockyards, was written in 1929–31. The story of Joan of Ark is transposed to the Chicago Stockyards during a lockout. Joan Dark is a member of the Black Strawhats, a religious movement whose aim is to lead the workers away from politics with prayers and the distribution of soup; but she soon changes sides and takes an active part in the struggle of the out-of-work and the strikers. Her well-meaning intercession with the meat magnate Pierpont Mauler proves disastrous for the working class. Joan's dream, reported here, takes place on the eve of a strike which will fail, partly because of her fear of violence. The dream is belied by the end of the play where Pierpont Mauler is ironically hailed as a saviour after taking over completely the meat industry.

Joan:
Listen to the dream I had one night
A week ago.
Before me in a little field, too small
To hold the shade of a middle-sized tree, hemmed in
By enormous houses, I saw a bunch
Of people: I could not make out how many, but
There were far more of them than all the sparrows
That could find room in such a tiny place –
A very thick bunch indeed, so that
The field began to buckle and rise in the middle
And the bunch was suspended on its edge, holding fast
A moment, quivering: then, stirred
By the intervention of a word – uttered somewhere or other
Meaning nothing vital – it began to flow.
Then I saw processions, streets, familiar ones, Chicago! You!
I saw you marching, then I saw myself:
I, silent, saw myself striding at your head
With warlike step and bloodstains on my brow
And shouting words that sounded militant
In a tongue I did not know; and while many processions
Moved in many directions all at once
I strode in front of many processions in manifold shapes:
Young and old, sobbing and cursing
Finally beside myself! Virtue and terror!

294 THEATRE OF SLEEP

Changing whatever my foot touched
Causing measureless destruction, visibly influencing
The courses of the stars, but also changing utterly
The neighbourhood streets familiar to us all.
So the procession moved, and I along with it
Veiled by snow from any hostile attack
Transparent with hunger, no target
Not to be hit anywhere, not being settled anywhere;
Not to be touched by any trouble, being accustomed
To all. And so it marches, abandoning the position
Which cannot be held: exchanging it for any other one.
That was my dream.
Today I see its meaning:
Before tomorrow morning we
Will start out from these yards
And reach their city, Chicago, in the grey of dawn
Displaying the full range of our wretchedness in public places
Appealing to whatever resembles a human being.
What will come after, I do not know.

Translated by F. Jones

WILDER

The Void

This passage is taken from Thornton Wilder's *The Ides of March*, published in 1948. It purports to be an extract from Caesar's Journal Letter to Lucius Mamilius Turrinus on the Island of Capri, one of several 'historical sources' on which the novel is constructed.

You once asked me, laughing, whether I had ever experienced the dream of the void. I told you I had, and I have dreamed it since.

It is perhaps occasioned by a chance posture of the sleeping body or by some indigestion or derangement within us, but the terror in the mind is no less real for that. It is not, as I once thought, the image of death and the grin of the skull. It is the state in which one divines the end of all things. This nothingness, however, does not present itself to us as a blank and a quiet, but as a total evil unmasked. It is at once laughter and menace. It turns into ridicule all delights and sears and shrivels all endeavour. This dream is the counterpart of that other vision which comes to me in the paroxysm of my illness. Then I seem to grasp the fair harmony of the world. I am filled with unspeakable happiness and confidence. I wish to cry out to all the living and all the dead that there is no part of the universe that is untouched by bliss.

MOSSADEGH

The Oil Commission

We found this report of a speech by Mohammad Mossadegh at a session of the Iranian parliament on 13 May 1951 in Jorge Luis Borges' *Libro de sueños*, published in Buenos Ayres in 1975.

In summer 1950, just a few months before the vote for the nationalization of oil, my physician prescribed a long period of rest. One month afterwards, while I was sleeping, I saw in my dream a luminous figure who told me: 'This is no time for rest. Get up and break the chains that fetter the Iranian people.' I responded to this call, and in spite of my extreme weariness, I went back to work in the oil commission. Two months later, when the commission agreed on the principle of nationalization, I had to admit that the figure in my dream had been a beneficial source of inspiration.

Translated from the Spanish by G. Almansi

SEFERIS

The Acropolis

The Greek poet George Seferis relates this dream in his *Glosses on Artemidorus of Daldis*, which was first published in Italian as an introduction to Artemidorus's *Interpretation of Dreams* in 1970. It was included in the posthumous edition of Seferis' essays in 1975.

During the first decade of this century and of my life, in the street where I was born in Smyrna, the pedlar was crying *The Great Oneirocritic*, selling popular versions of Artemidorus. During the same period, before the First World War, Freud climbed the Acropolis for the first time (the exact date: 3 September 1904). Many years later, in a Festschrift for Romain Rolland's seventieth birthday, when Freud himself was in his eighties, he happened to write a penetrating and moving analysis of the feelings that overwhelmed him as he had watched for the first time the Citadel. Freud, who was so familiar with classical culture that he used to write his diary in ancient Greek when he was a young man, was overpowered by a feeling of 'alienation', 'awe', 'loneliness', 'guilt' and 'filial piety' as he stood on top of the hill. He could not believe that he had actually arrived there, on the Acropolis of Athens.

Two generations have gone by; many things have happened. What have we learnt? I can't tell. In fact I find it more and more difficult to explain what *learning* may still mean. Yet the Acropolis has remained so far unchanged, at least by daytime. A few years ago I went up there myself, in a dream; and I jotted the dream down. I want to retell that experience here, as an homage to the great dream-detective of our post-Artemidorean age.

It was after my time – a few years must have gone by. It was as if I were coming back from a long exile. In the streets no one recognized me and I recognized no one. Early afternoon, but the sun was cloudy. I found myself on the Acropolis. I had a feeling that, in the meantime, civilization had made great progress. A restless crowd was facing the West front of the Parthenon. They were all watching the central columns, and moving about in simmering agitation. I asked someone who was gesticulating next to me. He answered:

'Boy! What a peasant! Where do you come from? Don't you know anything?' I stared at him blankly.

'There! The auction! Open your eyes! If the American toothpaste wins, our budget is safe for decades.'
I looked carefully at where he was pointing. Between the two central columns I made out a small table covered with a green cloth. Sitting behind it, there was a beardless gentleman wearing spectacles. He had on a black suit and was holding a small mother-of-pearl hammer in his hand. He looked like a surgeon. I was completely at a loss, and asked my neighbour, 'What auction?'

'Where do you live, stranger? It is the end of the world. This is a master-stroke by our government. They will lease these stones. What use are they to us?'

At this point the black-suited gentleman brought down his hammer. 'Gone!' someone yelled. 'Gone, gone!' repeated the rumbling crowd.

'The Americans have won!' my neighbour was shouting. He was beside himself, like a soccer fan.

Anxiety was welling up in me. 'And what will they do?' I managed to ask.

'They are real devils, aren't they?' he answered. 'They will carve up these columns in the shape of toothpaste tubes.'

I felt the crowd trickling away, leaving me all alone. Then I saw the Parthenon, awfully naked, without pediment, without frieze, its carved columns glistening like huge tubes. The nightmare threw me off my bed, howling, at five o'clock in the morning.

I am unable to analyse this dream. Just one remark about my dream-behaviour: I have often seen dreams which appeared to me with crystal clearness. If they are frightening, the nightmare works in depth and explodes at the end.

Translated by C. Béguin

PEREC

The Condemnation

For Georges Pérec's *La Boutique Obscure*, see page 107.

February 1972

I am compiling a mailing-list for Jean Duvignaud, that is, a list of people to whom he wishes to send off-prints of his publications.

P. and I are staying, just for the weekend, in a big hotel, possibly the Ritz. We have booked two very big apartments (or suites). We have brought so much luggage with us (trunks and hat-boxes) that the bell-boys have to make two journeys to get them into the lift.

In the lift. It is an immense lift, the size of a room. We are delighted in advance, almost to the point of vanity, with this luxurious weekend.

In P's room. It is a huge room, one part of which is taken up with a bar. A reception is in full swing. There is a little child stoking his mouth with spoonfuls of chili con carne.

I go down to the restaurant. P. is sitting at another table, looking very lovely. J.L. is sitting not far from me. At one point, he leads me into a corner of the room and starts telling me about an imminent landing in Cuba. He is talking too much, the room is crawling with spies.

That is when an old woman, a real witch, gets up and, pointing her finger at me, howls something along the lines of: 'We'll be saved, but he must die!'

At first, I am frightened, as if this menace would be carried out there and then, but then I calm down, convinced that the threat is an abstract one, a metaphysical certainty not defined in time. Meanwhile, I have been hoisted up on to a sort of pedestal and people have begun to adore me, that is, to lick my feet. No sooner have I grown used to this ritual than I realize that, sure enough, they are trying to kill me by knocking me off my pedestal. I finally fall, but manage to catch on to the rough parts of the wall (even though it is dangerously smooth), and land unhindered on the ground. From way up above, people are bombarding me with enormous rocks, but none hit me.

I have fled into the long grass; I have joined a horde and we have been wandering, for many years and many centuries, following the tracks of animals (perhaps I knew where in the book to find the passage about animals).

After long centuries of wandering, we return to the regions we fled from. Now a town has been built on the steppe. Its name is Texas. For the first time, we see firearms. . .

Texas is a new town, made out of wooden houses. Above all there are saloons. The Town Hall, where a meeting is about to be held, is situated in the double back room shared by two saloons. This arrangement is rather surprising at first, but when you think about it, it's really very clever.

Translated by J. Romney

The Jigsaw

April 1972

Accompanied by someone I am unable to identify (possibly my aunt) I am visiting a sort of colonial warehouse. At the very end of one of the halls, we come to a gigantic jigsaw puzzle, placed on a long, slightly tilted table. From a distance, you at first have the impression that there is a jigsaw in the centre, almost completed – it shows a Renaissance painting, in very bright, glossy colours – and other objects surrounding it. As you approach, you realize that in fact the whole thing is a jigsaw: the jigsaw itself (the painting) is only a fragment of a larger puzzle, which is incomplete, because it cannot be completed. For the curious thing about the puzzle is that it is made up of volumes (roughly speaking, cubes; or more precisely, irregular polyhedra), all the faces of which can be freely combined: all the faces of a cube 'A' can be matched with all the faces of a cube 'B', and not only two by two as in children's games (with building bricks). There is therefore, if not an infinity, at least an extremely large number of possible combinations. The painting is only one of them, the fragments surrounding it are sketches, rough drafts, proposals for other puzzles.

By way of proof of this almost unlimited permutability, I remove a piece from the edge of one of the fragments (I forgot to mention that, like the painting, they were not square or regular like most jigsaws, but, as it were, 'edgeless', without a rectilinear border); after handling it for a few moments I replace it on the edge of another fragment, into which it fits immediately.

We pass on to another hall, where we find my niece Sylvia. I think something very violent then takes place (perhaps we break something).

Translated by J. Romney

PADILLA

The Woof

According to Jorge Luis Borges, who is our only source of information, Gaston Padilla is the author of *Memorias de un prescindible*, published in 1974, which includes the following passage.

To our tired and distracted musing, what is visible in the carpet (the design of which never repeats itself) is probably the pattern for earthly existence; the reverse of the woof, the other side of the world (suppression of time and space or the insulting or glorious magnification of both); and the woof, the dreams. This was dreamt in Teheran by Moisés Neman, maker and seller of carpets whose premises look on to Ferdousi Square.

Translated by J. Lyons

RESNIK

The Wood

This text is taken from Salomon Resnik's *Il teatro del sogno*, published in 1982. Salomon Resnik is a psychoanalyst of Argentinian origin who now works in Paris. He studied with Mélanie Klein, Bion and Winnicott, and has specialized in child autism and psychosis.

... Another dream of the same patient will enable us to illustrate some of these concepts. It is a weird dream which forced me to get involved in the oneiric scene to such an extent that, through a sort of counter-transference, I was left hovering between dream and reality.

'I dreamt,' the patient told me, 'that I had gone to the theatre with my husband and our two daughters. The scene changed almost immediately, and I couldn't find my beloved ones. I started looking for them; I was in a wood; I felt like a child and I couldn't see anyone.'

There was a long silence, almost as if she were waiting for something. During this time I, as an analyst, was feeling lost in the wood like my patient. I asked her, 'Could you repeat the transition from the first to the second scene in your dream?' The patient became agitated and answered, 'You got lost!' 'Yes,' I said, 'I got lost in the wood of your narration!' Analysis, in the doctor's study which is a place of dramatic re-creation, had become a theatre in which the patient and I were both actors and spectators of what was being represented. The *skené* and the *théatron* confront each other till they end up merging. The reality of the psychoanalytic *séance* (today's dream) becomes ambiguous: actors are also spectators; the objectivity of contemplating the dream/tale and living its experience together merges with the reality of yesterday's dream. On the one hand, this is a transposition of the oneirical space of the patient to the space of the present analytic scene; on the other hand this is a meeting of two worlds, of two kinds of reality: the diurnal and nocturnal metaphors of the patient and of the analyst.

Translated by G. Almansi

Fantastic dreams

The dreams included in the 'fantastic' section seem cut off from their obvious source: the dreamer. They claim to lead an independent existence. The German language is endowed with a double verbal expression for the dreaming activity. You can say: 'Ich traume', 'I dream' – or 'Es träumt mir', with an impersonal form (as in verbs indicating natural phenomena, such as 'it rains', or 'it snows'), which could be translated as 'the dream comes to me'. There seem to be dreams that are not generated by the turmoil of instinct or by the drive towards symbolization, or even by the mimetic capacities of the individual who duplicates his waking experiences in his dreams. These dreams visit the dreamer, knock on his door and disturb, cheer, frighten or amuse him. 'People do not dream; they are dreamt. We undergo our dreams,' writes Jung, who sees in dreams the revelations and creations, not only of the Personal Unconscious, but also of the Collective Unconscious. Our dreams are a second life, according to Nerval; hence they do not belong to our first life. In what sense can I say that a dream is 'mine'? Because I have invented it, and it is *my* creation; because I need it, and it is *my* supply; because I undergo it, and it is *my* experience; because it concerns me, since it is part of *my* life. Or because I am the venue of the dream, it happens at *my* place. In the last case, the dreamer would be like a slave imprisoned in the universe of 'his' dream, which he cannot escape because he is unable to go elsewhere, to take a temporary abode outside his dream prison.

We may say that, in a sense, every dreamer is the slave of a despotic lord who is also his child, the dream he has engendered. This offspring progresses automatically: hard, inflexible and self-sufficient, submitting the dreamer to 'its' will and to 'its' tantrums (these last two possessives refer to an abstract entity, which in the absence of a more appropriate term we shall call the dream's individuality). The waking man can choose to change the situation and shut his eyes. But the dreamer cannot choose to open his eyes: he is condemned to live with his dream. His eyelids are bolted doors which shut him up in the cell of his hallucinating and delirious sleep. Perhaps the dreamer wants to be chaste, decorous, decent, balanced; the Dream – and I am using the capital letter with a sense of embarrassment – has decided for him on immodesty, indecorousness, indecency, imbalance. We wonder whether we can ever choose our dreams, *pace* the upholders of the therapeutic function of planned oneirism, those who want to teach the dreamers how to dream. At most, dreams choose us and knock at our door; or break in, like impatient gate-crashers and uncouth guests.

The dreams in this section are full of visitations, of inopportune interventions which are blown inside the dreamer by an act of magic, or by devilish influence, or by the random laws of games. Queen Mab visits the dreamers and raises havoc, according to the wonderful description in *Romeo and Juliet*: Mercutio 'talk[s] of nothing' because he 'talk[s] of dreams'. Of dreams we can only speak wildly, because any sane discourse would run contrary to our experience. We are faced with a categorical imperative of wildness, of which Mercutio is an undisputed master; and the natural enemy of this sublime divagation is the psychologist, or the oneiromancer, or whoever ventures to explain a dream. Queen Mab can take the form of 'a spirit [who] breathed through him', as in the passage by Novalis; or of the 'pale dream' that 'came to a lady', in Shelley's poem; or of the floating dreams caught in mid air by the BFG, the Big Friendly Giant, who blows them into the children's bedrooms with his trumpet (in the beautiful fantasy by Roald Dahl). Dream is identified with the *Traumtier*, the Dream Creature about to evaporate in Huch; or with the globes of light lined up at the back of the sky, which the dreamer Leiris, supposedly dead, must reach, hoisted like a dummy by a metallic rod drawn through his breast; or with Mother Durand, who sits like an *incubus* on Mocquet's rib-cage in Dumas' tale.

In a way, none of these dreams have an internal cause: they remain unjustified. God knows where they are born or why: they have no obvious or latent purpose (with all due respect to Freud), no natural or unnatural causes. 'Why these bizarre creatures?' asks Valéry. 'The Sick Gentleman' of Papini uses all the omnipotent violence of instinctive dreams, but there is no instinct world behind him to determine this aggressive outburst. Any study of their causes, or purposes, is banished, as well as any form of psychology. Dreams have no meaning, and can never have one, except in the fancies of their interpreters, whose explanations are in turn a form of dream. 'A trifle makes a dream, a trifle breaks it' (in Tennyson's poem). These are the favourite dreams of Roger Caillois – if we are to follow his fantasies in *L'incertitude qui vient des rêves* ('The Uncertainty Fostered by Dreams'). Are dreams dark and murky? We do not know. Caillois rejects one by one the traditional epithets of the oneiric world, even if in the end he cannot completely eliminate the sulphurous stench surrounding the castle of dreams. According to Caillois, dreams are not premonitory; they are no gateways to a world of wonders; their kernel hides no crucial secret. Caillois cannot even be bothered with their 'so-called poetic virtues', which are being upheld again by Charles Rycroft in his recent *The Innocence of Dreams* (Rycroft quotes approvingly the famous sentence by Darwin, actually borrowed from Jean Paul: 'The dream is an involuntary form of poetry').

Dreams are a medley of simulacra without any secret, and it is useless to examine them for a meaning, a confirmation, a hope, a revelation (but denying the meaning of dreams is as meaningless as asserting it: silence is the only fit comment). For Caillois, dreams have the same meaning as the shape of a cloud or the pattern on the wings of a butterfly: but beware, these two images are significant. Caillois, a great admirer of Mendeleiev (see his essay *Reconnaissance à Mendeleiev*, written for the centenary of the periodic table of elements), believes that the universe is finite and numerable. Mists and clouds hide a plan, and under the chaos of contingency we can make out the spare architecture of creation. Perhaps even the 'rainbows on spider-web horizons, petals on the grating bars' in the cell of Montale's prisoner, are part of a system. Hence the dreams, and the clouds, and the wings of the butterflies, and the stones, and the rainbows, belong to a plan which is for us in great part impossible to decipher, in spite of all our endeavours to decode the universe. Do we see in a glass darkly when we look at a cloud, or a butterfly, or a stone, or a rainbow, or even a dream? Apparently dreams signify nothing, but they have a thousand wiles to feign signification.

At the core of the dream question, or rather in its umbilicus – to use Freud's phrase against him – lies an indeterminacy principle. Descartes mentions 'this generalized uncertainty caused by dreams, which I could not tell apart from waking' (this is in fact the source of Caillois' title for the essay we have discussed here; but Descartes concludes that this position of *uncertainty* is 'ridiculous and hyperbolic'). At the bottom, there is a philosophical problem which has confronted all times and cultures: how can we find sure criteria to separate waking from dreaming? For many writers, the issue seems to bear more on the waking than on the dreaming state. Roger Caillois could, or should, have called his book *L'incertitude qui vient de la veille*, 'The Uncertainty Fostered by Waking'. Because the real difficulty with the question 'Am I dreaming or am I awake?' arises when we start doubting the reality of waking, and not the unreality of dreaming: 'Yet the issue [...] is not to avoid taking dreams for reality, but to discover why, when we are awake, we can feel entitled to the certainty that we are not dreaming,' writes Caillois.

As a corollary to this dilemma, we find the problem (treated as a joke, or as a paradox, or as a source of anxiety, or all three together) of how to vouch for the existence of a being who might belong to the world of dreams: from Carroll's classical *jeu d'esprit*, quoted here; to the deeply disturbing metaphor in Borges' *Circular Ruins*, whose protagonist, while trying to create a son by dreaming, discovers in the end that he himself has been engendered by a dream; to the 'figure in a dream' by Papini, a dreamed character in search of his dreamer, as his colleagues in Pirandello are in search of an author. In fact all dreams are subjects in search of an author; and there is a profound affinity between dream and show, between *La mise-en-scène du rêve* (the title of a book by the analyst Salomon Resnik, from which we have selected a patient's dream), and a theatrical production. This similarity is clearly pointed out in the dream by Leiris, included in our selection.

The 'otherness' of the fantastic dreams – even more radical than in other types of dreams – frees in part the dreamer from the responsibility for the events happening in them. Jean-Paul Sartre in *L'imaginaire* concludes his discussion on dreams by suggesting that the *I* in a dream is nothing but an image, although it is difficult to understand how one can explain the somatic and psychic reality of a nightmare in this 'detached' conception of oneiric experience; and surely when someone has an orgasm in a wet dream, in the morning the wet in the bed is his own, belongs to the 'I' (this problem is discussed by James Hillman). The dreams in this section show a variety of devices to escape the impact of nightmares: Huch's dreamer, or Huch as a dreamer if you prefer, thinks that the dentist's operations are no concern of his because he has got a spare head he can abandon to the drills and pincers; Damian duplicates himself in a little sculpted doll where he enjoys the eternal rest of death; and in Peter Handke's poem the inversion of all activity to passivity frees the dreamer from the duty to control what happens beyond the threshold of sleeping, and hence from the weight of remorse.

This is why all the dreams in this section, even the most anguishing, are more liberated, relaxed, carefree, imaginative, artificial. Nature itself is unnatural in Shelley's *Marianne's Dream*, and man's cultural products (buildings, columns, temples and triumphal arches) are non-cultural, exempt from the touch of a mortal instrument. In Michaux, New York presents unlikely mountains, whereas human and animal monsters proliferate in Nodier's tale. Demons and evil spirits obsess the dreamer (in Southey), but these dreams seem to come from outside, and are therefore less frightening than those which claim to articulate the emergencies of our deeper self, or of our desire to symbolize experience and duplicate reality. The man who is turned into a number in Desnos' dream, or the horses ridden by wolves who spur them with their tails in Euripides – these images may be frightening, but they are in part exorcized by the irresponsibility of the dreamer, who can then accept the most extreme and capricious experiences ('Caprices of the night' as Senancour puts it), from volcanoes more magnificent and awe-inspiring than earthly ones (again in Senancour) to the fantastic fauna and legendary characters of an earth where the sun has stopped in its course (in Apollinaire), or where the moon falls in a field (in Leopardi's poem, which is both a dream and a classical topos, derived from a long tradition which includes Virgil and Apuleius).

Dreams are spindrift, as in Novalis; or the unending waters in which Mocquet, Dumas' untiring hero, swims for days and days: 'Swim, Mocquet, swim' shout the watchers from the shore. This superhuman swimming feat is both a full nightmare from which the drunken sleeper wants to get out, and a moment of supreme liberty and irresponsibility for the swimmer and for the reader of the narrated dream.

EURIPIDES

The Wolves

This text is taken from *Rhesus*, a tragedy whose attribution to Euripides is still dubious and whose date is uncertain. The subject comes from the *Iliad* (IX, 299 ff.). During Achilles' wrath, the Trojans are successful: Hector has almost reached the Greeks' boats. But during the night, the fires are burning bright in the Greek camp. Hector decides to send a spy, Dolon, to find out what they are up to. At this point, his ally Rhesus arrives in Troy with his Thracian warriors. Hector assigns him quarters. Meanwhile, Ulysses and Diomedes have caught Dolon. Before killing him they have forced him to tell them the disposition of the Trojan army's night quarters. With this information they proceed to Troy, planning to kill Hector. But Athena convinces them that the real danger for the Greeks is Rhesus, and they kill him and steal his horses. In the ensuing confusion, Rhesus' charioteer arrives and tells Hector of his master's murder and of his own premonitory dream.

Charioteer:
Ill hath been wrought us – shame, to crown that 'ill',
The foulest shame! Yea, double ill is this!
To die with fame, if one must die, I trow,
Is bitterness to him who dies – how not?
Yet fame and honour crown his living kin.
But, as a fool dies, fameless we have died.
For, soon as Hector pointed us our quarters,
And told the watchword, couched on earth we slept,
Outworn with toil: our host no watchmen set
For nightlong guard, nor rank by rank were laid
Our arms, nor from the horses' yokes were hung
The car-whips, since our king had word that ye
Were camped triumphant nigh the galley-sterns:
So, careless all, we flung us down and slept.
Now I with heedful heart from slumber rose,
And dealt the steeds their corn with stintless hand,
Looking to yoke them with the dawn for fight.
Then spied I twain that prowled around our host
Through the thick gloom; but, soon as I bestirred me,
They cowered low, and straight drew back again.

I cried to them to come not near our host, –
Deeming some thieves from our allies drew nigh: –
Nought said they; neither added I thereto,
But to my couch went back and slept again.
And in my sleep a vision nightmared me: –
The steeds I tended, and at Rhesus' side
Drave in the car, I saw as in a dream
Mounted of wolves that rode upon their backs;
And with their tails these lashed the horses' flanks,
Scourging them on. They snorted, and outbreathed
Rage from their nostrils, tossing high their manes.
I, even in act to save from those fierce things
The steeds, woke: the night-horror smote me awake.
Then death-moans, as I raised my head, I heard;
And new-shed blood hot-welling plashed on me
As by my murdered lord's death-throes I lay.
Upright I leapt, with never a spear in hand.
But, as I peered and groped to find my lance,
From hard by came a sword-thrust 'neath my ribs
From some strong man – strong, for I felt the blade
Strike home, felt that deep furrow of the gash.
Face-down I fell: the chariot and the steeds
The robbers took, and fled into the night.
Ah me! Ah me!
Pain racketh me – O wretch! I cannot stand.
What ill befell I know – I saw it. How
The slain men perished, this I cannot tell,
Nor by what hand; but this do I divine –
Foully have they been dealt with by allies.

Translated by A. S. Way

SHAKESPEARE

Queen Mab

This passage is from *Romeo and Juliet*, I, iv.

Romeo I dream'd a dream tonight.
Mercutio   And so did I.
Romeo Well, what was yours?

Mercutio   That dreamers often lie.
Romeo In bed asleep, while they do dream things true.
Mercutio O! then, I see, Queen Mab hath been with you.
Benvotio Queen Mab! What's she?
Mercutio She is the fairies' midwife, and she comes
In shape no bigger than an agate-stone
On the fore-finger of an alderman,
Drawn with a team of little atomies
Athwart men's noses as they lie asleep:
Her waggon-spokes made of long spinners' legs;
The cover, of the wings of grasshoppers;
The traces, of the smallest spider's web;
The collars, of the moonshine's watery beams;
Her whip, of cricket's bone; the lash, of film;
Her waggoner, a small grey-coated gnat,
Not half so big as a round little worm
Prick'd from the lazy finger of a maid;
Her chariot is an empty hazel-nut,
Made by the joiner squirrel or old grub,
Time out o' mind the fairies' coach-makers.
And in this state she gallops night by night
Through lovers' brains, and then they dream of love;
O'er courtiers' knees, that dream on curtsies straight;
O'er lawyers' fingers, who straight dream on fees;
O'er ladies' lips, who straight on kisses dream;
Which oft the angry Mab with blisters plagues,
Because their breaths with sweetmeats tainted are.
Sometimes she gallops o'er a courtier's nose,
And then dreams he of smelling out a suit;
And sometimes comes she with a tithe-pig's tail,
Tickling a parson's nose as a' lies asleep,
Then dreams he of another benefice;
Sometime she driveth o'er a soldier's neck,
And then dreams he of cutting foreign throats,
Of breaches, ambuscadoes, Spanish blades,
Of healths five fathom deep; and then anon
Drums in his ear, at which he starts and wakes;
And, being thus frighted, swears a prayer or two,
And sleeps again. This is that very Mab
That plats the manes of horses in the night;
And bakes the elf-locks in foul sluttish hairs,
Which once untangled much misfortune bodes;
This is the hag, when maids lie on their backs,

That presses them and learns them first to bear,
Making them women of good carriage:
This is she —
Romeo Peace, peace! Mercutio, peace!
Thou talk'st of nothing.
Mercutio True, I talk of dreams,
Which are the children of an idle brain,
Begot of nothing but vain fantasy;
Which is as thin of substance as the air,
And more inconstant than the wind, who woos
Even now the frozen bosom of the north,
And, being anger'd, puffs away from thence,
Turning his face to the dew-dropping south.

CERVANTES

Miguel de Cervantes published the first part of *Don Quixote* in
1605, and the second part in 1615. This passage is situated
towards the end of the first part. Don Quixote, half starved after
his adventures on the Sierra Morena, has been brought back to
the Inn by his friends, who have decided to make use of his
fantasies in order to restore him to reason: to lure him back to the
Inn, they have staged the story of a lady in distress, Princess
Micomicona.

There remained but little more of the novel to be read, when Sancho Panza
burst forth in wild excitement from the garret where Don Quixote was lying,
shouting, 'Run, sirs! quick; and help my master, who is in the thick of the
toughest and stiffest battle I ever laid eyes on. By the living God he has given
the giant, the enemy of my lady the Princess Micomicona, such a slash that he
has sliced his head clean off as if it were a turnip.'

'What are you talking about, brother?' said the curate, pausing as he was
about to read the remainder of the novel. 'Are you in your senses, Sancho?
How the devil can it be as you say, when the giant is two thousand leagues
away?'

Here they heard a loud noise in the chamber, and Don Quixote shouting
out, 'Stand, thief, brigand, villain; now I have got thee and thy scimitar shall
not avail thee!' And then it seemed as though he were slashing vigorously at
the wall.

'Don't stop to listen,' said Sancho, 'but go in and part them or help my master: though there is no need of that now, for no doubt the giant is dead by this time and giving account to God of his past wicked life; for I saw the blood flowing on the ground, and the head cut off and fallen on one side, and it is as big as a large wine-skin.'

'May I die,' said the landlord at this, 'if Don Quixote or Don Devil has not been slashing some of the skins of red wine that stand full at his bed's head, and the spilt wine must be what this good fellow takes for blood;' and so saying he went into the room and the rest after him, and there they found Don Quixote in the strangest costume in the world. He was in his shirt, which was not long enough in front to cover his thighs completely and was six fingers shorter behind; his legs were very long and lean, covered with hair, and anything but clean; on his head he had a little greasy red cap that belonged to the host, round his left arm he had rolled the blanket of the bed, to which Sancho, for reasons best known to himself, owed a grudge, and in his right hand he held his unsheathed sword, with which he was slashing about on all sides, uttering exclamations as if he were actually fighting some giant: and the best of it was his eyes were not open, for he was fast asleep, and dreaming that he was doing battle with the giant. For his imagination was so wrought upon by the adventure he was going to accomplish, that it made him dream he had already reached the kingdom of Micomicon, and was engaged in combat with his enemy; and believing he was laying on to the giant, he had given so many sword cuts to the skins that the whole room was full of wine. On seeing this the landlord was so enraged that he fell on Don Quixote, and with his clenched fist began to pummel him in such a way, that if Cardenio and the curate had not dragged him off, he would have brought the war of the giant to an end. But in spite of all the poor gentleman never woke until the barber brought a great pot of cold water from the well and flung it with one dash all over his body, on which Don Quixote woke up, but not so completely as to understand what was the matter. Dorothea, seeing how short and slight his attire was, would not go in to witness the battle between her champion and her opponent. As for Sancho, he went searching all over the floor for the head of the giant, and not finding it he said, 'I see now that it's all enchantment in this house; for the last time, on this very spot where I am now, I got ever so many thumps and thwacks without knowing who gave them to me, or being able to see anybody; and now this head is not to be seen anywhere about, though I saw it cut off with my own eyes and the blood running from the body as if from a fountain.'

'What blood and fountains are you talking about, enemy of God and his saints?' said the landlord. 'Don't you see, you thief, that the blood and the fountain are only these skins here that have been stabbed and the red wine swimming all over the room? – and I wish I saw the soul of him that stabbed them swimming in hell.'

'I know nothing about that,' said Sancho; 'all I know is it will be my bad luck that through not finding this head my county will melt away like salt in water;' – for Sancho awake was worse than his master asleep, so much had his master's promises addled his wits.

The landlord was beside himself at the coolness of the squire and the mischievous doings of the master, and swore it should not be like the last time when they went without paying; and that their privileges of chivalry should not hold good this time to let one or other of them off without paying, even to the cost of the plugs that would have to be put to the damaged wine-skins. The curate was holding Don Quixote's hands, who, fancying he had now ended the adventure and was in the presence of the Princess Micomicona, knelt before the curate and said, 'Exalted and beauteous lady, your highness may live from this day forth fearless of any harm this base being could do you; and I too from this day forth am released from the promise I gave you, since by the help of God on high and by the favour of her by whom I live and breathe, I have fulfilled it so successfully.'

'Did not I say so?' said Sancho on hearing this. 'You see I wasn't drunk; there you see my master has already salted the giant; there's no doubt about the bulls; my county is all right!'

Who could have helped laughing at the absurdities of the pair, master and man? And laugh they did, all except the landlord, who cursed himself; but at length the barber, Cardenio, and the curate contrived with no small trouble to get Don Quixote on the bed, and he fell asleep with every appearance of excessive weariness. They left him to sleep, and came out to the gate of the inn to console Sancho Panza on not having found the head of the giant; but much more work had they to appease the landlord, who was furious at the sudden death of his wine-skins; and said the landlady, half scolding, half crying, 'At an evil moment and in an unlucky hour he came into my house, this knight-errant – would that I had never set eyes on him, for dear he has cost me; the last time he went off with the overnight score against him for supper, bed, straw, and barley, for himself and his squire and a hack and an ass, saying he was a knight adventurer – God send unlucky adventures to him and all the adventurers in the world – and therefore not bound to pay anything, for it was so settled by the knight-errantry tariff: and then, all because of him, came the other gentleman and carried off my tail, and gives it back more than two quartillos the worse, all stripped of its hair, so that it is no use for my husband's purpose; and then, for a finishing touch to all, to burst my wine-skins and spill my wine! I wish I saw his own blood spilt! But let him not deceive himself, for, by the bones of my father and the shade of my mother, they shall pay me down every quarto; or my name is not what it is, and I am not my father's daughter.' All this and more to the same effect the landlady delivered with great irritation, and her good maid Maritornes backed her up, while the daughter held her peace and smiled from time to time. The curate smoothed matters by promising to make good all losses to the best of his power, not only as regarded the wine-skins but also the wine, and above all the depreciation of the tail which they set such store by. Dorothea comforted Sancho, telling him that she pledged herself, as soon as it should appear certain that his master had decapitated the giant, and she found herself peacefully established in her kingdom, to bestow upon him the best county there was in it. With this Sancho consoled himself, and assured the princess she might rely upon it that he had seen the head of the giant, and more by token it had a beard that reached to the girdle, and that if it was not to be seen now it was because everything that happened in that house went by enchantment, as he himself had proved the last time he had lodged there. Dorothea said she fully believed it, and that he need not be uneasy, for all would go well and turn out as he wished.

Translated by J. Ormsby

NOVALIS

The Blue Flower

This extract is from the first chapter of *Henry von Ofterdingen*, Novalis' last novel which he left unfinished at his death in 1801. This novel is a *Bildungsroman*, partly inspired by Goethe's *Wilhelm Meister*, about the life and poetic formation of a thirteenth-century Minnesänger.

Henry's parents were already in bed and asleep; the clock on the wall was ticking monotonously; outside the rattling windows the wind whistled by. From time to time the moon's glimmer lit up the room. The youth lay restless on his bed and thought about the stranger and his stories. 'It is not the treasures which have awakened such an inexpressible longing in me,' he said to himself. 'There is no greed in my heart; but I yearn to get a glimpse of the blue flower. It is perpetually in my mind, and I can write or think of nothing else. I have never felt like this before; it seems as if I had a dream just then, or as if slumber had carried me into another world. For in the world where I had always lived, who ever bothered about flowers? Besides, such a strange passion for a flower is something I never heard of before.

I wonder where the stranger really came from? None of us has ever seen a person like him. Still I can't understand why I was the only one to be so touched by his stories. The others experienced nothing like it even though they heard the same tales. And to think I can't even talk about my singular condition! Often I feel so rapturously happy; and only when I do not have the flower clearly before my mind's eye does a deep inner turmoil seize me. This cannot and will not be understood by anyone. I would think I were mad if I did not see and think so clearly. Indeed since then everything is much clearer to me.

'Once I heard tell of the days of old, how animals and trees and cliffs talked with people then. I feel just as though they might start any moment now and I could tell by their looks what they wanted to say to me. There must be many words I do not know; if I knew more, I could grasp everything much better. Once I liked to dance; now I prefer to meditate on music.'

Little by little the youth lost himself in sweet fantasies and fell asleep. First he dreamed of immeasurable distances and wild unfamiliar regions. He wandered over oceans with inconceivable ease; he saw strange creatures; he lived with many kinds of people, in war, in wild tumult, and in quiet huts. He fell into captivity and into most ignominious affliction. Every sensation within him mounted to hitherto unknown heights. He went through an infinite variety of experiences; he died and came to life again, loved most passionately, and was then separated from his loved one forever.

Finally toward morning as daybreak appeared, his soul became calmer, and the images became clearer and more abiding. It seemed he was walking alone through a dark forest. Only rarely did the sun gleam through the green net. Soon he came to a rocky gorge that rose steeply. He had to climb over mossy stones, which former floods had carried down. The higher he climbed, the more sparse the forest became. At length he reached a small meadow which lay on the slope of the mountain. Behind the meadow jutted a crag, at the foot of which he perceived an opening that appeared to be the beginning of a passageway cut into the rock. The passage led him comfortably onward for a while and then widened into a large expanse from which a bright light had welcomed him from afar. As he entered he became aware of a mighty beam of light which rose as from a fountain to the very ceiling of the cave and dashed there into countless mistlike sparks that were gathered in a large basin below. The beam glistened like flaming gold. Not the faintest sound was to be heard; a holy stillness enveloped the glorious spectacle.

He approached the basin which surged and quivered in endless colours. This fluid, which was not hot but cool, covered the walls of the cave, where it emitted only a faint bluish light. He dipped his hand into the basin and wet his lips. It was as though a spirit breathed through him, and he felt deeply refreshed and strengthened. An irresistible longing to bathe seized him; he undressed and stepped down into the basin. It seemed as if a sunset cloud was enveloping him; a heavenly sensation flowed through his soul; with voluptuous delight countless thoughts strove to mingle within him. New images never seen before arose and interfused and became visible beings around him, and every wave of the lovely element clung to him like a tender bosom. The waves appeared to be charming girls dissolved, which momentarily embodied themselves as they touched the youth.

Intoxicated with rapture and yet conscious of every impression, he swam easily with the luminous stream as it flowed out of the basin into the cliff. A kind of sweet slumber fell upon him in which he dreamed of indescribable events and out of which he was awakened by another illumination. He found himself on soft turf by the edge of a fountain, which shot up into the air and seemed to consume itself there. Dark blue cliffs with bright veins arose at a distance; the daylight round about him was brighter and milder than ordinary daylight, and the sky was dark blue and wholly clear. But what attracted him with great force was a tall, pale blue flower, which stood beside the spring and touched him with its broad glistening leaves. Around this flower were countless others of every hue, and the most delicious fragrance filled the air. He saw nothing but the blue flower and gazed upon it long with inexpressible tenderness. Finally, when he wanted to approach the flower, it all at once began to move and change; the leaves became more glistening and cuddled up to the growing stem; the flower leaned towards him and its petals displayed an expanded blue corolla wherein a delicate face hovered. His sweet amazement increased with the strange transformation, when suddenly the voice of his mother woke him and he found himself in his parents' living room already gilded by the morning sun. He was too enraptured to be cross at this disturbance; indeed he bade his mother a cheerful good-morning and returned her cordial hug.

'You slug-abed,' said his father, 'how long have I already been sitting here, planing and polishing. I have not been able to do any hammering on account of you; mother wanted to let her dear son sleep. I also had to wait for breakfast. You have shrewdly chosen teaching as your profession, for which we wake and work. But a competent scholar, as I have heard, also has to call the night to his aid in order to study the great works of our wise forebears.'

'Dear father,' Henry answered, 'do not get angry at my sleeping so long, something you are not accustomed to having me do. I did not fall asleep until late and had many disquieting dreams until I finally dreamed a pleasant dream I shall long remember. Indeed it seems to me to have been more than a mere dream.'

'Dear Henry,' said his mother, 'I'm sure you slept on your back or went woolgathering during evening prayers last night. You look quite strange, too. Eat and drink so you will feel refreshed again.'

His mother went out; his father kept on working steadily and said to him: 'Dreams are spindrift, whatever your learned men may think of them; and you will do well to turn your mind away from such useless and harmful reflections. The times are past when divine apparitions appeared in dreams, and we cannot and will not fathom the state of mind of those chosen men the Bible speaks of. The nature of dreams as well as of the world of men must have been different in those days.

'In the age we live in there is no longer any direct intercourse with heaven. The old stories and records form our only source of knowledge, in so far as we need it, of the supernatural world; and in place of those express revelations the Holy Ghost now speaks to us indirectly through the minds of wise and well-disposed men and through the way of life and the fortunes of the pious. Our present-day miracle-working images have never edified me especially, and I have never believed the great deeds our divines credit them with. However, anyone who wants to may derive edification from them, and I am careful not to make another stray from his faith.'

'But my dear father, what makes you so opposed to dreams? Their strange transformations and their lightsome and tender nature certainly do promote our meditations. Is not every dream, even the most confused one, a remarkable phenomenon, which apart from any notion of its being sent from God is a significant rent in the mysterious curtain that hangs a thousandfold about our inner life? In the wisest books we find countless authentic stories of dreams, and just call to mind the dream the venerable court chaplain told us lately; it seemed remarkable even to you.

'But even without these stories, if you had a dream for the first time in your life, how astonished you would be, and you certainly would not let anyone talk you out of the miraculous nature of this happening which has merely become commonplace to us. Dreams seem to me to be a defence against the regularity and routine of life, a playground where the hobbled imagination is freed and revived and where it jumbles together all the pictures of life and interrupts the constant soberness of grown-ups by means of a merry child's play. Without dreams we should certainly grow old sooner; and so we can regard dreams, if not as directly sent from heaven above, at least as divine gifts, as friendly companions on our pilgrimage to the holy sepulchre. Certainly the dream I dreamed last night will not have been an ineffectual accident in my life, for I feel that it reaches into my soul as into a giant wheel, impelling it onward with a mighty swing.'

His father smiled pleasantly and said, looking at Henry's mother who stepped in just then, 'Mother, Henry cannot deny the hour in which he came into the world. There brews in his talk the fiery Italian wine I had brought along from Rome and which glorified our wedding night. At that time I was still quite a different fellow, too. The southern air had thawed me out, I was overflowing with boldness and high spirits and you were also an ardent, adorable girl. We had a high time then in your father's house: musicians and singers had come from far and near, and it was long since a gayer wedding had been celebrated in Augsburg.'

'You were just now talking about dreams,' the mother said. 'Do you remember you told me at that time about a dream you had dreamed in Rome, which put it into your head to come to Augsburg and try for my hand?'

'You remind me just at the right time,' he said; 'I had quite forgotten the strange dream which at that time occupied me long enough; but even that dream proves what I have been saying about dreams. One could not have a more vivid and orderly dream; I still remember every detail precisely; and yet what did it mean? That I dreamt about you and that soon afterwards I was seized by a longing to possess you was quite natural, for I already knew you. Your sweet and gentle nature had touched me deeply from the very beginning, and only the desire for foreign parts restrained my wish to possess you. At the time of the dream my curiosity had been pretty well satisfied, so that my affection could more easily make itself felt.'

'Do tell us that strange dream of yours,' said his son.

'One evening,' his father began, 'I had been wandering about. The sky was clear, and the moon clothed the old pillars and walls with a pale uncanny light. My companions went out with girls, but homesickness and love drove me out into the open country. Finally I got thirsty and entered the first farm home I encountered to ask for a drink of wine or milk. An old man came out, likely taking me for a doubtful visitor. I presented my request for a drink of wine or milk; and when he learned I was a foreigner and a German, he invited me in like a friend and brought out a bottle of wine. He asked me to have a seat and inquired about my trade. The room was full of books and antiquities. We got into a rather long conversation; he told me much about ancient times, about painters, sculptors, and poets. I had never heard anyone talk about them in this fashion. I felt as though I had landed in a new world. He showed me signet rings and other old art works; then with fiery animation he read me some glorious poems, and in this way the time passed like a moment. My heart still cheers up whenever I recall the motley crowd of strange thoughts and feelings that filled me that night. He was at home in the pagan ages and yearned with incredible fervour to return to that grey antiquity. Finally he took me to a room where I might pass the rest of the night, saying that it was already too late to return.

'I soon fell asleep, and then it seemed to me I was back home in Eisenach, sauntering out of the city gate. It seemed I had to go somewhere and do something, but I could not tell where I was to go or what I was to do. I walked very briskly towards the Harz region, happy as a bridegroom on the way to his wedding. I did not stick to the road but cut across the fields over hill and dale, soon coming to a high mountain. When I had climbed it, I saw a golden meadow-land and surveyed the length and breadth of Thuringia, since not a mountain round about cut off my view. Opposite me lay the Harz ridge with its dark mountains, and I saw countless monasteries, castles and villages. And as I began to feel a hearty satisfaction, I thought of the old man at whose place I was sleeping, and it seemed to me I had been with him a long time ago.

'Soon I noticed a stairway that led into the mountain. I went down the steps and after a long while came to a spacious cavern; there an old man in a flowing cloak sat at an iron table and stared continually at a beautiful girl carved in marble before him. His beard had grown through the iron table and covered his feet. He had a serious and kindly look and reminded me of an old bust I had seen at the country home that night. A bright light flooded the cave. As I was standing there and looking at the old man, my host suddenly tapped me on my shoulder, took me by my hand, and led me away with him through long passages. After a while I saw a dim light at a distance as though daylight were about to break in. I hurried towards it, and found myself on a green plain; but everything seemed to me quite different than in Thuringia. Mammoth trees with large glistening leaves cast a broad shade round about. The air was very warm and yet not oppressive. Everywhere fountains and flowers, and among all the flowers *one* pleased me especially, and it seemed to me that the others leaned towards this one.'

'Ah, dearest father, please tell me what colour it was,' the lad said with violent agitation.

'I cannot remember that, although the other details are still clearly impressed on my mind.'

'Was it not blue?'

'Maybe it was,' the father continued without paying any attention to Henry's strange vehemence. 'This much I still remember; I was in an extraordinary state of mind and for a long time paid no attention to my guide. When I finally turned to him, I noticed that he was observing me closely and smiling at me with heartfelt joy. How I got away from this place I can't remember any more. Presently I was up on the mountain again. My companion was with me and said, 'You have seen the greatest wonder of the world. It rests with you to become the happiest creature on earth and in addition a famous man. Heed carefully what I tell you: if you come back here again towards evening on St John's day and pray earnestly to God for the meaning of this dream, then the highest earthly lot will be yours. Then be sure to pay heed to a small blue flower which you will find up here; break it off and humbly resign yourself to heavenly guidance.'

'After that dream I found myself among the most glorious shapes and people, and endless periods of time fluttered by in manifold changes. My tongue was as though set free, and my words had the ring of music. Then everything became dark and confined and ordinary again. I saw your mother with an amiable, abashed look before me. She held a shining child in her arms and handed it to me, when all of a sudden the child visibly grew, becoming more and more radiant and bright. And finally on dazzling-white wings it soared over us, and taking us both in its arms it flew so high that the earth looked like a golden bowl with the neatest carving. After that I only remember that the flower and the mountain and the old man appeared again. But I awoke soon after and felt stirred by violent love. I took leave of my hospitable host, who begged me to visit him often; I promised to and would have kept my world had I not soon after left Rome and travelled impetuously to Augsburg.'

Translated by P. Hilty

SENANCOUR

Dreams

This is an extract from the eighty-fifth letter in Ernest Pivert de Senancour's *Oberman*, first published in 1804. *Oberman* is, rather than an actual epistolary novel, a sort of rambling diary, a logbook of *états d'âme*, written by a man overwhelmed by the boredom and meaninglessness of life. At first it was not understood by the contemporary readership, but was recognized around 1830 as one of the first expressions of the *mal-du-siècle*.

At other times I find myself in a vague but delightful condition between sleeping and waking. I enjoy the blending and confusion of the ideas of daytime with those of sleep. Often there lingers with me a trace of the gentle agitation left by some vivid, startling, and remarkable dream, with those mysterious associations and that picturesque incoherence so dear to the imagination.

Man's genius in his waking hours cannot equal the caprices of the night. Some time ago I dreamed of a volcanic eruption, but never was real volcano so grand, awe-inspiring, and magnificent in its terror. I seemed to be watching it from the window of a palace on a lofty site, with several others near me. It was night, but everything was lighted up. The moon and Saturn were visible in the sky between scattered and hurrying clouds, though all around was calm. Saturn was near the horizon and seemed larger than the moon, its ring, like white-hot metal on the point of fusion, lighted up the vast, cultivated and populous plain. In the far distance, but distinctly visible, a long and regular chain of lofty snow-clad mountains linked the plain with the sky. While I gazed a terrible wind swept over the landscape, tearing up and sweeping away every trace of cultivation, forests, and dwellings, and in two seconds nothing remained but a desert of arid sand, red and glowing as if with internal fire. Then the ring of Saturn detached itself and shot downward through the sky until it touched the pinnacles of snow, while they began to shudder and upheave from their very roots, rising and rolling in great billows like huge sea waves raised by some vast earth-tremor. In a few moments the flames that spurted from the crests of these white waves fell back from the skies and rolled down in blazing streams. The mountains were alternately pale or glowing as they rose and fell in weird pulsation, and the great catastrophe was wrought amid a silence more weird still.

No doubt you will fancy that in this wreck of the world I awoke in horror before the climax, but my dream did not end according to rule. I did not wake; the flames died down, and a great calm ensued. Darkness fell on the scene; we shut the windows, began chatting in the drawing-room on the subject of fireworks, and my dream went on.

I have heard it stated again and again that our dreams are suggested by what has impressed us on the previous day. I quite admit that our dreams, like all our ideas and sensations, are composed entirely of elements with which experience has already made us familiar, but I think the resultant whole has often no other relation to the past. Whatever we imagine can only be built up of existing materials; but we dream, just as we imagine, new combinations, and often they have no traceable connection with what we have previously seen. Some of these dreams constantly recur in the same way, identical in many of their smallest details, though we may never have thought of them in the meantime. I have seen in dreams lovelier views than any I could have imagined, and have always seen them alike. Ever since my childhood I have dreamed of being near one of the chief cities in Europe. The landscape is entirely different from that which actually surrounds this capital, which I have never seen, and yet every time I have dreamed of approaching this town in my travels, the landscape has looked just as it did when I dreamed of it first, and not as I know it to be.

Some twelve or fifteen times I have seen in a dream a place in Switzerland that I was previously familiar with, and yet in these dream visits it looks quite different from the reality, and always exactly as I saw it the first time I dreamed of it.

Some weeks ago I saw a delightful valley, so perfectly in harmony with my tastes that I question whether such a place can exist. Last night I saw it again, and found there also an old man, quite alone, eating some coarse bread at the door of a wretched little cabin. 'I was expecting you,' said he; 'I knew you would come; in a few days I shall be here no more, and you will see everything changed.' Then we went on the lake, in a little boat which he upset by jumping overboard. I went to the bottom, and woke up in the act of drowning.

Fonsalbe maintains that a dream like this must be prophetic, and that I shall see such a lake and valley. To make the dream come true we have decided that if I ever discover such a place I shall go on the water, provided the boat is well built, the weather calm, and no old man about.

Translated by Y. A. Barnes

SOUTHEY

Evil Spirits

This is a passage from a diary Robert Southey (1774–1843), the Romantic poet, kept of his dreams.

About ten days ago, a very valuable dream which I had, has induced me to commence this record. I was haunted by evil spirits, of whose presence, though unseen, I was aware. There were also dead bodies near me, though I saw them not. Terrified as I was, far beyond any fear that I ever experienced in actual life, still I reasoned and insisted to myself that all was delirium and weakness of mind, and even sent away the person who I thought was present with me, that I might be left alone to exert myself. When alone, the actual presence of the tormentors was more certain, and my horrors increased, till at length an arm appeared through the half-opened door, or rather a long hand. Determined to convince myself that all was unsubstantial and visionary, though I saw it most distinctly, I ran up and caught it. It was a hand, and a lifeless one. I pulled at it with desperate effort, dragged in a sort of shapeless body into the room, trampled upon it, crying out aloud the while for horror. The extreme efforts I made to call for help succeeded so far as to wake Edith, who immediately delivered me from the most violent fear that ever possessed me.

This is a valuable dream, for an old monk would have believed all to have been verily what it appeared and I now perfectly understand by experience what their contests with the devil are.

SHELLEY

Marianne's Dream

An occasional poem written in 1817 by Percy Bysshe Shelley.
Marianne Hunt, the wife of Leigh Hunt, was scraping down and
restoring the plaster statues in the library, and had this dream
which she recounted to Shelley. *Marianne's Dream* was first published, anonymously, in Leigh Hunt's *The Literary Pocketbook*.

Marianne's Dream

I

A pale dream came to a Lady fair,
   And said, 'A boon, a boon, I pray –
I know the secrets of the air,
   And things are lost in the glare of day,
Which I can make the sleeping see,
If they will put their trust in me.

II

And thou shalt know of things unknown,
   If thou wilt let me rest between
The veiny lids, whose fringe is thrown
   Over thine eyes so dark and sheen:'
And half in hope and half in fright,
The Lady closed her eyes so bright.

III

At first all deadly shapes were driven
   Tumultuously across her sleep,
And o'er the vast cope of bending Heaven
   All-ghastly-visaged clouds did sweep;
And the Lady ever looked to spy
If the golden sun shone forth on high.

IV

And as towards the East she turned,
   She saw aloft in the morning air,
Which now with hues of sunrise burned,
   A great black Anchor rising there;
And wherever the Lady turned her eyes,
It hung before her in the skies.

V

The sky was blue as the summer sea,
   The depths were cloudless over head,
The air was calm as it could be,
   There was no sight or sound of dread
But that black Anchor floating still
Over the piny eastern hill.

VI

The Lady grew sick with a weight of fear,
   To see that Anchor ever hanging,
And veiled her eyes; she then did hear
   The sound as of a dim low clanging,
And looked abroad if she might know
Was it aught else, or but the flow
Of the blood in her own veins, to and fro.

VII

There was a mist in the sunless air,
   Which shook as it were with an earthquake's shock,
But the very weeds that blossomed there
   Were moveless, and each might rock
Stood on its basis steadfastly;
The Anchor was seen no more on high.

VIII

But piled around, with summits hid
   In lines of cloud at intervals,
Stood many a mountain pyramid
   Among whose everlasting walls
Two mighty cities shone, and ever
Thro' the red mist their domes did quiver.

IX

On two dread mountains, from whose crest
   Might seem, the eagle, for her brood,
Would ne'er have hung her dizzy nest,
   Those tower-encircled cities stood.
A vision strange such towers to see,
Sculptured and wrought so gorgeously,
Where human art could never be.

X

And columns framed of marble white,
   And giant fanes, dome over dome
Piled, and triumphal gates, all bright
   With workmanship, which could not come
From touch of mortal instrument.
Shot o'er the vales, or lustre lent
From its own shapes magnificent.

XI

But still the Lady heard that clang
   Filling the wide air far away;
And still the mist whose light did hang
   Among the mountains shook alway,
So that the Lady's heart beat fast,
As half in joy, and half aghast,
On those high domes her look she cast

XII

Sudden, from out that city sprung
   A light which made the earth grow red;
Two flames, that each with quivering tongue
   Licked its high domes, and overhead
Among those mighty towers and fanes
Dropped fire, as a volcano rains
Its sulphurous ruin on the plains.

XIII

And hark! a rush as if the deep
   Had burst its bonds; she looked behind
And saw over the eastern steep
   A raging flood descend, and wind
Thro' that wide vale; she felt no fear,
But said within herself, 'tis clear
These towers are Nature's own, and she
To save them has sent forth the sea.

XIV

And now those raging billows came
   Where that fair Lady sate, and she
Was borne towards the showering flame
   By the wild waves heaped tumultuously,
And, on a little plank, the flow
Of the whirlpools bore her to and fro.

XV

The waves were fiercely vomited
   From every tower and every dome,
And dreary light did widely shed
   O'er that vast flood's suspended foam,
Beneath the smoke which hung its night
On the stained cope of heaven's light.

XVI

The plank whereon that Lady sate
   Was driven through the chasms, about and about
Between the peaks so desolate
   Of the drowning mountains, in and out,
As the thistle-beard on a whirlwind sails –
While the flood was filling those hollow vales.

XVII

At last her plank an eddy crost,
   And bore her to the city's wall,
Which now the flood had reached almost;
   It might the stoutest heart appal
To hear the fire roar and hiss
Thro' the rifts of those mighty palaces.

XVIII

The eddy whirled her round and round
  Before a gorgeous gate, which stood
Piercing the clouds of smoke, which bound
  Its aëry arch with light like blood;
She looked on that gate of marble clear,
With wonder that extinguished fear.

XIX

For it was filled with sculptures rarest,
  Of forms most beautiful and strange,
Like nothing human, but the fairest
  Of wingèd shapes, whose legions range
Throughout the sleep of those that are,
Like this same Lady good and fair.

XX

And as she looked, still lovelier grew
  Those marble forms; – the sculptor sure
Was a strong spirit, and the hue
  Of his own mind did there endure
After the touch, whose power had braided
Such grace, was in some sad change faded.

XXI

She looked, the flames were dim; the flood
  Grew tranquil as a woodland river
Winding thro' hills in solitude;
  Those marble shapes then seemed to quiver,
And their fair limbs to float in motion,
Like weeds unfolding in the ocean.

XXII

And their lips moved; – one seemed to speak,
  When suddenly the mountains crackt,
And thro' the chasm the flood did break
  With an earth-uplifting cataract;
The statues gave a joyous scream,
And on its wings the pale thin Dream
Lifted the Lady from the stream.

XXIII

The dizzy flight of that phantom pale
   Waked the fair Lady from her sleep,
And she arose, while from the veil
   Of her dark eyes the dream did creep.
And she walked about as one who knew
That sleep has sights as clear and true
As any waking eyes can view.

KEATS

Endymion

John Keats wrote 'Endymion', of which we give here an extract, in 1817.

So she was gently glad to see him laid
Under her favourite bower's quiet shade,
On her own couch, new made of flower leaves,
Dried carefully on the cooler side of sheaves
When last the sun his autumn tresses shook,
And the tann'd harvesters rich armfuls took.
Soon was he quietened to slumbrous rest:
But ere it crept upon him; he had prest
Peona's busy hand against his lips,
And still, a-sleeping, held her finger-tips
In tender pressure. And as a willow keeps
A patient watch over the stream that creeps
Windingly by it, so the quiet maid
Held her in peace – so that a whispering blade
Of grass, a wailful gnat, a bee bustling
Down in the blue-bells, or a wren light rustling
Among sere leaves and twigs, might all be heard.

O magic sleep! O comfortable bird,
That broodest o'er the troubled sea of the mind
Till it is hushed and smooth! O unconfined
Restraint! Imprisoned liberty! Great key
To golden palaces, strange minstrelsy,
Fountains grotesque, new trees, bespangled caves,

Echoing grottoes, full of tumbling waves
And moonlight – aye, to all the mazy world
Of silvery enchantment! Who, upfurled
Beneath thy drowsy wing a triple hour,
But renovates and lives? Thus, in the bower,
Endymion was calmed to life again.
Opening his eyelids with a healthier brain,
He said: 'I feel this thine endearing love
All through my bosom: thou art as a dove
Trembling its closèd eyes and sleekèd wings
About me; and the pearliest dew not brings
Such morning incense from the fields of May
As do those brighter drops that twinkling stray
From those kind eyes, the very home and haunt
Of sisterly affection. Can I want
Aught else, aught nearer heaven, than such tears?
Yet dry them up in bidding hence all fears
That, any longer, I will pass my days
Alone and sad. No, I will once more raise
My voice upon the mountain-heights; once more
Make my horn parley from their foreheads hoar;
Again my trooping hounds their tongues shall loll
Around the breathèd boar; again I'll poll
The fair-grown yew tree for a chosen bow,
And, when the pleasant sun is getting low,
Again I'll linger in a sloping mead
To hear the speckled thrushes, and see feed
Our idle sheep. So be thou cheerèd, sweet,
And if thy lute is here, softly intreat
My soul to keep in its resolvèd course.'

LEOPARDI

Nocturnal Fright

Giacomo Leopardi, the great Italian poet of the Romantic period,
wrote this poem in 1819, but it was first published in 1826. It was
excluded from the 1831 edition of his collected *Canti*, but rein-
troduced among the 'fragments' in the 1835 edition.

Alcetas:
Hearken, Melissus: I will tell to you
A dream of yester-night, which yonder moon
Brings back into my mind. Methought I stood
Beside the window facing toward the field,
And gazed up at the sky: when suddenly
The moon dropped out of heaven; and as it fell,
The nearer it approached, the larger grew
Its disk unto the sight, till down it crashed
In the middle of my paddock; and it was
A bucket's girth in size and vomited
A cloud of sparks, which made a hissing sound
As loud as when a man dips and puts out
A glowing coal in water. Even so
The moon, there in the meadow as I said,
Was put out and grew momently more black,
And round about it all the herbage smoked.
Then, looking up, I saw left in the sky
A kind of gleam or mark, or rather niche,
From where it had been torn; I froze with fear
To see it, and have not recovered yet.

Melissus:
No wonder, when you think how easily
The moon might tumble down into your field.

Alcetas:
Why, do we not in summer often see
Stars falling?

Melissus:
But there are so many stars,
That 'tis no harm, tho' one or two should fall,
When thousands still remain. But only one
Moon is there in the sky, and no one yet
Has ever seen it fall except in dreams.

Translated by G. L. Bickersteth

NODIER

The Bailiff of the Isle of Man

Charles Nodier was the host of the first Romantic circle, which included Victor Hugo and Alfred de Vigny. *La Fée aux miettes*, 'The Crumb-Picking Fairy', from which this passage is taken, was published in 1832. Michel, a young carpenter, has befriended, at first out of compassion, a strange old woman who begs for her food (hence her nickname, the Crumb-picking Fairy), under the porch of the church of Granville, in Normandy. But he is soon fascinated by her charm and wisdom, and accepts quite readily that she is in fact Belkiss, the Queen of Sheba. He follows her to Scotland, but loses track of her in Greenock. He gets employment as a carpenter with Master Finewood, who finds him a room at Mrs Speaker's Inn. At this point our passage begins.

... So saying, I rested my head on my hand, haunted by the vague and confused ideas which habitually take possession of me after any vivid impressions; I suppose the same is true of others subject to an all-absorbing and passionate imagination.

A movement close by me compelled me to open my eyes and I discovered that I was being served.

'You should congratulate yourself, Michel,' Mistress Speaker said as she set before me a pair of grouse *à l'estragon* and two bottles of port. 'The bailiff of the Isle of Man, who has come to Greenock to change the dues of his province into banknotes, does you the honour of wishing to dine with you for the pleasure of your conversation, because he has heard of your learning and exemplary conduct.'

I hastened to rise and greet the bailiff of the Isle of Man, whose bearing was of the most worthy that you can imagine, and in whose person were combined the imposing exterior of holders of high office, and the refined manners of the choicest society. What surprised me more than I have words to express was the fact that there sat upon his shoulders the magnificent head of a Great Dane, and that I alone of Mistress Speaker's numerous guests seemed to notice it. This circumstance threw me into some consternation, because I was not at all certain in what language to address him, and because I had some difficulty in understanding his, which consisted of a series of small barks, delivered with the gravest of inflections, and accompanied by extremely expressive gestures. What is beyond doubt is that he understood me perfectly, and that after a quarter of an hour of conversation, I was as surprised at the concision of his language and the exquisite subtlety of his judgements as I had been on first catching sight of the novelty of his physiognomy. It is truly embarrassing to think of the time people waste rummaging through dictionaries, when one has had the pleasure of spending time in conversation with a well-educated Great Dane such as the bailiff of the Isle of Man.

We took our leave of each other with effusive marks of affection on both sides, which no longer caused me any surprise. There are such curious sources of fellow-feeling in this world of ours! But since the port, to which I was wholly unaccustomed, made me feel sleepy, I wasted no time in retiring to the fine eiderdown bed that Master Finewood had had prepared for me. There I said my goodnights to the portrait of Belkiss, which still had the same laughter playing about its lips, and was soon dozing off, when I heard the voice of Mistress Speaker insinuating itself into my ear like a breath of wind.

'Forgive me for waking you, my child', she said, 'but there is such a terrible turmoil in my house, what with all these travellers setting sail tomorrow on the great 'Queen of Sheba', that I don't know where to put them all, and you would be obliging me considerably if you would share your bed with the honourable gentleman who kept you company at supper.'

'I am only too glad to do so,' I replied, 'and it is such an insignificant inconvenience for a working man to sleep double in such a spacious and accommodating bed, that you should not even have troubled to mention it.'

However I did half turn over to make sure that I was not mistaken about my bedfellow; and in fact I saw the bailiff of the Isle of Man quietly putting on a nightgown of a kind to give complete reassurance to those most sensitive about cleanliness, then slipping a fat morocco wallet with a clasp under the pillow, and finally creeping between the sheets with a silent and seemly discreetness, keeping a decent distance between himself and me, which I had taken the trouble to make easy for him to do. I was only made aware of his presence by the warmth of his breath which reached me from afar without disturbing me, for it is obvious that a Great Dane can only sleep comfortably on its side. After a few minutes, he started snoring, but in a manner so rhythmical and harmonious that I took no more notice. And I likewise fell asleep.

At that particular time, I was not in the habit of dreaming much, or rather I felt that my faculty for dreaming had undergone a change. It seemed to me that it was no longer connected with the impressions of sleep, but rather with those of real life, and that it was in real life that it had taken refuge with all its manifold illusions. To tell the truth, I only entered a bizarre and imaginary world when I had done with sleeping; and that surprised and derisive eye we usually cast, when we awaken, on the dreams of the previous night, I cast, not without shame, on the dreams of the dawning day, before yielding myself up to them completely as to one of the inescapable imperatives of my destiny. The particular night of which I am speaking was, however, troubled by strange dreams and by real events stranger still, and the memory of it never recurs to my mind without all my limbs being at the same time traversed by a shudder of fear.

It all began with the shrill sound of a window slowly turning on its hinges, through which I felt the insidious air of damp September mists creep in. 'Oh! Oh!' I said to myself, 'the wind has its way as much in the Caledonian Hotel, if I am not mistaken, as in the artisan's garret!' And I put it out of my mind. – A moment later, I thought I heard confused movements, sinister murmurings in whispered undertones, a vague noise of muffled words and stifled laughter which buzzed in my ears. 'So that's how it is,' I continued. 'The storm is going to play its nasty tricks at Mistress Speaker's; but it would be a stupid man who, sleeping on such a magnificent eiderdown bed, troubled his head about it!' And I merely drew the eiderdown up over my companion and myself, and snuggled into the down again, so afraid was I of losing the somnolence of that soothing repose, a repose I had not enjoyed since the days of my childhood at my father's, when my Uncle André, on his way to bed, would come and lift the overflowing mattress from between the planks of the bedstead and kiss my forehead.

'The other one is asleep,' muttered a hoarse voice, immediately drowned in unintelligible grunts.

And while I held my breath to listen, the luminous globe of a lantern, whose heat I could almost feel, transfixed me with its piercing rays, which penetrated between my eyelids like fiery wedges; for in the vague turmoil of a half-interrupted sleep, I had automatically turned towards the middle of the room. – I then saw (how horrible to recall it!) four enormous heads rising up above the blazing lantern, as though they belonged to the same body, and on which its light was reflected with as much brilliance as if it had had two mutually intensifying sources. They were indeed extraordinary and forbidding faces! The head of a wild cat, growling in a low, lugubrious and unbroken mumble, through the red vapours which played round the lamp's window, and fixing on me eyes more dazzling than the rounded belly of the glass but which, instead of being circular, were centres of refraction, thin, narrow, oblique and pointed like flaming slits. – A mastiff's head, its hair bristling, blood foaming from its mouth, and with shapeless, but still living, pulsating, groaning hunks of flesh hanging from its fangs. – A horse's head more cleanly picked, sharper and whiter, than those drying out on the municipal dump, half charred by the sun; it was set on a kind of camel's neck and swung backwards and forwards with the regularity of a pendulum, shaking out of its empty eye-sockets, in all directions and with each oscillation, several feathers left there by the crows. – Behind these three heads, there rose – and hideous, hideous it was – the head of a man or some other monster, which stood much taller than all the others, and whose features, arranged in reverse order to our own, seemed to have exchanged not only their places but also their organs and attributes, so that its eyes gnashed their teeth right and left as stridently as metal resisting the locksmith's file; and its disproportionate mouth, whose lips were twisted in terrible convulsions, like the eye-balls of an epileptic, threatened me with looks like daggers. It seemed to me that this head was supported from below by a vast hand which had a tight grip on its hair, and brandished it like a terrifying rattle to amuse an uproarious multitude hanging by their feet from the panels in the ceiling, which creaked under their stamping; this mass of creatures clapped their thousands of dangling hands in our direction to register their applause and good humour.

Faced with this terrifying sight, I gave the bailiff of the Isle of Man a sharp push, but he fell back on me like a corpse, because by dint of hiding away in the depths of the bed so as not to get in his way, I had made a hollow for myself, and I could no longer see what was going on, except by the ray of light let in by his long muzzle pointing out from between his small, straight ears. However, a lever of some sort, muscular, black and hairy, an arm perhaps, rummaging under our pillow, brushed against my neck with the raw, stabbing coldness of ice and alerted me to the fact that they had designs on his wallet. I leapt up, seized the knife which I had bought that morning for the crossing, and rushed in among the phantoms, striking about me, at the cat, at the mastiff, at the horse, at the monster, cutting through the owls which were beating their wings against my head, through the snakes which encircled me with their coils, twining round my limbs and biting my shoulders, through the black and yellow salamanders which were gnawing at my toes and encouraging each other with the assurance that I would soon be brought down. At last I managed to snatch my friend's fortune. . . from whom? I don't know! – for my dagger plunged into bodies with no more consistency than clouds, – and then I saw them gather together, leaping and bounding through the open window, mingling together in a pack, wheeling round each other pell-mell, momentarily scattered by collision with a stone, reuniting again on the slope down to the jetty, still wheeling in their uninterrupted flight, and finally plunging into the sea with the crash of an avalanche.

I came back in triumph, but panting with weariness and terror, – searching for all the doors, but they were walled up, or offered so narrow and meagre an egress that even a snake would not have dared to slither through, – pulling all the bell-cords, but they jangled their squirrel's-tail clappers against their cork rims to no avail, – crying out for someone to speak, just one word; but my cries, which were audible only to me, could not find a way out of my all but bursting chest and died away on my mute lips like the echo of a breath.

I was found the next day, lying prone by my bed, the bailiff's wallet in one hand and a knife in the other.

I was asleep.

Translated by C. Scott

NERVAL

The Second Life

For Gérard de Nerval's *Aurélia*, from which this dream is taken, see page 280.

Our dreams are a second life. I have never been able to penetrate without a shudder those ivory or horned gates which separate us from the invisible world. The first moments of sleep are an image of death; a hazy torpor grips our thoughts and it becomes impossible for us to determine the exact instant when the 'I', under another form, continues the task of existence. Little by little a vague underground cavern grows lighter and the pale, gravely immobile shapes that live in limbo detach themselves from the shadows and the night. Then the picture takes form, a new brightness illumines these strange apparitions and gives them movement. The spirit world opens before us.

Swedenborg called these visions *Memorabilia*; he owed them more often to musing than to sleep; *The Golden Ass* of Apuleius, Dante's *Divine Comedy*, are two poetic models of such studies of the human soul. Following their example I am going to try to describe the impressions of a long illness which took place entirely within the mysteries of my soul; I do not know why I use the word '*illness*', for as far as my physical self was concerned, I never felt better. Sometimes I thought my strength and energy were doubled, I seemed to know everything, understand everything. My imagination gave me infinite delight. In recovering what men call reason, do I have to regret the loss of those joys?

Translated by G. Wagner

DUMAS

Mocquet's Nightmare

The following passasge is taken from a short story by Alexandre Dumas (Père), which was first published as *Le cauchemar de Mocquet* in a weekly, *Le Monte-Cristo* on 8 October 1857. It was then republished as *Un voyage à la lune* in *Causeries*, vol. I, 1857. The passage given here is situated at the beginning of the story.

I have often told you in my *Mémoires* and in other books, of a gamekeeper of my father's, who gave me my first fencing-lessons.

This man was called Mocquet.

He was a worthy fellow, but very superstitious, and never would let you throw any doubts on the truth of the legends which the old folk told about the forest of Villers-Cotterets. He vowed he had seen with his own eyes the White Lady of the Tower on the Mount; he had carried on his shoulder the Ghostly Sheep of the Goat's Knoll; and (as you may know) it was he who told me the story of Thibaut the Werewolf, which I have lately retold to my readers.

For the last few months of my father's life, when he was suffering from the complaint of which he died, we were all living at the little old castle known as the 'Château des Fossés', and just at this time Mocquet was possessed with a strange fancy.

He believed that an old woman of Haramont (a little village a mile and a half away from our house) haunted him in his sleep, and gave him the nightmare.

This old woman was called Mother Durand.

Mocquet's tale was, that as soon as he fell asleep, the old woman came and sat upon his chest and weighed more and more heavily upon him till he choked for breath.

Then he would begin in his dreams to go through a series of adventures which made him suffer so acutely that when he awoke the poor man was quite sure that what he had just endured was not a dream at all, but had really happened.

So persuaded was he of this, that I have more than once known his hearers to be shaken in their disbelief; and as for myself, child-like, I never doubted in the least but that Mocquet had seen and done the things which he said he had seen and done.

After one of these dreams he would awake, panting, pale, and trembling. It was pitiful to see the poor fellow using every possible means to keep himself from sleeping, so afraid was he of what sleep would bring. Sometimes he would beg his neighbours to come in and play cards with him, would order his wife to pinch him black and blue if he should give way and close his eyes, and, further, to keep himself from drowsiness, he would drink cup after cup of coffee, just as anybody else would drink water.

But it was all in vain. His neighbours, who were forced to be up early next morning, could seldom be persuaded to play at cards later than eleven o'clock. His wife, after keeping on pinching him until one o'clock in the morning, ended by going to sleep herself. And lastly, the coffee, which at first had the desired effect, little by little ceased to keep him awake, and ended by being no more helpful to poor Mocquet than any ordinary drink.

Mocquet struggled his very hardest; he walked up and down, he sang, he cleaned his gun; but at last his legs gave way under him, his voice died away in his throat, and his gun fell from his hands.

Knowing what was going to happen Mocquet uttered many a bitter groan whilst all this was going on; but his cries gave way to a sort of rattling in his throat, which showed that the nightmare was beginning to take hold of him, and that the old witch, who was riding upon the poor man as if he were her broom, was in the saddle once more!

Then the poor dreamer lost all idea of time and of space and had the strangest fancies about the length of time he had slept. He insisted that he had slept twelve hours, or eight hours, or eight days, or a month, just as it happened; and the things which he had seen, the places he had visited, the deeds he had done in his sleeping hours, were so fresh and real to him, that whatever one might say, however much you might try to prove to him the absurdity of what he said, nothing would shake his belief in the truth of his dreams.

One day he walked into my father's room looking so pale and upset that the General saw at once something alarming had happened to Mocquet, not in real life – for the poor fellow had ceased to care about the events of his waking hours – but in one of his bad dreams.

And indeed, when asked what his news was, Mocquet replied that he had been to the Moon.

My father's face showed that he did not quite believe this; but the keeper was quite certain of it, and as his bare word did not seem to have any great weight with my father, Mocquet went on to tell the whole story from beginning to end.

I was sitting in a corner of the room; I heard it all, and as I was always fond of wonderful stories I didn't lose a word of the strange tale which I am going to tell you.

'You remember, General,' began Mocquet, 'that seven or eight days ago you sent me with a letter to General Charpentier, at Oigny.'

Here my father stopped the speaker.

'You're mistaken, Mocquet,' he said, 'it was only yesterday!'

'General, I know what I'm talking about,' Mocquet went on.

'Yes, and, good heavens, so do I!' cried my father. 'And the proof is, that yesterday was Sunday, when I sent you – and today's Monday.'

'Yesterday was Sunday, yes,' Mocquet replied, 'and today's Monday – that's all right. But it wasn't yesterday, but a *week* yesterday, that you sent me to Oigny.'

My father knew that on this subject it was no use trying to set Mocquet right, so he merely said –

'Let it be so, then. We'll suppose it was eight days ago.'

'There's no "suppose" about it, General; I was eight days in doing the journey I've just returned from; and you'll see that eight days wasn't a bit too long, and that I've got the time quite right.'

'Ah! And so you've been to the Moon, eh, Mocquet?'

'I have been there, General, as sure as there's a sun in heaven.'

'Well, well, tell us all about it, Mocquet; it ought to have been a very interesting trip.'

'I should think so! But you'll see. I must first tell you, General, that as luck or ill-luck would have it, old daddy Berthelin was married for the second time eight days ago. He saw me just as he was coming out of church, and cried out –

' "Hallo! Is that you? I wouldn't have bothered you to come and see me for such a trifle as my wedding, but now that you're here, you must come and dine with us at Port-aux-Perches!"

' "I ask nothing better," I answered. "The General has given me leave until tomorrow, and so long as I turn up at nine in the morning I'm free till then!"

' "Good! You know your way back home, don't you?"

' "I should think I do!"

' "We'll let you off at midnight, and you'll be at the château before daylight."

' "Right!" I said, "that's settled!"

'And I gave my arm to fat old Dame Berchu, who had no beau, and there was I, one of the wedding party!

'The breakfast was held at Father Tellier's of Corcy, who had provided the food; General Charpentier had sent fifty bottles of wine, and Tellier had brought fifty himself. There were twenty-five guests, seven of them being women, and so reckoning a bottle each for the ladies, that left four or five each for us men, which was rather too big a share. So I said to Berthelin –

' "Fifty bottles for twenty-five of us will be enough, Berthelin."

'But he only answered –

' "Bah! The wine's drawn: we must drink it."

'And we did.

'You quite understand, General, that when a man has five bottles of wine under his waistcoat he doesn't walk very straight or see very clearly. So I don't quite know how the thing happened, but I suddenly found myself standing on the bank of the little river Ourcq, on the wrong side.

'I knew a place where there was, not a bridge, unluckily, but a tree-trunk thrown across the stream. I walked along the bank until I found it, and started off bravely to cross it.

'But just as I reached the middle my foot slipped, and splash! there I was in the river!

'Luckily I can swim like a fish, and I struck out for the other bank; but I don't know how it was – perhaps the river turned and twisted, perhaps the current was too strong, perhaps the other side drew back as fast as I approached – but anyhow, I swam on, following the stream, but never being able to get any nearer to either side.

'At dawn I found myself entering a much broader river.

'It was the Marne.

'I went on swimming. As the morning grew lighter I began to pass people on the banks. Everyone stopped to watch me, and I heard them say, "There's a fine swimmer for you! Where's he off to, I wonder?"

'And others would reply, "Oh, very likely to Havre – or England, or America – or—"

'Then I cried out, "No, no, my friends, I'm not going so far as that! I'm on my way to the Château des Fossés, to carry Comte Charpentier's reply to the General. – Kind friends, in Heaven's name, send off a boat to pick me up! I swear to you I've no business in America, or England, or even at Havre!"

'But they began to laugh, and cried out, "No, no, no! You swim too well! Swim, Mocquet, swim!"

'I wondered how these people whom I'd never seen before knew my name; but I couldn't puzzle it out, and as in spite of my struggles I could get no nearer the side, I was forced to go on swimming.

'About four o'clock in the afternoon I came to another river, larger still, and as I passed a little shop with the sign, "To Charenton Bridge: fried fish sold", I guessed I was in the Seine.

'My doubts were set at rest when about five o'clock I saw Bercy. I was going to pass through Paris!

'I felt very glad at this, for I said to myself, "The dickens is in it, if all the way through the great city I can't find some boat to catch hold of, some kind soul who'll throw me a rope, or some good Newfoundland dog to rescue me."

'Well, General, I found nothing of the sort! The quays and the bridges were covered with people, who seemed to have come out on purpose to see me swim past. I shouted out to the men, to the women, and even to the children, "My good friends! I shall end by being drowned, as you well may see, if you don't pull me out. Help! Help!"

'But one and all – men, women, and children – began to laugh, crying out, "What, you drown! You'll take good care you don't! Swim, Mocquet, swim!"

'And I heard others saying, "If he goes on at this rate he'll be at Havre tomorrow night, England day after tomorrow, and reach America in two months!"

'And it was all in vain that I cried, "That's not what I want at all: I've a message for the General, and he's waiting for it. Take me up – take me up, please!"

'But they only answered, "Take you up, Mocquet? We've no right to do that: you haven't stolen anything! Swim, Mocquet, swim!"

'And swim I did, not being able to get hold of the washing-womens' boats, or the piles under the bridges, and I swam on, past the Hôtel de Ville, leaving the Louvre on my right, the Academy on my left, on past the Tuileries Gardens and the Champs Elysées, until at last I left Paris behind me.

'Night came on. I swam all night.

'Next morning I found myself at Rouen.

'The more I progressed the more the river widened, and the further away the banks became. I said to myself, "And they call this the *inferior* Seine! They are nice ones, aren't they!"

'At Rouen I aroused the same curiosity as at Charenton and Paris; and the people there answered me, just as the others had done, by bidding me swim on, and reckoning to each other, just as the folk had done at Charenton and Paris, how long it would take me to get to Havre, England, and America at the rate I was going.

'At three in the afternoon I saw a boundless stretch of waters open before me, with a big town at the right corner and a little town at the left corner.

'I supposed that the little town on the left was Honfleur, the big town, built in a curve, was Havre, and the great field of water the sea.

'I was too far from the shore to attract the attention of the people. I only met fishermen in their boats, who stopped in their fishing to watch me as I passed, and to say,

' "That wretched Mocquet! See how he swims: he's worse than a duck, hang him!"

'And I answered them, grinding my teeth with rage,

' "Away, you vile set of fish-pots!"

'But, meanwhile, it was I who was "away"-ing, at a fine pace, I warrant you. And soon I knew by the swell of the waves that I was in the open sea.

'Night came on.

'I might have been able to turn to left or right if I had wanted, but as there was no reason why I should go either way, I kept on swimming straight ahead.

'Towards daybreak I saw something like a shadow in front of me. I made an effort to stand up in the water so as to see above the waves. I managed to do so, and spied what seemed to me like an island.

'I redoubled my efforts, and as the day became brighter I found that I had not been mistaken.

'An hour later I set foot on solid ground.

'It was high time, for I was beginning to be tired . . .'

Translated by H. A. Spurr

TENNYSON

Sea Dreams

This is a fragment from the poem *Sea Dreams*, first published in
Macmillan's Magazine in January 1860 with the subtitle *An Idyll*. A
small clerk, who had invested his slender fortunes to buy some
shares in some Peruvian mines, goes to the seaside with his family.
During a stormy night he has this dream.

> Had you ill dreams?
>   'O yes,' he said, 'I dreamed
> Of such a tide swelling toward the land,
> And I from out the boundless outer deep
> Swept with it to the shore, and entered one
> Of those dark caves that run beneath the cliffs.
> I thought the motion of the boundless deep
> Bore through the cave, and I was heaved upon it
> In darkness: then I saw one lovely star
> Larger and larger. "What a world," I thought,
> "To live in!" but in moving on I found
> Only the landward exit of the cave,
> Bright with the sun upon the stream beyond:
> And near the light a giant woman sat,
> All over earthy, like a piece of earth,
> A pickaxe in her hand: then out I slipt
> Into a land all sun and blossom, trees
> As high as heaven, and every bird that sings:
> And here the night-light flickering in my eyes
> Awoke me.'
>   'That was then your dream,' she said,
> 'Not sad, but sweet.'
>   'So sweet, I lay,' said he,
> 'And mused upon it, drifting up the stream
> In fancy, till I slept again, and pieced
> The broken vision: for I dreamed that still
> The motion of the great deep bore me on,
> And that the woman walked upon the brink:
> I wondered at her strength, and asked her of it:
> "It came," she said, "by working in the mines:"
> O then to ask her of my shares, I thought:
> And asked; but not a word; she shook her head.

And then the motion of the current ceased,
And there was rolling thunder; and we reached
A mountain, like a wall of burs and thorns;
But she with her strong feet up the steep hill
Trod out a path: I followed; and at top
She pointed seaward: there a fleet of glass,
That seemed a fleet of jewels under me,
Sailing along before a gloomy cloud
That not one moment ceased to thunder, past
In sunshine: right across its track there lay,
Down in the water, a long reef of gold,
Or what seemed gold: and I was glad at first
To think that in our often-ransacked world
Still so much gold was left; and then I feared
Lest the gay navy there should splinter on it,
And fearing waved my arm to warn them off;
An idle signal, for the brittle fleet
(I thought I could have died to save it) neared,
Touched, clinked, and clashed, and vanished, and I woke,
I heard the clash so clearly. Now I see
My dream was Life; the woman honest Work;
And my poor venture but a fleet of glass
Wrecked on a reef of visionary gold,'
    'Nay,' said the kindly wife to comfort him,
'You raised your arm, you tumbled down and broke
The glass with little Margaret's medicine in it;
And, breaking that, you made and broke your dream:
A trifle makes a dream, a trifle breaks.'

CARROLL

Through the Looking Glass

This passage is taken from Chapter IV of Lewis Carroll's *Through the Looking Glass*, first published in 1871.

She checked herself in some alarm, at hearing something that sounded to her like the puffing of a large steam-engine in the wood near them, though she feared it was more likely to be a wild beast. 'Are there any lions or tigers about here?' she asked timidly.

'It's only the Red King snoring,' said Tweedledee.

'Come and look at him!' the brothers cried, and they each took one of Alice's hands, and led her up to where the King was sleeping.

'Isn't he *a lovely* sight?' said Tweedledum.

Alice couldn't say honestly that he was. He had a tall red night-cap on, with a tassel, and he was lying crumpled up into a sort of untidy heap, and snoring loud—'fit to snore his head off!' as Tweedledum remarked.

'I'm afraid he'll catch cold with lying on the damp grass,' said Alice, who was a very thoughtful little girl.

'He's dreaming now,' said Tweedledee: 'and what do you think he's dreaming about?'

Alice said, 'Nobody can guess that.'

'Why, about *you*!' Tweedledee exclaimed, clapping his hands triumphantly. 'And if he left off dreaming about you, where do you suppose you'd be?'

'Where I am now, of course,' said Alice.

'Not you!' Tweedledee retorted contemptuously. 'You'd be nowhere. Why, you're only a sort of thing in his dream!'

'If that there King was to wake,' added Tweedledum, 'you'd go out – bang! – just like a candle!'

'I shouldn't!' Alice exclaimed indignantly. 'Besides, if *I'm* only a sort of thing in his dream, what are *you*, I should like to know?'

'Ditto,' said Tweedledum.

'Ditto, ditto!' cried Tweedledee.

He shouted this so loud that Alice couldn't help saying, 'Hush! You'll be waking him, I'm afraid, if you make so much noise.'

'Well, it's no use *your* talking about waking him,' said Tweedledum, 'when you're only one of the things in his dream. You know very well you're not real.'

'I *am* real!' said Alice, and began to cry.

'You won't make yourself a bit realler by crying,' Tweedledee remarked: 'there's nothing to cry about.'

'If I wasn't real,' Alice said – half laughing through her tears, it all seemed so ridiculous – 'I shouldn't be able to cry.'

'I hope you don't suppose those are *real* tears?' Tweedledum interrupted in a tone of great contempt.

RIMBAUD

Dawn

'Dawn' belongs to *Les Illuminations*, and it was first published in 1886 in *La Vogue*, the periodical directed by the symbolist poet Gustave Kahn. *Les Illuminations* were probably written in 1872–3. According to Verlaine, the title of the collection derives from one of the English acceptations of the word *illuminations*, meaning 'coloured plates'.

I have kissed the summer dawn.

Before the palaces, nothing moved. The water lay dead.
Battalions of shadows still kept the forest road.

I walked, waking warm and vital breath,
While stones watched, and wings rose soundlessly.

My first adventure, in a path already gleaming
With a clear pale light,
Was a flower who told me its name.

I laughed at the blond *Wasserfall*
That threw its hair across the pines:
On the silvered summit, I came upon the goddess.

Then, one by one, I lifted her veils.
In the long walk, waving my arms.
Across the meadow, where I betrayed her to the cock.
In the heart of town she fled among steeples and domes,
And I hunted her, scrambling like a beggar on marble wharves.

Above the road, near a thicket of laurel,
I caught her in her gathered veils,
And smelled the scent of her immense body.
Dawn and the child fell together at the bottom of the wood.

When I woke, it was noon.

Translated by P. Schmidt

WAGNER

Sausages and Music

This dream of Richard Wagner was written down by his wife Cosima in her *Diary* on 6 January 1876.

Thursday, January 6   R. dreamed that he had to conduct the Ninth Symphony, in Dresden or Munich, and passed beforehand through a railway-station restaurant which had frankfurters; being very hungry, he ordered some; coming back to fetch them, he sees two men eating his portion, the assistant at the buffet maliciously insolent, also the manageress, who refuses him not only the sausages, but beer as well; he is angry, then tries friendly words, all to no avail. In the end he leaves the restaurant, cursing, arrives at the concert hall, walks through the orchestra, is greeted with applause, but has to climb, relies on his agility, but comes to a place which is too steep; when he cannot jump over it, he wakes up! ... He says, 'All one needs is bad experiences to stop the brain from carrying out the task it is there to do, for demons of all kinds to take control and produce nothing but horrible images!' ...

Translated by G. Skelton

MAUPASSANT

Dreams

Guy de Maupassant's 'Dreams' was first published in 1885 in *Contes du jour et de la nuit*.

It was after a dinner of friends, of old friends. There were five of them, a writer, a doctor, and three rich bachelors without any profession.

They had talked about everything, and a feeling of lassitude came on, that feeling of lassitude which precedes and leads to the departure of guests after festive gatherings. One of those present, who had for the last five minutes been gazing silently at the surging boulevard starred with gas-lamps, and rattling with vehicles, said suddenly:

'When you've nothing to do from morning till night, the days are long.'

'And the nights, too,' assented the guest who sat next to him. 'I sleep very little; pleasures fatigue me; conversation is monotonous. Never do I come across a new idea, and I feel, before talking to anyone, a violent longing to say nothing and listen to nothing. I don't know what to do with my evenings.'

And the third idler remarked:

'I would pay a great deal for anything that would enable me to pass merely two pleasant hours every day.'

Then the writer, who had just thrown his overcoat across his arm, turned round to them and said:

'The man who could discover a new vice, and introduce it among his fellow-creatures, even though it were to shorten their lives, would render a greater service to humanity than the man who found the means of securing to them eternal salvation and eternal youth.'

The doctor burst out laughing, and, while he chewed his cigar, he said:

'Yes, but 'tis not so easy as that to discover it. Men have, however crudely, been seeking for and working for the object you refer to since the beginning of the world. The men who came first reached perfection at once in this way. We are hardly equal to them.'

One of the three idlers murmured:

"Tis a pity!'

Then, after a minute's pause, he added:

'If we could only sleep, sleep well without feeling hot or cold, sleep with that perfect unconsciousness we experience on nights when we are thoroughly fatigued, sleep without dreams.'

'Why without dreams?' asked the guest sitting next to him.

The other replied:

'Because dreams are not always pleasant, and they are always fantastic, improbable, disconnected, and because when we are asleep we cannot have the sort of dreams we like. We require to be awake when we dream.'

'And what's to prevent you from being so?' asked the writer.

The doctor flung away the end of his cigar.

'My dear fellow, in order to dream when you are awake you need great power and great exercise of will, and when you try to do it, great weariness is the result. Now, real dreaming, that journey of our thoughts through delight-ful visions, is assuredly the sweetest experience in the world; but it must come naturally, it must not be provoked in a painful manner, and must be accom-panied by absolute bodily comfort. This power of dreaming I can give you provided you promise that you will not abuse it.'

The writer shrugged his shoulders:

'Ah! yes, I know – haschich, opium, green tea – artificial paradises. I have read Baudelaire, and I even tasted the famous drug, which made me very sick.'

But the doctor, without stirring from his seat, said:

'No: ether, nothing but ether, and I would suggest that you literary men ought to use it sometimes.'

The three rich men drew closer to the doctor.

One of them said:

'Explain to us the effects of it.'

And the doctor replied:

'Let us put aside big words, shall we not? I am not talking of medicine or morality; I am talking of pleasure. You give yourselves up every day to excesses which consume your lives. I want to indicate to you a new sensation, only possible to intelligent men, let us say even very intelligent men, dangerous, like everything that overexcites our organs, but exquisite. I might add that you would require a certain preparation, that is to say, a practice to feel in all their completeness the singular effects of ether.

'They are different from the effects of haschich, from the effects of opium and morphia, and they cease as soon as the absorption of the drug is interrupted, while the other generators of day dreams continue their action for hours.

'I am now going to try to analyse as clearly as possible the way one feels. But the thing is not easy, so facile, so delicate, so almost imperceptible, are these sensations.

'It was when I was attacked by violent neuralgia that I made use of this remedy, which perhaps I have since slightly abused.

'I had in my head and in my neck acute pains, and an intolerable heat of the skin, a feverish restlessness. I took up a large flagon of ether, and lying down, I began to inhale it slowly.

'At the end of some minutes, I thought I heard a vague murmur, which ere long became a sort of humming, and it seemed to me that all the interior of my body had become light, light as air, that it was dissolving into vapour.

'Then came a sort of torpor of the soul, a somnolent sense of comfort in spite of the pains which still continued, but which, however, had ceased to make themselves felt. It was one of those sensations which we are willing to endure and not any of those frightful wrenches against which our tortured body protests.

'Soon, the strange and delightful sense of emptiness which I felt in my chest extended to my limbs, which, in their turn, became light, as light as if the flesh and the bones had been melted and the skin only were left, the skin necessary to enable me to realize the sweetness of living, of bathing in this well-being. Then I perceived that I was no longer suffering. The pain had gone, melted also, evaporated. And I heard voices, four voices, two dialogues, without understanding what was said. At one time, there were only indistinct sounds, at another time a word reached my ear. But I recognized that this was only the humming I had heard before, accentuated. I was not asleep; I was not awake: I comprehended, I felt, I reasoned with the utmost clearness and depth, with extraordinary energy and intellectual pleasure, with a singular intoxication arising from this separation of my mental faculties.

'It was not like the dreams caused by haschich or the somewhat sickly visions that come from opium; it was an amazing acuteness of reasoning, a new way of seeing, judging, and appreciating the things of life, and with the certainty, the absolute consciousness that this was the true way.

'And the old image of the Scriptures suddenly came back to my mind. It seemed to me that I had tasted of the Tree of Knowledge, that all the mysteries were unveiled, so much did I find myself under the sway of a new, strange, and irrefutable logic. And arguments, reasonings, proofs, rose up in a heap before my brain only to be immediately displaced by some stronger proofs, reasoning, argument. My head had in fact, become a battle-ground of ideas. I was a superior being, armed with invincible intelligence, and I experienced a huge delight at the manifestation of my power.

'It lasted a long, long time. I still kept inhaling the ether from the opening of my flagon. Suddenly I perceived that it was empty.'

The four men exclaimed at the same time:

'Doctor, a prescription at once for a litre of ether!'

But the doctor, putting on his hat, replied:

'As for that, certainly not; go and get poisoned by others!'

And he left them.

Ladies and gentlemen, what is your idea on the subject?

Anonymous translation

APOLLINAIRE

Oneirocritique

Oneirocritique is a section of *L'Enchanteur pourrissant*, a long story Apollinaire published in *Le Festin d'Esope*, the review he edited in 1903–4.

The sky's embers were so close that their heat filled me with fear. They were on the point of burning me. But I was conscious of the differing eternities of man and of woman. Two dissimilar animals were coupling and the rose-trees were propagating vines weighed down with bunches of moonlight. From the monkey's throat shot flames that branded the world with a fleur-de-lys. In the myrtle-groves, an ermine was turning white. We asked it the reason for the false winter. I swallowed flocks of tanned sheep. Orkenise appeared on the horizon. We set off for that town though we missed the vales where the apple-trees sang, whistled and roared. But the song of the tilled fields was marvellous:

In through the gates of Orkenise
A carter seeks his entry
Out of the gates a ne'er-a-care
Is leaving past the sentry

And the sentries of the town
Pounce on this ne'er-a-care
'What are you taking from the town?'
'I've left my whole heart there.'

And the sentries of the town
Pounce upon the carter
'What are you bringing to the town?'
'My heart there for to barter.'

All those hearts in Orkenise!
The guards burst into laughter.
Ne'er-a-care, the road is hard,
But love is harder, carter.

The jolly sentries of the town
Knitted in their glory
And all the gates of Orkenise
Closed upon this story.

But I was conscious of the differing eternities of man and of woman. The sky was suckling its wildcat cubs. It was then that I noticed some crimson blotches on my hand. Towards morning, pirates made off with nine ships anchored in the port. The monarchs were carousing. And the women would not weep for the dead. They prefer the old kings, who are better at love than old dogs. A sacrificial priest asked to perish in place of the victim. They opened up his belly. Inside I could see four I's, four O's and four D's. We were served fresh meat and after eating it, I suddenly began to grow. Monkeys which looked like their own trees were violating ancient tombs. I called to one of these beasts, which had laurel leaves growing all over it. It brought me a head made from a single pearl. I took the head in my arms and questioned it, threatening to throw it back into the sea if it did not reply. But the pearl knew nothing and the sea swallowed it up.

But I was conscious of the differing eternities of man and of woman. Two dissimilar animals loved one another. But the kings alone did not die of this laughter and twenty blind tailors arrived to cut and sew a veil, which was to cover the sardonyx. I directed them myself, stepping backwards. Towards evening, the trees flew away, the monkeys were frozen motionless and I saw myself multiplied a hundredfold. The herd of me sat down by the seashore. Great golden ships were passing on the horizon. And when night was complete, a hundred flames came to meet me. I procreated a hundred male children who took the moon and the hillside as nursemaids. They took immediately to the flabby kings who were being shaken about on the balcony. Coming to the edge of a river, I took it in both hands and held it aloft. This sword quenched my thirst. And the languishing spring warned me that if I stopped the sun, I would see that it was really square. Multiplied a hundredfold, I swam towards an archipelago. A hundred sailors welcomed me and led me to a palace, where they killed me ninety-nine times. At that moment I burst out laughing and broke into dance as they wept. I began to dance on all four paws. The sailors did not dare to move, for I was in the frightening guise of a lion.

On all four paws, on all four paws.

My arms and legs all looked alike and my eyes, multiplied, crowned me with attention. Then I rose up to dance like hands and leaves.

I was wearing gloves. The islanders led me into their orchards so that I could gather fruit which looked like women. The island drifted in to fill up a gulf where red trees instantly sprouted from the sand. A soft beast covered in white feathers was singing ineffably and a whole race of people listened, never tiring of it. On the ground I found the head made from a single pearl; it was crying. I held the river aloft and the crowd dispersed. Old men were eating water-parsley and, immortal, suffered no more than the dead. I felt free, free as a flower in its season. The sun is no freer than a ripe fruit. A herd of trees grazed on the invisible stars and dawn was hand in hand with the tempest. In the myrtle-groves, darkness was exerting its influence. A whole race of people piled up in a wine-press were bleeding as they sang. Men were born out of the liquor that flowed from the press. They were brandishing other rivers that clashed with a sound of silver. The shadows emerged from the myrtle-groves and disappeared into the little gardens that the sucker of a tree was spraying with the eyes of men and beasts.

The handsomest of the men took me by the throat, but I managed to bring him down. On his knees, he bared his teeth. I touched them; out came sounds which changed into snakes the colour of chestnuts, and their tongue was called Sainte-Fabeau. They unearthed a transparent root and ate from it. It was as thick as a radish. And my restful river washed over them without drowning them. The sky was full of faeces and onions. I cursed the unworthy stars which bathed the earth with light. Not a living creature could be seen. But songs were rising all around. I visited empty towns and abandoned cottages. I gathered up the crowns of all the kings and made of them the immobile minister of the loquacious world. Golden ships, sailorless, were passing on the horizon. Gigantic shapes cast their shadows on the distant sails. Several centuries separated me from these shadows. I lost all hope. But I was conscious of the differing eternities of man and of woman. Dissimilar shadows darkened with their love the scarlet rigging, while my eyes were multiplied in the rivers, in the towns and in the mountain snows.

Translated by J. Romney

PAPINI

The Sick Gentleman's Last Visit

Giovanni Papini, a prolific Italian writer and polemist, author of about one hundred books, published this short story in 1906 in a volume entitled *Il tragico quotidiano*.

No one ever knew the real name of the man we all called the Sick Gentleman. Since his sudden disappearance everything that was his has vanished as well, everything except the memory of his unforgettable smile, and a portrait by Sebastiano del Piombo which shows him half hidden in the soft shadow of a fur coat, one gloved hand drooping delicately like the hand of someone asleep. A few of those who loved him truly – and I count myself as one of the few – also remember his remarkable skin of a transparent and pale yellow hue, the almost feminine lightness of his step, and his constantly vacant look. He enjoyed talking for hours on end but no one ever grasped the full meaning of his words. I even know of some who did not wish to understand him because the things he said were too horrible. His presence lent a fantastic tint to the simplest things: when his hand touched an object, the object seemed to enter and become part of the world of dreams. His eyes reflected not things that were there but other unknown and faraway things not seen by those who were with him. No one ever asked him what his illness was, or why he did not seem to try to cure it. He spent his time walking, always, day and night, without stopping. No one knew where he lived; no one ever met his parents or his brothers or sisters. One day he just appeared in town and then another day, some years later, he vanished.

The day before his disappearance he came to my room to wake me, very early, when dawn was just beginning to break. I felt the soft touch of his glove on my forehead and saw him standing in front of me, wrapped in his furs, with the ghost of a smile on his lips and his eyes more absent than ever. I realized, seeing his red eyelids, that he had been awake all night, and that he must have waited for dawn with great anxiety because his hands were trembling and his entire body seemed to shake with fever.

'What is the matter?' I asked. 'Is your illness causing you more discomfort than usual?'

'My illness?' he answered. 'My illness? Do you too believe, like the others, that I *have* an illness? That there is such a thing as my illness? Why not say that I *myself* am an illness? There is nothing that is mine, don't you understand? There is nothing that actually belongs to me! It is I, I who belong to someone, and that someone is my master!'

Accustomed as I was to his strange talk, I didn't answer. I continued to look at him and my look must have been gentle because he came even nearer to my bed and again touched my forehead with his soft glove.

'You do not seem to have a temperature,' he said. 'You are perfectly healthy and calm. Your blood runs peacefully through your veins. I can therefore tell you something that perhaps will frighten you: I can tell you who I am. Listen carefully, please, because I may not be able to say the same things twice. But it is necessary that I say them at least once.'

With this, he let himself fall into a purple armchair beside my bed, and carried on in a stronger voice.

'I am not a real man. I am not a man like others, a man of flesh and blood, a man born of woman. I did not come into this world like your fellow men. No one rocked me in my cradle, or watched over my growing years. I have not known the restlessness of adolescence, or the comfort of family ties. I am – and I will say this out loud though perhaps you may not want to believe me – I am but *a figure in a dream*. In me, Shakespeare's image has become literally and tragically exact: I am *such stuff as dreams are made on*! I exist because someone is dreaming me, someone who is now asleep and dreaming and sees me act and live and move, and in this very moment is dreaming that I am saying these very words. When this *someone* began to dream me, I began my existence. When he wakes, I will cease to be. I am an imagination, a creation, a guest of his long nightly fantasies. This someone's dream is lasting and intense to such a degree that I have become visible even to those who are awake. But the world of watchfulness, the world of solid reality is not mine. I feel uncomfortable in the midst of your tangible and vulgar existence! My life flows slowly in the soul of my sleeping creator . . .

'Don't think I speak symbolically or in riddles. What I am saying is the truth – the whole, simple and tremendous truth.

'To be an actor in a dream is not what pains me most. There are poets who have said that man's life is but the shadow of a dream, and philosophers who have hinted that all reality is but hallucination. I, instead, am haunted by another thought: *who is this someone who dreams me?* Who is this nameless, unknown being to whom I belong, who suddenly brought me out of the darkness of his tired brain and whose awakening will just as suddenly extinguish me, like a flame in the wind? How many days have I spent thinking of this master of mine, asleep; thinking of my creator busy with the course of my ephemeral life! He must be someone great and powerful, a being for whom our years are minutes, someone who can live the entire life of a man in just one of his nights. His dreams must be so vivid and powerful and deep that they can cast forth images in such a way that they seem real. Perhaps the whole world is but the ever-changing result of the crossing of dreams dreamt by beings identical to him. But I won't generalize: let us leave metaphysical trifling to reckless philosophers! For me, it is enough to know with absolute certainty that I am the imaginary creature of a vast, enormous dreamer.

'But who is he? That is the question that's been troubling me for so long, ever since I discovered the nature of the stuff I was made on. Surely you understand how important this question is to me? On its answer hinges my entire fate. The actors in dreams enjoy ample freedom, and for that reason my life has not been entirely determined by my birth but to a large extent by my free will. However, it has become necessary for me to know who it was that was dreaming me in order to choose my way of life. At first I was terrified by the idea that the slightest thing might wake him – that is, destroy me. A shout, a noise, a whisper might suddenly fling me into nothingness. In those days I used to care for life, so I would torture myself in vain trying to guess the tastes and passions of my unknown master, trying to give to my existence the attributes and shapes that might please him. All the time I trembled with the thought that I might commit an act that would offend him, frighten him – and therefore wake him. For a while I imagined him to be a sort of paternalistic, evangelic deity, and I tried to lead the most virtuous and saintly of lives. At another time I pictured him as a classic pagan hero, and I would crown myself with vine-leaves and sing songs in praise of wine and dance with young nymphs in forest clearings. Once I even believed that I was part of the dream of a pure and immortal sage who managed to live in a superior spiritual world, and I spent long sleepless nights counting the stars and measuring the Earth and trying to find out how living creatures were made.

'But in the end I grew tired, humiliated to think I was but the spectacle of this unknown and unknowable master. I realized that this fiction of a life was not worth such base and servile flattery. And I began to wish ardently for that which in the beginning had caused me such terror – his awakening. I deliberately filled my life with gruesome images so that the sheer horror might wake him. I tried everything to achieve the peace of annihilation, I did all within my power to interrupt the sad comedy of my apparent life, to destroy this ridiculous larva of a life that somehow likens me to men.

'I left no crime untouched, no infamy untasted. With refined tortures I murdered innocent old people, I poisoned the waters of entire cities, I set fire to the hair of hundreds of women. Grown wild through my death-wish, I tore apart with my teeth the children I met on my way. At night I sought the company of monstrous dark giants forgotten by mankind. I took part in the incredible villainies of trolls, demons and ghosts. I threw myself from the top of a mountain into a broken and naked valley surrounded by caverns full of white bones. Witches taught me the shrieks of wild beasts that at night put fear into the hearts of the bravest of men. But it seems that he who dreams me isn't frightened by those things which make ordinary men tremble. Perhaps he enjoys watching horrible sights, perhaps he doesn't care or perhaps it doesn't affect him. Until this day I have not been able to wake him, so I must drag on with this ignoble life, wretched and unreal.

'Who will free me from my dreamer? When will the dawn come that will put an end to his work? When will the bell toll, the cock crow, the voice call that will wake him? I have been waiting so long for my day of freedom! I have been waiting so eagerly for the end of this foolish dream in which I play so monotonous a part!

'What I am doing now is my last attempt. I am telling my dreamer that I am a dream. I want him to dream that he is dreaming. That is something that happens to men, doesn't it? And don't they wake, once they realize they are dreaming? That's why I have come to see you and that's why I have told you everything. I hope he who has created me understands that at this very minute I do not exist as a real man, for as soon as he does I shall cease to exist, even as an unreal image. Do you think I will succeed? Do you think that by repeating it and shouting it I will manage to startle and awaken my invisible master?'

And while he was saying these words, the Sick Gentleman tossed and turned in the armchair, pulling off and putting on the glove of his left hand, staring at me with eyes that seemed to grow more and more vacant. It was as if he expected something terrible and marvellous to happen at any minute. His face took on an agonized expression. From time to time he would stare at his own body as if expecting to see it dissolve into thin air, and he would nervously pass a hand across his damp forehead.

'Do you believe all this to be true?' he asked me. 'Or do you think I'm lying? But why can't I disappear, why can't I be free of it all? Is it that I'm part of an everlasting dream, the dream of an immortal sleeper, of an eternal dreamer? Help me get rid of this terrible notion! Console me, find me some plan, some way to escape from this horror! I beg you, help me! Will no one pity this poor, bored apparition?'

As I remained silent, he stared at me once again and then stood up. He seemed to me taller than before, and once again I noticed his almost diaphanous skin. One could see he was suffering terribly. His whole body seemed convulsed: he looked like an animal trying to escape from a net. The soft gloved hand shook mine, for the last time. Murmuring something very gently he left my room, and *only one person* has seen him since.

Translated by A. Manguel

HUCH

The Poem

For Huch, see page 81.

K. reads out a poem to me. I like it, but I say: that kind of thing isn't a poem; I'll show you a poem. And with that I reach into my waistcoat-pocket and bring out some broad, brownish-gold gently tapered sunbeams that I gathered in the early morning from off the floor in front of my bedroom window.

Translated by M. Hollington

Dream Creature

It seemed as if I was about to wake up. Then I became aware of something rustling right by my ear, and I knew it was the dream creature, about to escape as the dream evaporated; I made a quick grab for it and held it in my hand. But it got thinner and thinner; I feared it would vanish altogether. Yet I had it in a firm grip, and it could not escape. I filled a goldfish-bowl shaped glass vessel with water, and put it in there. Silky, diaphanous, golden-brown, it slid in slender, delicate movements into the bowl.

Translated by M. Hollington

The Second Head

I am at a dentist's, sitting in the patients' chair. The dentist says to me: you've still got quite some pain to go through today! This alarms me, but I suddenly think of a way out of it. I say to the dentist: Yes, but the head I have on isn't my own at all. You know of course that my head is that one on the table beside us, and this one here is only an artificial one, and I won't feel a thing! Gently I use both hands to turn my head to the left: it feels as if it were turning on a screw. And I am overcome with the most terrifying and chilling anxiety at the thought that at one point during all the procedures I shall have to undergo to get my real head back on again I shan't have a head at all.

Translated by M. Hollington

VALERY

Let me, dream, look you in the eye

This text and the following ones by Valéry were written between 1908 and 1919. Some of them appeared in the *Nouvelle Revue Française*, but most were published for the first time under the editorship of J. Levaillant in the *Cahiers Paul Valéry*, No. 3, 1979, under the title *Questions du rêve*.

Let me, dream, look you in the eye. What is it that dies as we look at it? Yet starts to swell, growing in the shadows to one side? Like the liar, when the eye dives in as if to touch the real.

Its eye fears the eye's gaze. It knows too much to hold out.

The liar would be truthful if he could forget the truth.

What must the dream forget in order to be dreamt, what is this omission which allows such novelties, gardens never before seen?

Dream

A locomotive of a kind which does not exist. I know the form of these machines very well. I have a host of memories. – Yes, but not you, he dreams.

Why, wherefore this bizarre *creation*?

Hypotheses

I have interpreted something as a locomotive. If exactly a locomotive – it was no longer a dream – what is conserved?

If we had the exact interpretation – the observer himself is a dream – the theory would easily follow. You might say it is not possible to observe a dream properly. That is almost a definition – (for I do not much trust dreams which claim to be reported exactly) –

Dreamt, all the less; the more exactly you think you remember them. It is like trying to study liquid iron from the solid...

In dream, you do not remember explicitly. What distinguishes dreaming from waking is that the waking state contains dreamt passages. In dream, all is dreamt – therefore nothing is dreamt – (until we wake).

Dream is thus, from this point of view, a translation of a text whose original sense is different from the dream. But the text suits both well enough.

My dreaming self is to my waking self as a reader is to an author. The same text is common to us both. The *text* in the dream is more or less garbled. The text is composed of the dreamer's present state – sensations, vestiges of his waking state, residues, etc...

Memory supplies the dreamer – with isolated images, not generalizable ones. There remains the system of combination. Known secondary facts: to believe in, or to doubt ... lapses become of capital importance in the dream (surface tension).

Noting this dream, I write it like a story, making a *resumé* or summary of a story, by memory. This is the fundamental error when it comes to narrating a dream. Unfortunately there is no other way around it. To obtain the synthesis of a dream you would have to express it in its 'atomic' constituents. For the story – *which one remembers*, is only a secondary fabrication, following an initial state that is non-chronological, non-resumable, *non-integrable*.

Translated by J. Romney

DESNOS

Dreams

For the note on Robert Desnos, see page 198.

1916
I find myself transformed into a number. I fall into a well which is at the same time a sheet of paper, and I pass from one equation to another, desperate in the knowledge that I am moving farther and farther away from the light of day and from a landscape which is the chateau of Ferrières (Seine-et-Marne) seen from the Eastern Railways track.

During the winter of 1918–19
I am lying down and can see myself as I am in real life. The electric light is on. The mirrored door of my cupboard opens by itself. I can see the books inside. On one shelf is a brass paper-knife (there is also one there in real life) in the shape of a yataghan. It rises up on the end of its blade, remains unstably balanced for a moment, then lays itself slowly down again upon the shelf. The door closes. The light goes out.

Translated by J. Romney

WEST

The Trojan Horse

This is from the opening pages of *The Dream Life of Balso Snell*, the first novel by Nathanael West first published in 1931.

While walking in the tall grass that has sprung up around the city of Troy, Balso Snell came upon the famous wooden horse of the Greeks. A poet, he remembered Homer's ancient song and decided to find a way in.

On examining the horse, Balso found that there were but three openings: the mouth, the navel, and the posterior opening of the alimentary canal. The mouth was beyond his reach, the navel proved a cul-de-sac, and so, forgetting his dignity, he approached the last. O Anus Mirabilis!

Along the lips of the mystic portal he discovered writings which after a little study he was able to decipher. Engraved in a heart pierced by an arrow and surmounted by the initial N, he read, 'Ah! Qualis . . . Artifex . . . Pereo!' Not to be outdone by the actor-emperor, Balso carved with his penknife another heart and the words 'O Byss! O Abyss! O Anon! O Anan!' omitting, however, the arrow and his initial.

Before entering he prayed:

'O Beer! O Meyerbeer! O Bach! O Offenbach! Stand me now as ever in good stead.'

Balso immediately felt like the One at the Bridge, the Two in the Bed, the Three in the Boat, the Four on Horseback, the Seven Against Thebes. And with a high heart he entered the gloom of the foyer-like lower intestine.

After a little while, seeing no one and hearing nothing, Balso began to feel depressed. To keep his heart high and yet out of his throat, he made a song.

> Round as the Anus
> Of a Bronze Horse
> Or the Tender Buttons
> Used by Horses for Ani
>
> On the Wheels of His Car
> Ringed Round with Brass
> Clamour the Seraphim
> Tongues of Our Lord
>
> Full Ringing Round
> As the Belly of Silenus
> Giotto Painter of Perfect Circles
> Goes . . . One Motion Round

Round and Full
Round and Full as
A Brimming Goblet
The Dew-Loaded Navel
Of Mary
Of Mary Our Mother

Round and Ringing Full
As the Mouth of a Brimming Goblet
The Rust-Laden Holes
In Our Lord's Feet
Entertain the Jew-Driven Nails.

He later gave this song various names, the most successful of which were: *Anywhere Out of the World, or a Voyage Through the Hole in the Mundane Millstone* and *At Hoops with the Ani of Bronze Horses, or Toe Holes for a Flight of Fancy*.

But despite the gaiety of his song, Balso did not feel sure of himself. He thought of the Phoenix Excrementi, a race of men he had invented one Sunday afternoon while in bed, and trembled, thinking he might well meet one in this place. And he had good cause to tremble, for the Phoenix Excrementi eat themselves, digest themselves, and give birth to themselves by evacuating their bowels.

Hoping to attract the attention of an inhabitant, Balso shouted as though overwhelmed by the magnificence of his surroundings:

'O the Rose Gate! O the Moist Garden! O Well! O Fountain! O Sticky Flower! O Mucous Membrane!'

A man with 'Tours' embroidered on his cap stalked out of the shadow. In order to prove a poet's right to trespass, Balso quoted from his own works:

'If you desire to have two parallel lines meet at once or even in the near future,' he said, 'it is important to make all the necessary arrangements beforehand, preferably by wireless.'

The man ignored his little speech. 'Sir,' he said, 'you are an ambassador from that ingenious people, the inventors and perfectors of the automatic water-closet, to my people who are the heirs of Greece and Rome. As your own poet has so well put it, The Grandeur that was Greece and the Glory that was Rome' . . . I offer you my services as guide. First you will please look to the right where you will see a beautiful Doric prostate gland swollen with gladness and an over-abundance of good cheer.'

This speech made Balso very angry. 'Inventors of the automatic water-closet, are we?' he shouted. 'Oh, you stinker! Doric, bah! It's Baptist '68, that's what it is. And no prostate gland either, simply an atrophied pile. You call this dump grand and glorious, do you? Have you ever seen the Grand

Central Station, or the Yale Bowl, or the Holland Tunnel, or the New Madison Square Garden? Exposed plumbing, stinker, that's all I see – and at this late date. It's criminally backward, do you hear me?'

The guide gave ground before Balso's rage. 'Please sir,' he said, 'please ... After all, the ages have sanctified this ground, great men have hallowed it. In Rome do as the Romans do.'

'Stinker,' Balso repeated, but less ferociously this time.

The guide took heart. 'Mind your manners, foreigner. If you don't like it here, why don't you go back where you came from? But before you go let me tell you a story – an old tale of my people, rich in local colour. And, you force me to say it, apropos, timely. However, let me assure you that I mean no offence. The title of the story is 'Visitors'.

'A traveller in Tyana, who was looking for the sage Appolonius, saw a snake enter the lower part of a man's body. Approaching the man, he said:

' "Pardon me, my good fellow, but a snake just entered your ...' He finished by pointing.

' "Yes sir, he lives there," was the astounding rejoinder.

' "Ah, then you must be the man I'm looking for, the philosopher-saint, Appolonius of Tyana. Here is a letter of introduction from my brother George. May I see the snake please? Now the opening. Perfect!" '

Balso echoed the last word of the story. 'Perfect! Perfect! A real old-world fable. You may consider yourself hired.'

'I have other stories to tell,' the guide said, 'and I shall tell them as we go along. By the way, have you heard the one about Moses and the Burning Bush? How the prophet rebuked the Bush for speaking by quoting the proverb, "Good wine needs no bush"; and how the Bush insolently replied, "A hand in the Bush is worth two in the pocket." '

Balso did not consider this story nearly as good as the other; in fact he thought it very bad, yet he was determined to make no more breaks and entered the large intestine on the arm of his guide. He let the guide do all the talking and they made great headway up the tube. But, unfortunately, coming suddenly upon a place where the intestine had burst through the stomach wall, Balso cried out in amazement.

'What a hernia! What a hernia!'

The guide began to splutter with rage and Balso tried to pacify him by making believe he had not meant the scenery. 'Hernia,' he said, rolling the word on his tongue. 'What a pity childish associations cling to beautiful words such as hernia, making their use as names impossible. Hernia! What a beautiful name for a girl! Hernia Hornstein! Paresis Pearlberg! Paranoia Puntz! How much more pleasing to the ear (and what other sense should a name please?) than Faith Rabinowitz or Hope Hilkowitz...'

BORGES

The Circular Ruins

For the notice about the author, see page 219. 'The Circular
Ruins' belongs to the volume *Ficciones*, first published in 1944.

And if he left off dreaming about you . . .
    Through the Looking Glass, IV

Nobody saw him come ashore in the encompassing night, nobody saw the
bamboo craft run aground in the sacred mud, but within a few days everyone
knew that the quiet man had come from the south and that his home was
among the numberless villages upstream on the steep slopes of the mountain,
where the Zend language is barely tainted by Greek and where lepers are rare.
The fact is that the grey man pressed his lips to the mud, scrambled up the
bank without parting (perhaps without feeling) the brushy thorns that tore his
flesh, and dragged himself, faint and bleeding, to the circular opening
watched over by a stone tiger, or horse, which was once the colour of fire and
is now the colour of ash. This opening is a temple which was destroyed ages
ago by flames, which the swampy wilderness later desecrated, and whose god
no longer receives the reverence of men. The stranger laid himself down at
the foot of the image.

Wakened by the sun high overhead, he noticed – somehow without amazement – that his wounds had healed. He shut his pale eyes and slept again, not
because of weariness but because he willed it. He knew that this temple was
the place he needed for his unswerving purpose; he knew that downstream the
encroaching trees had also failed to choke the ruins of another auspicious
temple with its own fire-ravaged, dead gods; he knew that his first duty was to
sleep. At about midnight, he was awakened by the forlorn call of a bird.
Footprints, some figs, and a water jug told him that men who lived nearby had
looked on his sleep with a kind of awe and either sought his protection or else
were in dread of his witchcraft. He felt the chill of fear and searched the
crumbling walls for a burial niche, where he covered himself over with leaves
he had never seen before.

His guiding purpose, though it was supernatural, was not impossible. He
wanted to dream a man; he wanted to dream him down to the last detail and
project him into the world of reality. This mystical aim had taxed the whole
range of his mind. Had anyone asked him his own name or anything about his
life before then, he would not have known what to answer. This forsaken,
broken temple suited him because it held few visible things, and also because
the neighbouring villagers would look after his frugal needs. The rice and fruit

of their offerings were nourishment enough for his body, whose one task was to sleep and to dream.

At the outset, his dreams were chaotic; later on, they were of a dialectic nature. The stranger dreamed himself at the centre of a circular amphitheatre which in some way was also the burnt-out temple. Crowds of silent disciples exhausted the tiers of seats; the faces of the farthest of them hung centuries away from him and at a height of the stars, but their features were clear and exact. The man lectured on anatomy, cosmography, and witchcraft. The faces listened, bright and eager, and did their best to answer sensibly, as if they felt the importance of his questions, which would raise one of them out of an existence as a shadow and place him in the real world. Whether asleep or awake, the man pondered the answers of his phantoms and, not letting himself be misled by impostors, divined in certain of their quandaries a growing intelligence. He was in search of a soul worthy of taking a place in the world.

After nine or ten nights he realized, feeling bitter over it, that nothing could be expected from those pupils who passively accepted his teaching, but that he might, however, hold hopes for those who from time to time hazarded reasonable doubts about what he taught. The former, although they deserved love and affection, could never become real; the latter, in their dim way, were already real. One evening (now his evenings were also given over to sleeping, now he was only awake for an hour or two at dawn) he dismissed his vast dream-school forever and kept a single disciple. He was a quiet, sallow, and at times rebellious young man with sharp features akin to those of his dreamer. The sudden disappearance of his fellow pupils did not disturb him for very long, and his progress, at the end of a few private lessons, amazed his teacher. Nonetheless, a catastrophe intervened. One day, the man emerged from his sleep as from a sticky wasteland, glanced up at the faint evening light, which at first he confused with the dawn, and realized that he had not been dreaming. All that night and the next day, the hideous lucidity of insomnia weighed down on him. To tire himself out he tried to explore the surrounding forest, but all he managed, there in a thicket of hemlocks, were some snatches of broken sleep, fleetingly tinged with visions of a crude and worthless nature. He tried to reassemble his school, and barely had he uttered a few brief words of counsel when the whole class went awry and vanished. In his almost endless wakefulness, tears of anger stung his old eyes.

He realized that, though he may penetrate all the riddles of the higher and lower orders, the task of shaping the senseless and dizzying stuff of dreams is the hardest that a man can attempt – much harder than weaving a rope of sand or of coining the faceless wind. He realized that an initial failure was to be expected. He then swore he would forget the populous vision which in the beginning had led him astray, and he sought another method. Before attempting it, he spent a month rebuilding the strength his fever had consumed. He gave up all thoughts of dreaming and almost at once managed to sleep a reasonable part of the day. The few times he dreamed during this period he did not dwell on his dreams. Before taking up his task again, he waited until the moon was a perfect circle. Then, in the evening, he cleansed himself in the waters of the river, worshipped the gods of the planets, uttered the prescribed syllables of an all-powerful name, and slept. Almost at once, he had a dream of a beating heart.

He dreamed it throbbing, warm, secret. It was the size of a closed fist, a darkish red in the dimness of a human body still without a face or sex. With anxious love he dreamed it for fourteen lucid nights. Each night he perceived it more clearly. He did not touch it, but limited himself to witnessing it, to observing it, to correcting it now and then with a look. He felt it, he lived it from different distances and from many angles. On the fourteenth night he touched the pulmonary artery with a finger and then the whole heart, inside and out. The examination satisfied him. For one night he deliberately did not dream; after that he went back to the heart again, invoked the name of a planet, and set out to envision another of the principal organs. Before a year was over he came to the skeleton, the eyelids. The countless strands of hair were perhaps the hardest task of all. He dreamed a whole man, a young man, but the young man could not stand up or speak, nor could he open his eyes. Night after night, the man dreamed him asleep.

In the cosmogonies of the Gnostics, the demiurges mould a red Adam who is unable to stand on his feet; as clumsy and crude and elementary as that Adam of dust was the Adam of dreams wrought by the nights of the magician. One evening the man was at the point of destroying all his handiwork (it would have been better for him had he done so), but in the end he restrained himself. Having exhausted his prayers to the gods of the earth and river, he threw himself down at the feet of the stone image that may have been a tiger or a stallion, and asked for its blind aid. That same evening he dreamed of the image. He dreamed it alive, quivering; it was no unnatural cross between tiger and stallion but at one and the same time both these violent creatures and also a bull, a rose, a thunderstorm. This manifold god revealed to him that its earthly name was Fire, that there in the circular temple (and in others like it) sacrifices had once been made to it, that it had been worshipped, and that through its magic the phantom of the man's dreams would be wakened to life in such a way that – except for Fire itself and the dreamer – every being in the world would accept him as a man of flesh and blood. The god ordered that, once instructed in the rites, the disciple should be sent downstream to the other ruined temple, whose pyramids still survived, so that in that abandoned place some human voice might exalt him. In the dreamer's dream, the dreamed one awoke.

The magician carried out these orders. He devoted a period of time (which finally spanned two years) to initiating his disciple into the riddles of the universe and the worship of Fire. Deep inside, it pained him to say goodbye to his creature. Under the pretext of teaching him more fully, each day he drew out the hours set aside for sleep. Also, he reshaped the somewhat faulty right shoulder. From time to time, he was troubled by the feeling that all this had already happened, but for the most part his days were happy. On closing his eyes he would think, 'Now I will be with my son.' Or, less frequently. 'The son I have begotten awaits me and he will not exist if I do not go to him.'

Little by little, he was training the young man for reality. On one occasion he commanded him to set up a flag on a distant peak. The next day, there on the peak, a fiery pennant shone. He tried other, similar exercises, each bolder than the one before. He realized with a certain bitterness that his son was ready – and perhaps impatient – to be born. That night he kissed him for the first time and sent him down the river to the other temple, whose whitened ruins were still to be glimpsed over miles and miles of impenetrable forest and swamp. At the very end (so that the boy would never know he was a phantom, so that he would think himself a man like all men), the magician imbued his disciple with total oblivion of his long years of apprenticeship.

His triumph and his peace were blemished by a touch of weariness. In the morning and evening dusk, he prostrated himself before the stone idol, perhaps imagining that his unreal son was performing the same rites farther down the river in other circular ruins. At night he no longer dreamed, or else he dreamed the way all men dream. He now perceived with a certain vagueness the sounds and shapes of the world, for his absent son was taking nourishment from the magician's decreasing consciousness. His life's purpose was fulfilled; the man lived on in a kind of ecstasy. After a length of time that certain tellers of the story count in years and others in half-decades, he was awakened one midnight by two rowers. He could not see their faces, but they spoke to him about a magic man in a temple up north who walked on fire without being burned. The magician suddenly remembered the god's words. He remembered that of all the creatures in the world, Fire was the only one who knew his son was a phantom. This recollection, comforting at first, ended by tormenting him. He feared that his son might wonder at this strange privilege and in some way discover his condition as a mere appearance. Not to be a man but to be the projection of another man's dreams – what an unparalleled humiliation, how bewildering! Every father cares for the child he has begotten – he has allowed – in some moment of confusion or happiness. It is understandable, then, that the magician should fear for the future of a son thought out organ by organ and feature by feature over the course of a thousand and one secret nights.

The end of these anxieties came suddenly, but certain signs foretold it. First (after a long drought), a far-off cloud on a hilltop, as light as a bird; next, towards the south, the sky, which took on the rosy hue of a leopard's gums; then, the pillars of smoke that turned the metal of the nights to rust; finally, the headlong panic of the forest animals. For what had happened many centuries ago was happening again. The ruins of the fire god's shrine were destroyed by fire. In a birdless dawn the magician saw the circling sheets of flame closing in on him. For a moment, he thought of taking refuge in the river, but then he realized that death was coming to crown his years and to release him from his labours. He walked into the leaping pennants of flame. They did not bite into his flesh, but caressed him and flooded him without heat or burning. In relief, in humiliation, in terror, he understood that he, too, was an appearance, that someone else was dreaming him.

Translated by N. T. Di Giovanni

LEIRIS

Death

For Michel Leiris' *Nights without Night and Some Days without Day*, see page 98.

15–16 March 1923

I am dead. I can see the sky filled with dust like the cone of air crossed by the rays of a projector in a theatre auditorium. Several luminous globes, milky-white, are lined up in the back of the sky. Out of each stretches a long metallic rod, and one of these pierces my chest right through, without my feeling anything but great euphoria. I am moving towards the globes of light, gliding slowly along the rod, and rising upwards in a gentle slope. With each hand, I am holding on to the two men nearest me in a chain of others who, like me, are rising towards the sky, each following the rail that perforates him. There is no sound but the soft rasp of the steel in the flesh of our chests.

One of my immediate neighbours is Max Jacob (who for about a year and a half has been giving me poetry lessons, in our daytime existence).

Translated by J. Romney

MONTALE

The Prisoner's Dream

This is one of the rare 'political' poems by the Italian poet Eugenio
Montale. It belongs to his third collection of poems, *La bufera e
altro*, published in 1956.

Dawns and nights here differ by few signs.

The zigzagging of formations upon the look-out towers
on days of battle, my only wings,
a needle of artic draught,
the head-gaoler's eye at the peephole,
report of cracking nuts, an oily
hissing from the depths, roasting jacks
real or imagined – but the straw is gold,
the wine-red lantern is fireside,
if, sleeping, I am at your feet.

The purge has gone on since time began, senselessly.
They say whoever retracts and signs
can save himself from this massacre of geese,
that whoever sobs and gravely accuses
and confesses and denounces, grabs hold of the server
instead of ending in the *pâté*
marked for the apocalyptic gods.

Slow-witted, riddled
by the prickling mattress I have grown one with
the flight of the moth-thing drilling my soles
to powder on the tiles,
with the iridescent kimonos of the window spaces
held out to the dawn from bastions,
I have sniffed on the wind the burnt odour
of rock-cakes from the ovens,
I have looked about, I have conjured
rainbows on spider-web horizons,
petals on the grating bars,
I have risen I have fallen back
into the depth where century is minute

and the blows resound again and the footsteps,
and I still do not know if at the banquet
I shall be stuffer or stuffed. The wait is long,
my dream of you has not ended.

Translated by G. Kay

HANDKE

The Inverted World

For Peter Handke, see also page 111. This poem was written in 1967 and first published in German in the collection *Die innere Welt der äusseren Welt der inneren Welt* ('The Inner World of the Outer World of the Inner World') in 1969.

I wake up asleep:
I don't look at the objects, and the objects look at me;
I don't move, and the ground under my feet moves me;
I don't see myself in the mirror, and I in the mirror see myself;
I don't pronounce words, and words pronounce me;
I go to the window and I am opened.

I lie there upright:
I don't open my eyes, but my eyes open me;
I don't listen to sounds, but sounds listen to me;
I don't swallow water, but water swallows me;
I don't reach for objects, but objects reach for me;
I don't take off my clothes, but my clothes take me off;
I don't talk words into myself, but words talk me out of myself;
I go to the door, and the handle presses me down.
The shutters are rolled up and it becomes
Night, and to catch a breath of air I dive under water:

I step on the stone floor and sink in ankle-deep;
I sit on the box of the coach and put one foot before the other;
I see a woman with a parasol and break out in a cold sweat;
I raise my arm in the air and it catches fire;
I reach for an apple and I am bitten;
I walk on bare feet and feel a stone in my shoe;
I tear the bandaid from the wound and the cut is in the bandaid;

I buy a newspaper and I am scanned;
I frighten someone to death and am left aghast;
I stuff cotton in my ears and scream;
I hear sirens wailing and the Corpus Christi procession passes by;
I open the umbrella and the ground singes my feet;
I run into the open and am arrested.

It is over the floor that I trip,
and with a wide open mouth that I make conversations,
and with the palm of my hand that I scratch myself,
and with the police whistle that I laugh,
and out of the ends of my hair that I bleed,
and on opening the newspaper that I choke,
and caviar that I regurgitate,
and I tell about the future,
and I talk to things,
and it is through *myself* that I see,
and corpses that I kill.

And I see sparrows firing at cannons;
and I see the catatonic in ecstasy;
and I see the newborn baby actually having wishes;
and I see the milkman at night:

and the letter carrier? asks for the mail;
and the preacher? rolls on the ground;
and the firing squad? lines up against the wall;
and the clown? flings a grenade among the spectators;
and the murder? does not occur until the eyewitnesses appear.

And the mortician cheers his soccer team;
And the head of state attempts to assassinate the baker's apprentice;
And the field marshal is named after a side street;
And nature is faithfully reproduced after a painting;
And the Pope is counted out standing up –

and listen! The watch ticks outside itself!
And look! The guttering candles are growing!
And listen! The scream is whispered!
And look! The wind petrifies the grass!
And listen! The folk song is bellowed!
And look! The raised arm points down!
And listen! The question mark is commanded!
And look! The starved man is fat!
And smell! The snow is rotting!

And it is morningfall,
and the table stands on one leg,
and the escapee assumes the lotus position,
and the trolley stops on the forty-ninth floor:

Listen! It is deathly quiet! – It is rush hour.

I fell asleep awake
and fled the unbearable dream for gentle reality
and am humming hue and cry to myself, merrily as they say –
listen to my mouth watering: I see a corpse!

Translated by M. Roloff

PEREC

Balls and Masks

For the note on Pérec's *La Boutique Obscure*, from which this text is
taken, see page 107.

August 1971
Walking in the street, I stop to watch a game of tennis, and mingle with the
players, who are apparently indistinguishable from the other passers-by. We
are at the end of a service and I catch a rather tricky ball, thus earning the
compliments of one of the players (who is none other than Marcel C.). That
sets off a misunderstanding: he thinks I can play, I don't dare disabuse him,
and he offers me the service.

Although the ball is extremely large and my racket ridiculously small, things
do not go too badly at first. There is no net: the idea is to knock the ball over
the fence, into the park. I manage to knock my first two balls on to the other
side, much too far for my opponent to catch them (he doesn't even try), and
we score 30-love. But the ball expands, and ends up looking like a rather soft
leather punch-ball, and I can no longer hit it over the fence. I thought I had
lost only one point, but my partner (Bernard L.) informs me in severe tones
that we are 50–40 down, and that if I don't even the score, the service is lost
(the service alone is not so serious; we'll then be one game all). I explain that I
cannot hit such a heavy ball with such a small racket, and he offers to lend me
one of his. In fact, under his arm he has two rackets that he is not using, and
which he has even put back in their presses (which are tall diamond-shapes in
wood, held down with four wing-nuts). These rackets are curious: they look

more like 'old rackets' (what viols are to violins, or crumhorns to bassoons): one of them has an extremely bulky wooden frame, and the racket proper (the strings) consists of a minuscule hole, round rather than oval, which quite obviously has no strings at all. This is the one Bernard L. hands to me; I tell him it is unstrung and that I cannot play with it. He begins to unscrew the press of his second racket, then changes his mind, and almost angrily, hands me the first one, insisting the strings are perfect. In fact, looking at it closely, I can see that the hole is strung with a very fine network of gossamer threads.

At first, I try to serve by throwing the ball myself. But the ball and racket are much too heavy. My partner throws the ball, while I grasp my racket handle with both hands. I manage to hit the ball, but my stroke is not powerful enough; the ball falls within the net, a bad serve...

Translated by J. Romney

MICHAUX

The Mother

This text is taken from Henri Michaux's *Poteaux d'angle*, ('Main-stays' – but the title is untranslatable), published first in *Les Cahiers de l'Herne* (1971). It was reprinted in 1978 and 1981. *Poteaux d'angle* is a kind of elaborate scrap-book, with brief thoughts and longer narrative texts intermingling.

N. has just landed in New York in the course of a journey. It is in a dream, but he doesn't know it.

He is alone, and climbing.

The place he's heading for is a hotel, a majestic palace on top of a mountain. A mountain in New York! N. knows very well there aren't any!

But he can't see any contradiction. There is a road leading up, so incredibly sloped that it sometimes gives the impression of an almost vertical rock-face.

The walk up has turned into a climb, although N. is not particularly bothered.

And just then, just before he arrives, he's caught! Mother! She's there! Mother! he'd forgotten all about her. She's found him...

In one bound, she's ambushed him, she's almost on top of him, possessed by rage, a rage made out of a hundred angers and disgusts accumulated in an entire lifetime. She immobilizes him with one look, he's that taken by surprise, that stupefied. This diabolical rage is holding him down, preventing him from getting away, it's a rage out to slake itself, a rage that bursts out of her face and out of those tiny little pale grey eyes, set in their sickly pale skin – it's her all the same, although he's never seen her like this before, quite so full of hate, and truer than she's ever shown herself in all her life; more extraordinary. It's a passion at the moment of paroxysm, filled with the crazy joy of no longer having to hold back after so many years, now that she's faced with the object of her hate, and falling on his defenceless throat. Why defenceless? Why indeed?

N. wakes up in time, still stupefied. Nevertheless he starts to think. Where could this dream have come from? They no longer knew each other... He goes back to sleep. It begins again, still in New York, and once again she's found him, in this town which definitely brings him bad luck. 'There he is!' she cries out to Father, who remains a little way behind, to one side.

She approaches, carried by hatred, which, as it accumulates in the presence of her 'prey', transfigures her and actually propels her forward by psychic force, without her seeming to make any movement, and she's already leaning over him, face twisted under the incredible augmented voltage of her fury, she's about to get him, to deal him the death blow when . . . he wakes up.

Enough. He'll keep the light on in his room.

Surprising, this dream. He's never travelled with them, except as a child, and not much even then. They haven't seen each other in ages. They'd had nothing to say to each other. They'd never had anything to say to each other. Besides, they've both been dead for forty or fifty years, and where they lived was a country he has never visited. As for dreaming about them, it simply doesn't happen. Where he lives, nothing reminds him of them.

. . . now he comes to think of it, *there has been one thing recently*, which if they were alive and knew what he was doing, might well have struck them, a sort of success which in their eyes would have seemed obviously undeserved, and which might have irritated, scandalized them. (Ah yes. . .that 'climb'!)

That lazy good-for-nothing who caused them so much worry and shame, he didn't deserve 'success' (!!). He mustn't reach the top. It must not be. Mother – for it was her above all – SHE *had come back from the dead* at the very last minute *to stand in his way*.

. . . she had returned.

Translated by J. Romney

CALVINO

Zobeide

This text is taken from Italo Calvino's *Invisible Cities*, first published in Italian in 1972 and translated into English in 1974. Kubla Khan listens to the description of imaginary cities visited by Marco Polo, or invented by him to relieve the Emperor from his melancholy.

From there, after six days and seven nights, you arrive at Zobeide, the white city, well exposed to the moon, with streets wound about themselves as in a skein. They tell this tale of its foundation: men of various nations had an identical dream. They saw a woman running at night through an unknown city; she was seen from behind, with long hair, and she was naked. They dreamed of pursuing her. As they twisted and turned, each of them lost her. After the dream they set out in search of that city; they never found it, but they found one another; they decided to build a city like the one in the dream. In laying out the streets, each followed the course of his pursuit; at the spot where they had lost the fugitive's trail, they arranged spaces and walls differently from the dream, so she would be unable to escape again.

This was the city of Zobeide, where they settled, waiting for that scene to be repeated one night. None of them, asleep or awake, ever saw the woman again. The city's streets were streets where they went to work every day, with no link any more to the dreamed chase. Which, for that matter, had long been forgotten.

New men arrived from other lands, having had a dream like theirs, and in the city of Zobeide, they recognized something of the streets of the dream, and they changed the positions of arcades and stairways to resemble more closely the path of the pursued woman and so, at the spot where she had vanished, there would remain no avenue of escape.

The first to arrive could not understand what drew these people to Zobeide, this ugly city, this trap.

Translated by W. Weaver

GOYTISOLO

The Good Little Wolf

This poem by José Agustin Goytisolo belongs to the collection *Palabras para Julia y otras canciones*. Goytisolo has often collaborated with the Spanish singer Paco Ibañez, who has set this poem to music.

> The lambs were horrible
> The little wolf was good
> They chased it and abused it
> In the wood
>
> The handsome prince was nasty
> The evil witch was pretty
> The pirate was an honourable man
> In my ditty
>
> All these strange things
> Occurred in my town
> Where every night I used to dream
> A world upside down.

Translated by G. Almansi

DAHL

The BFG

This passage comes from *The BFG*, one of the many children's books by that most prolific author, Roald Dahl. The BFG, i.e. the Big Friendly Giant, catches dreams floating in the air with a butterfly net and blows the most pleasant ones with a trumpet into children's bedrooms.

The Big Friendly Giant was seated at the great table in his cave and he was doing his homework.

Sophie sat cross-legged on the table-top near by, watching him at work.

The glass jar containing the one and only good dream they had caught that day stood between them.

The BFG, with great care and patience, was printing something on a piece of paper with an enormous pencil.

'What are you writing?' Sophie asked him.

'Every dream is having its special label on the bottle,' the BFG said. 'How else could I be finding the one I am wanting in a hurry?'

'But can you really and truly tell what sort of a dream it's going to be simply by listening to it?' Sophie asked.

'I can,' the BFG said, not looking up.

'But *how*? Is it by the way it hums and buzzes?'

'You is less or more right,' the BFG said. 'Every dream in the world is making a different sort of buzzy-hum music. And these grand swashboggling ears of mine is able to read that music.'

'By music, do you mean tunes?'

'I is not meaning tunes.'

'Then what *do* you mean?'

'Human beans is having their own music, right or left?'

'Right,' Sophie said. 'Lots of music.'

'And sometimes human beans is very overcome when they is hearing wonderous music. They is getting shivers down their spindels. Right or left?'

'Right,' Sophie said.

'So the music is saying something to them. It is sending a message. I do not think the human beans is knowing what that message is, but they is loving it just the same.'

'That's about right,' Sophie said.

'But because of these jumpsquiffling ears of mine,' the BFG said, 'I is not only able to *hear* the music that dreams is making but is *understanding* it also.'

'What do you mean *understanding* it?' Sophie said.

'I can read it,' the BFG said. 'It talks to me. It is like a langwitch.'

'I find that just a little hard to believe,' Sophie said.

'I'll bet you is also finding it hard to believe in quogwinkles,' the BFG said, 'and how they is visiting us from the stars.'

'Of course I don't believe that,' Sophie said.

The BFG regarded her gravely with those huge eyes of his. 'I hope you will forgive me,' he said, 'if I tell you that human beans is thinking they is very clever, but they is not. They is nearly all of them notmuchers and squeakpips.'

'I *beg* your pardon,' Sophie said.

'The matter with human beans,' the BFG went on, 'is that they is absolutely refusing to believe in anything unless they is actually seeing it right in front of their own schnozzles. Of course quogwinkles is existing. I is meeting them oftenly. I is even chittering to them.' He turned away contemptuously from Sophie and resumed his writing. Sophie moved over to read what he had written so far. The letters were printed big and bold, but were not very well formed. Here is what it said:

THIS DREAM IS ABOUT HOW I IS SAVING MY TEECHER FROM DROWNING. I IS
DIVING INTO THE RIVER FROM A HIGH BRIDGE AND I IS DRAGGING MY TEECHER
TO THE BANK AND THEN I IS GIVING HIM THE KISS OF DEATH...

'The kiss of *what?*' Sophie asked.

The BFG stopped writing and raised his head slowly. His eyes rested on
Sophie's face. 'I is telling you once before,' he said quietly, 'that I is never
having a chance to go to school. I is full of mistakes. They is not my fault. I do
my best. You is a lovely little girl, but please remember that *you* is not exactly
Miss Knoweverything yourself.'

'I'm sorry,' Sophie said. 'I really am. It is very rude of me to keep correcting
you.'

The BFG gazed at her for a while longer, then he bent his head again to his
slow laborious writing.

'Tell me honestly,' Sophie said. 'If you blew this dream into my bedroom
when I was asleep, would I really and truly start dreaming about how I saved
my teacher from drowning by diving off the bridge?'

'More,' the BFG said. 'A lot more. But I cannot be squibbling the whole
gropefluncking dream on a titchy bit of paper. Of course there is more.'

The BFG laid down his pencil and placed one massive ear close to the jar.
For about thirty seconds he listened intently. 'Yes,' he said, nodding his great
head solemnly up and down. 'This dream is continuing very nice. It has a very
dory-hunky ending.'

'How does it end?' Sophie said. '*Please* tell me.'

'You would be dreaming,' the BFG said, 'that the morning after you is
saving the teacher from the river, you is arriving at school and you is seeing all
the five hundred pupils sitting in the assembly hall, and all the teachers as
well, and the head teacher is then standing up and saying, 'I is wanting the
whole school to give three cheers for Sophie because she is so brave and is
saving the life of our fine arithmatic teacher, Mr Figgins, who was unfortunately pushed off the bridge into the river by our gym-teacher, Miss Amelia
Upscotch. So three cheers for Sophie!' And the whole school is then cheering
like mad and shouting bravo well done, and, for ever after that, even when you
is getting your sums all gungswizzled and muggled up, Mr Figgins is always
giving you ten out of ten and writing *Good Work Sophie* in your exercise book.
Then you is waking up.'

'I like that dream,' Sophie said.

'Of course you like it,' the BFG said. 'It is a phizzwizard.' He licked the
back of the label and stuck it on the jar. 'I is usually writing a bit more than this
on the labels,' he said. 'But you is watching me and making me jumpsy.'

'I'll go and sit somewhere else,' Sophie said.

'Don't go,' he said. 'Look in the jar carefully and I think you will be seeing
this dream.'

Sophie peered into the jar and there, sure enough, she saw the faint translucent outline of something about the size of a hen's egg. There was just a touch of colour in it, a pale sea-green, soft and shimmering and very beautiful. There it lay, this small oblong sea-green jellyish thing, at the bottom of the jar, quite peaceful, but pulsing gently, the whole of it moving in and out ever so slightly, as though it were breathing.

'It's moving!' Sophie cried. 'It's alive!'

'Of course it's alive.'

'What will you feed it on?' Sophie asked.

'It is not needing any food,' the BFG told her.

'That's cruel,' Sophie said. 'Everything alive needs food of some sort. Even trees and plants.'

'The north wind is alive,' the BFG said. 'It is moving. It touches you on the cheek and on the hands. But nobody is feeding it.'

Sophie was silent. This extraordinary giant was disturbing her ideas. He seemed to be leading her towards mysteries that were beyond her understanding.

'A dream is not needing anything,' the BFG went on. 'If it is a good one, it is waiting peaceably for ever until it is released and allowed to do its job. If it is a bad one, it is always fighting to get out.'

The BFG stood up and walked over to one of the many shelves and placed the latest jar among the thousands of others.

'Please can I see some of the other dreams?' Sophie asked him.

The BFG hesitated. 'Nobody is ever seeing them before,' he said. 'But perhaps after all I is letting you have a little peep.' He picked her up off the table and stood her on the palm of one of his huge hands. He carried her towards the shelves. 'Over here is some of the good dreams,' he said. 'The phizzwizards.'

'Would you hold me closer so I can read the labels,' Sophie said.

'My labels is only telling bits of it,' the BFG said. 'The dreams is usually much longer. The labels is just to remind me.'

Sophie started to read the labels. The first one seemed long enough to her. It went right round the jar, and as she read it, she had to keep turning the jar. This is what it said:

TODAY I IS SITTING IN CLASS AND I DISCOVER THAT IF I IS STARING VERY HARD AT MY TEECHER IN A SPHESHAL WAY, I IS ABLE TO PUT HER TO SLEEP. SO I KEEP STARING AT HER AND IN THE END HER HEAD DROPS ON TO HER DESK AND SHE GOES FAST TO SLEEP AND SNORKLES LOUDLY. THEN IN MARCHES THE HEAD TEACHER AND HE SHOUTS 'WAKE UP MISS PLUMRIDGE! HOW DARE YOU GO TO SLEEP IN CLASS! GO FETCH YOUR HAT AND COTE AND LEAVE THIS SCHOOL FOR EVER! YOU IS SACKED!' BUT IN A JIFFY I IS PUTTING THE HEAD TEECHER TO SLEEP AS WELL, AND HE JUST CRUMPLES SLOWLY TO THE FLOOR LIKE A LUMP OF JELLY

AND THERE HE LIES ALL IN A HEAP AND STARTS SNORKELLING EVEN LOWDER
THAN MISS PLUMRIDGE. AND THEN I IS HEARING MY MUMMY'S VOICE SAYING
WAKE UP YOUR BREKFUST IS REDDY.

'What a funny dream,' Sophie said.

'It's a ringbeller,' the BFG said. 'It's whoppsy.'

Inside the jar, just below the edge of the label, Sophie could see the
putting-to-sleep dream lying peacefully on the bottom, pulsing gently, sea-
green like the other one, but perhaps a trifle larger.

'Do you have separate dreams for boys and for girls?' Sophie asked.

'Of course,' the BFG said. 'If I is giving a girl's dream to a boy, even if it was
a really whoppsy girl's dream, the boy would be waking up and thinking what a
rot-bungling grinksludging old dream that was.'

'Boys would,' Sophie said.

'These here is all girls' dreams on this shelf,' the BFG said.

'Can I read a boy's dream?'

'You can,' the BFG said, and he lifted her to a higher shelf. The label on
the nearest boy's-dream jar read as follows:

I IS MAKING MYSELF A MARVELUS PAIR OF SUCTION BOOTS AND WHEN I PUT
THEM ON I IS ABLE TO WALK STRATE UP THE KITSHUN WALL AND ACROSS THE
CEILING. WELL, I IS WALKING UPSIDE DOWN ON THE CEILING WEN MY BIG SISTER
COMES IN AND SHE IS STARTING TO YELL AT ME AS SHE ALWAYS DOES, YELLING
WOT ON EARTH IS YOU DOING UP THERE WALKING ON THE CEILING AND I LOOKS
DOWN AT HER AND I SMILES AND I SAYS I *TOLD* YOU YOU WAS DRIVING ME UP
THE WALL AND NOW YOU HAS DONE IT.

'I find that one rather silly,' Sophie said.

'Boys wouldn't,' the BFG said, grinning. 'It's another ringbeller. Perhaps
you has seen enough now.'

'Let me read another boy's one,' Sophie said.

The next label said:

THE TELLYFONE RINGS IN OUR HOUSE AND MY FATHER PICKS IT UP AND SAYS IN
HIS VERY IMPORTANT TELLYFONE VOICE 'SIMPKINS SPEAKING'. THEN HIS FACE
GOES WHITE AND HIS VOICE GOES ALL FUNNY AND HE SAYS *'WHAT! WHO?'*
AND THEN HE SAYS 'YES SIR I UNDERSTAND SIR BUT SURELY IT IS *ME* YOU IS
WISHING TO SPEKE TO SIR NOT MY LITTLE SON?' MY FATHER'S FACE IS GOING
FROM WHITE TO DARK PURPEL AND HE IS GULPING LIKE HE HAS A LOBSTER
STUCK IN HIS THROTE AND THEN AT LAST HE IS SAYING 'YES SIR VERY WELL SIR I
WILL GET HIM SIR' AND HE TURNS TO ME AND HE SAYS IN A RATHER RESPECKFUL
VOICE 'IS YOU KNOWING THE PRESIDENT OF THE UNITED STATES?' AND I SAYS
'NO BUT I EXPECT HE IS HEARING ABOUT ME.' THEN I IS HAVING A LONG TALK ON
THE FONE AND SAYING THINGS LIKE 'LET ME TAKE CARE OF IT, MR PRESIDENT.
YOU'LL BUNGLE IT ALL UP IF YOU DO IT YOUR WAY'. AND MY FATHER'S EYES IS

GOGGLING RIGHT OUT OF HIS HEAD AND THAT IS WHEN I IS HEARING MY
FATHER'S REAL VOICE SAYING GET UP YOU LAZY SLOB OR YOU WILL BE LATE FOR
SKOOL.

'Boys are crazy,' Sophie said. 'Let me read this next one.' Sophie started
reading the next label:

I IS HAVING A BATH AND I IS DISCOVERING THAT IF I PRESS QUITE HARD ON MY
TUMMY BUTTON A FUNNY FEELING COMES OVER ME AND SUDDENLEY MY LEGS
IS NOT THERE NOR IS MY ARMS. IN FACT I HAS BECOME ABSOLOOTLY INVISIBLE
ALL OVER. I IS STILL THERE BUT NO ONE CAN SEE ME NOT EVEN MYSELF. SO MY
MUMMY COMES IN AND SAYS 'WHERE IS THAT CHILD! HE WAS IN THE BATH A
MINIT AGO AND HE CAN'T POSSIBLY HAVE WASHED HIMSELF PROPERLY!' SO I
SAYS 'HERE I IS' AND SHE SAYS 'WHERE?' AND I SAYS 'HERE!' AND SHE SAYS
'WHERE?' AND I SAYS 'HERE!' AND SHE YELLS 'HENRY! COME UP QUICK!' AND WHEN
MY DADDY RUSHES IN I IS WASHING MYSELF AND MY DADDY SEES THE SOAP
FLOATING AROUND IN THE AIR BUT OF CORSE HE IS NOT SEEING ME AND HE
SHOUTS 'WHERE ARE YOU BOY?' AND I SAYS 'HERE' AND HE SAYS 'WHERE?' AND I
SAYS 'HERE' AND HE SAYS *'WHERE?'* AND I SAYS *'HERE!'* AND HE SAYS 'THE
SOAP, BOY! THE SOAP! IT'S FLYING IN THE AIR!' THEN I PRESS MY TUMMY BUTTON
AGAIN AND NOW I IS VISIBLE. MY DADDY IS SQUIFFY WITH EXCITEMENT AND HE
SAYS 'YOU IS THE INVISIBLE BOY!' AND I SAYS 'NOW I IS GOING TO HAVE SOME
FUN,' SO WHEN I IS OUT OF THE BATH AND I HAVE DRIED MYSELF I PUT ON MY
DRESSING GOWN AND SLIPPERS AND I PRESS MY TUMMY BUTTON AGAIN TO
BECOME INVISIBLE AND I GO DOWN INTO THE TOWN AND WALK IN THE STREETS.
OF COURSE ONLY ME IS INVISIBLE BUT NOT THE THINGS I IS WEARING SO WHEN
PEEPLE IS SEEING A DRESSING GOWN AND SLIPPERS FLOATING ALONG THE
STREET WITH NOBODY IN IT THERE IS A PANIC WITH EVERYBODY YELLING 'A
GHOST! A GHOST!' AND PEEPLE IS SCREAMING LEFT AND RIGHT AND BIG STRONG
POLICEMEN IS RUNNING FOR THEIR LIVES AND BEST OF ALL I SEE MR GRUMMIT
MY ALGEBRA TEECHER COMING OUT OF A PUB AND I FLOAT UP TO HIM AND SAY
'BOO!' AND HE LETS OUT A FRIGHTSOME HOWL AND DASHES BACK INTO THE PUB
AND THEN I IS WAKING UP AND FEELING HAPPY AS A WHIFFSQUIDDLER.

'Pretty ridiculous,' Sophie said. All the same, she couldn't resist reaching
down and pressing her own tummy button to see if it worked. Nothing
happened.

'Dreams is very mystical things,' the BFG said. 'Human beans is not
understanding them at all. Not even their brainiest professors is understanding them. Has you seen enough?'

'Just this last one,' Sophie said. 'This one here.'

She started reading:

I HAS RITTEN A BOOK AND IT IS SO EXCITING NOBODY CAN PUT IT DOWN. AS
SOON AS YOU HAS RED THE FIRST LINE YOU IS SO HOOKED ON IT YOU CANNOT

STOP UNTIL THE LAST PAGE. IN ALL THE CITIES PEEPLE IS WALKING IN THE STREETS BUMPING INTO EACH OTHER BECAUSE THEIR FACES IS BURIED IN MY BOOK AND DENTISTS IS READING IT AND TRYING TO FILL TEETHS AT THE SAME TIME BUT NOBODY MINDS BECAUSE THEY IS ALL READING IT TOO IN THE DENTIST'S CHAIR. DRIVERS IS READING IT WHILE DRIVING AND CARS IS CRASH-ING ALL OVER THE COUNTRY. BRAIN SURGEONS IS READING IT WHILE THEY IS OPERATING ON BRAINS AND AIRLINE PILOTS IS READING IT AND GOING TO TIM-BUCTOO INSTEAD OF LONDON. FOOTBALL PLAYERS IS READING IT ON THE FIELD BECAUSE THEY CAN'T PUT IT DOWN AND SO IS OLIMPICK RUNNERS WHILE THEY IS RUNNING. EVERYBODY HAS TO SEE WHAT IS GOING TO HAPPEN NEXT IN MY BOOK AND WHEN I WAKE UP I IS STILL TINGLING WITH EXCITEMENT AT BEING THE GREATEST RITER THE WORLD HAS EVER KNOWN UNTIL MY MUMMY COMES IN AND SAYS I WAS LOOKING AT YOUR ENGLISH EXERCISE BOOK LAST NITE AND REALLY YOUR SPELLING IS ATROSHUS SO IS YOUR PUNTULASHON.

'That's enough for now,' the BFG said. 'There is dillions more but my arm is getting tired holding you up.'

'What are all those over there?' Sophie said. 'Why have they got such tiny labels?'

'That,' the BFG said, 'is because one day I is catching so many dreams I is not having the time or energy to write out long labels. But there is enough to remind me.'

'Can I look?' Sophie said.

The long-suffering BFG carried her across to the jars she was pointing to. Sophie read them rapidly, one after the other:

I IS CLIMBING MOUNT EVERAST WITH JUST MY PUSSY-CAT FOR CUMPANY.

I IS INVENTING A CAR THAT RUNS ON TOOTHPASTE.

I IS ABLE TO MAKE THE ELEKTRIK LITES GO ON AND OFF JUST BY WISHING IT.

I IS ONLY AN EIGHT YEAR OLD LITTLE BOY BUT I IS GROWING A SPLENDID BUSHY BEARD AND ALL THE OTHER BOYS IS JALOUS.

I IS ABEL TO JUMP OUT OF ANY HIGH WINDOW AND FLOTE DOWN SAFELY.

I HAS A PET BEE THAT MAKES ROCK AND ROLL MUSIK WHEN IT FLIES.

Index

Gibbon, Edward 266
Gide, André 291
Goethe, J.W. von 276
Gomez de la Serna, Ramon 98
Goytisolo, José Augustin 372
Graves, Robert 205
Grillparzer, Franz 154
Groussac, Paul 191

Handke, Peter 111, 366
Hebbel, Friedrich 155
Herodotus 126
Hoffmann, E.T.A. 52
Huch, Friedrich 81, 193, 287, 354

Ibsen, Henrik 285

Jean Paul 269
Jensen, W.H. 188
Jouve, Pierre Jean 90

Keats, John 327
Kerouac, Jack 210

La Fontaine, Jean de 149
La Motte-Fouque, Friedrich de 272
Lautreamont, Comte de 72
Le Fanu, Joseph Sheridan 76
Leiris, Michel 98, 211, 364
Lenau 66
Leopardi, Giacomo 328
Lincoln, Abraham 161
Lobel, Arnold 114
Lucretius 133
Lynkaeus, Joseph Popper 185

Machado, Antonio 193, 287
Malerba, Luigi 99
Mandiargues, Andre Pieyre 97
Maupassant, Guy de 344
Melville, Hermann 282
Mérimée, Prosper 163
Michaux, Henri 369
Montaigne, Michel Eyquem 145
Montale, Eugenio 365
Mossadegh, Mohammad 295

Nerval, Gérard de 280, 334
Nodier, Charles 330
Novalis 313

Ovid 242

Padilla, Gaston 299
Papini, Giovanni 350
Pascal, Blaise 150
Perec, Georges 107, 217, 297, 368
Petrarch, Francesco 139
Pirandello, Luigi 198
Plato 21, 128
Plutarch 243
Proust, Marcel 82
Pushkin, Alexander 56

Quevedo y Villegas, Francisco Gomez de 146

Rabelais, François 257
Racine, Jean 40
Resnik Salomon 299
Rimbaud, Arthur 74, 343
Roland, Song of *see* Song of Roland

Guy Davenport
The Geography of the Imagination £3.50

Forty essays in criticism, each a tour of the history of ideas and imagination in philosophy, art and literature, witty, wide-ranging and erudite. Subjects include Greek culture Whitman, Spinoza, Tolkien, Pound, Olson, Moore, Ives and Wittgenstein

'Anyone who cares for order and for grace in the exposed life of American letters is abundantly in Davenport's debt'
GEORGE STEINER, NEW YORKER

'The best explicator of the arts alive, because he assumes that the artists – painters, poets, describers of natural wonders – have the sort of mind he has, quick, unpredictable, alert for gaps to traverse toward the unexpected terminus' HUGH KENNER

Eclogues £2.95

Eight extraordinary new stories, a fiction of historical and linguistic collage, mixtures of myth and fable, inspired by Plutarch, Montaigne, Acts of the Apostles, and the daily newspaper

'Davenport is the last *pataphysician* . . we could say we are lucky he's alive and taking the time to bewitch us with brilliance' VILLAGE VOICE

'Among the few truly original, truly autonomous voices now audible . . He rivals, he echoes Thoreau and Mark Twain in the knowing sensuality of his immersions in the American Arcadia' NEW YORKER

'Davenport's conception of the short-story form is remarkable. He has given it some of the intellectual density of the learned essay, some of the lyric concision of the modern poem' NEW YORK TIMES

All these books are available at your local bookshop or newsagent, or can be ordered direct from the publisher. Indicate the number of copies required and fill in the form below.

Send to: **CS Department, Pan Books Ltd., P.O. Box 40, Basingstoke, Hants.   RG21 2YT.**

or phone: 0256 469551 (Ansaphone), quoting title, author and Credit Card number.

Please enclose a remittance* to the value of the cover price plus: 60p for the first book plus 30p per copy for each additional book ordered to a maximum charge of £2.40 to cover postage and packing.

*Payment may be made in sterling by UK personal cheque, postal order, sterling draft or international money order, made payable to Pan Books Ltd.

Alternatively by Barclaycard/Access:

Card No.   ☐☐☐☐☐☐☐☐☐☐☐☐☐☐☐

Signature:

Applicable only in the UK and Republic of Ireland.

While every effort is made to keep prices low, it is sometimes necessary to increase prices at short notice. Pan Books reserve the right to show on covers and charge new retail prices which may differ from those advertised in the text or elsewhere.

NAME AND ADDRESS IN BLOCK LETTERS PLEASE:

....

Name————————————————————————————

Address—————————————————————————————

————————————————————————————————

————————————————————————————————

————————————————————————————————

3/87